CGP

Cambridge International GCSE

Biology

Cambridge International GCSE Biology is tricky, but this lovingly-made CGP book explains everything you need to know — facts, theory, practical skills... the lot.

What's more, we've included lots of exam-style questions to put your knowledge to the test. There's even a set of realistic practice papers in the back. Amazing!

It's great for both the Core and Extended courses — the supplement content for the Extended course is clearly marked up throughout the book.

How to access your free Online Edition

This book includes a free Online Edition to read on your PC, Mac or tablet. You'll just need to go to **cgpbooks.co.uk/extras** and enter this code:

0851 0181 8887 5943

By the way, this code only works for one person. If somebody else has used this book before you, they might have already claimed the Online Edition.

Complete
Revision & Practice

Everything you need to pass the exams!

Contents

Practical Skills

Practice Papers

Some of the content in the specification is 'Supplemental'. This content will only be assessed if you're taking the Extended version of the Cambridge International GCSE. We've marked up all the content that's only for the Extended course with purple brackets, like the ones on this box, or the example below:

⌐Information or questions with a bracket like this are for the
└Extended course only.

Published by CGP

From original material by Paddy Gannon.

Editors:
Ellen Burton, Laura Collins, Katie Fernandez, Daniel Fielding, Emily Forsberg, Camilla Sheridan, Hayley Thompson.

With thanks to Janet Cruse-Sawyer, Glenn Rogers and Rachael Rogers for the proofreading.

ISBN: 978 1 78908 475 7
With thanks to Emily Smith for the copyright research.

DDT diagram on page 148 from Biological Science Combined Volume Hardback, 1990, Soper, Green, Stout, Taylor. © Cambridge University Press 1984, 1990. Reproduced with permission of the Licensor through PLSclear.

Page 217 contains public sector information licensed under the Open Government Licence v 3.0.
http://www.nationalarchives.gov.uk/doc/open-government-licence/version/3/

Printed by Bell and Bain Ltd, Glasgow.

Clipart from Corel®

Illustrations by: Sandy Gardner Artist, email sandy@sandygardner.co.uk

Based on the classic CGP style created by Richard Parsons.

Characteristics of Living Organisms

Welcome to the wonderful world of Biology. It's wonderful because it's all about living organisms — which includes you. And all living organisms share the same seven basic characteristics...

The Seven Basic Characteristics Are...

The table below shows the seven characteristics in the left-hand column, with their definitions in the right-hand column. You need to make sure you know them all:

KEY TERM

Characteristic	Definition
Movement	An action by organisms or parts of organisms causing a change of place or position.
Respiration	The chemical reactions that happen in cells to break down nutrient molecules and release energy for metabolism (see p.78).
Sensitivity	The ability of an organism to detect and respond to changes in the environment (see p.87).
Growth	A permanent increase in the size of an organism.
Reproduction	The processes that make more of the same kind of organism (see p.105).
Excretion	The removal of the waste products of metabolism, toxic materials and substances that are in excess of what the organism needs (see p.83).
Nutrition	The taking in of materials for energy, growth and development.

This could be to move towards things like water and food, or away from things like predators and poisons. Even plants can move a bit.

These changes are called stimuli and they can be internal or external. *(Supplement)*

An increase in size can be by an increase in cell number, cell size, or both. Growth can also be an increase in the dry mass of an organism. *(Supplement)*

Metabolism is the chemical reactions that happen in cells, including respiration. *(Supplement)*

Plants and animals require slightly different materials. Plants need light, carbon dioxide, water and ions. Animals require ions and organic compounds, and usually need water. *(Supplement)*

Remember "Mrs Gren"

REVISION TIP

It's important you learn all seven characteristics and their definitions. Use the first letter of each characteristic to help you remember them — they spell out "Mrs Gren".

Classification

I hope you like organising things, because it's time to put millions of organisms into groups...

Classification is Organising Living Organisms into Groups

1) There are millions of different organisms living on Earth and they come in a huge range of shapes and sizes — from small and simple (like bacteria) to large and complex (like blue whales). They also have a wide variety of physical features — e.g. wings, beaks, claws, teeth, leaves, branches, etc.

2) All of these organisms can be organised into groups. For example:

- Plants can be divided into two major groups — flowering plants (e.g. daisies) and non-flowering plants (such as ferns and mosses).
- Animals can also be divided into two major groups — invertebrates (which lack a backbone, e.g. insects) and vertebrates (which have a backbone, e.g. mammals).

3) There are different ways of classifying organisms, e.g. they can be grouped based on the features that they share.

4) One way of classifying organisms is the five kingdom system. In this system, living things are first divided into five groups, called kingdoms:

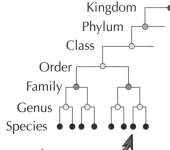

- Animals — fish, mammals, reptiles, etc.
- Plants — grasses, trees, etc.
- Fungi — mushrooms and toadstools, yeasts, mould.
- Prokaryotes — single-celled organisms without a nucleus.
- Protoctists — eukaryotic single-celled or simple multicellular organisms, e.g. algae.

5) These are then subdivided into smaller and smaller groups that have common features.

6) The smallest group in this system is called a species.

> A species is a group of similar organisms that can reproduce to give fertile offspring.

Each Organism has its Own Two-Part Scientific Name in Latin

Organisms are named according to the binomial system.

> The binomial system is an internationally agreed system to scientifically name organisms using their genus and species.

1) The first part of a binomial name refers to the genus that the organism belongs to. This gives you information on the organism's ancestry. The second part refers to the species. E.g. humans are known as *Homo sapiens*. '*Homo*' is the genus and '*sapiens*' is the species.

2) The binomial system is used worldwide and means that scientists in different countries or who speak different languages all refer to a particular species by the same name — avoiding potential confusion.

Classification

Here's some more information about classification systems, and a diagram of an odd-looking tree.

Classification Systems have Changed Over Time

1) Traditionally, organisms were classified according to similarities and differences in their morphological and anatomical characteristics (features of their internal and external structure).
2) As technology improved, this included things you can see with a microscope, e.g. cell structure.
3) These characteristics were used to classify organisms in the five kingdom classification system.
4) The five kingdom classification system is still used, but it's now a bit out of date.
5) This is because over time technology has developed further and our understanding of things like biochemical processes and genetics has increased.
6) For example, we are now able to determine the sequence (order) of DNA bases in different organisms' genes and compare them — the more similar the sequence of a gene, the more closely related the organisms.

There's more on DNA on pages 30 and 126.

7) Scientists are also able to compare amino acid sequences in proteins in a similar way. DNA base sequencing and amino acid sequencing are more accurate methods of classification.

Classification Systems Reflect Evolutionary Relationships

1) Evolutionary trees show how scientists think different species are related to each other.
2) They show common ancestors and relationships between species. The more recent the common ancestor, the more closely related the two species — and the more characteristics they're likely to share.
3) Scientists analyse lots of different types of data to work out evolutionary relationships. For living organisms, they use the current classification data (e.g. DNA analysis and structural similarities).
4) Organisms which share a more recent ancestor have more similar DNA base sequences than organisms that only share a distant ancestor.

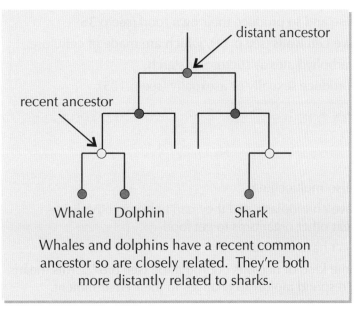

Whales and dolphins have a recent common ancestor so are closely related. They're both more distantly related to sharks.

Classification systems have been around for thousands of years

The more scientists find out about organisms, the more information they have to be able to classify them into different groups. New technology has made this even easier. Clever stuff.

Features of Organisms

As you saw on page 2, living organisms can be arranged into groups called kingdoms, according to the features they have in common. Two of the kingdoms are plants and animals.

Different **Components** Make Up **Cells**

1) Cells make up all living organisms. There are a few different features of cells, each with its own role. These features can be used to help classify organisms into different kingdoms. These are the cell features you need to know:

- Cytoplasm — contains smaller structures and is where reactions happen
- Cell membrane — holds the cell together, responsible for what comes in and out of the cell
- DNA — genetic material responsible for the proteins made within the cell

- Ribosomes — involved in protein synthesis
- Enzymes — involved in respiration

Supplement

2) There are two different types of cell. Eukaryotic cells have their genetic material in a structure called a nucleus. Prokaryotic cells do not have a nucleus — their genetic material is in the cytoplasm.

Learn the **Features** of **Plants** and **Animals**

Plant and animals are eukaryotic organisms — they are made up of eukaryotic cells. If you've ever wondered what features you share with a housefly, then this section is for you. Read on to find out more...

For more on the structure of plant and animal cells, see page 11.

Plants

1) Plants are multicellular.
2) They have chloroplasts (see p.11), which means they can photosynthesise and so produce their own food (see p.36).
3) Their cells have cell walls (see p.11), which are made of cellulose.
4) Plants store carbohydrates as sucrose or starch.
5) Plants can reproduce sexually or asexually (see p.105).

Animals

1) Animals are also multicellular.
2) They don't have chloroplasts and they can't photosynthesise — they have to eat other organisms to get food.
3) Their cells don't have cell walls.
4) Most have some kind of nervous coordination (see p.87). This means that they can respond rapidly to changes in their environment.
5) They can usually move around from one place to another.
6) They often store carbohydrate in the form of glycogen.
7) Most animals reproduce sexually.

Features of Organisms

Here are a few more kingdoms you need to know about, and a group that isn't a kingdom at all...

Fungi are Eukaryotic Organisms

1) Some are single-celled, but others have a structure called a mycelium. The mycelium is made up of hyphae (thread-like structures) which contain lots of nuclei.
2) They can't photosynthesise, so they feed off other organisms.
3) Their cells have cell walls made of chitin.
4) They can store carbohydrate as glycogen.
5) They reproduce using spores.

'Nuclei' is the plural of 'nucleus'.

Protoctists are Eukaryotic Organisms Too

1) These are mostly single-celled and microscopic (really tiny). Some are multicellular and quite big (e.g. seaweed).
2) Some have chloroplasts and are similar to plant cells. Others are more like animal cells or fungal cells.

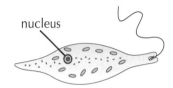

nucleus

Prokaryotes Include Bacteria

1) Prokaryotes are single-celled and microscopic.
2) They don't have a nucleus but they do have a cell wall.
3) They have a circular chromosome of DNA.
4) Some can photosynthesise. Most bacteria feed off other organisms — both living and dead. Some are pathogens — they cause disease (see p.69).

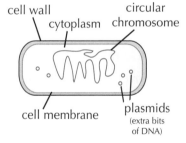

cell wall
cytoplasm
circular chromosome
cell membrane
plasmids (extra bits of DNA)

Viruses are Not One of the Kingdoms

1) Viruses are particles, rather than cells, and are smaller than bacteria.
2) They don't have a cellular structure (e.g. a cell membrane or cytoplasm) — instead they have a protein coat around some genetic material (either DNA or RNA).
3) They can only reproduce inside other living cells — they are parasites. They're also all pathogens.

There's more on DNA on p.30. RNA is a similar type of molecule to DNA.

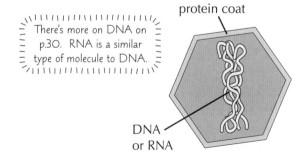

protein coat

DNA or RNA

Organisms can be classified according to their features

Viruses are not living organisms — they rely on other organisms to reproduce. If you're studying the Extended course, you still need to know a few of their features, as well as the features for the five kingdoms.

Supplement

More on Features of Organisms

The organisms in different kingdoms have to be divided into different groups. You need to know about the main features that are used to classify the organisms in the animal kingdom.

Animals are Divided into Vertebrates and Invertebrates

1) Vertebrates are all species of animals with a backbone and an internal skeleton.
2) Invertebrates do not have these structures, although some have an external skeleton (exoskeleton).
3) Vertebrates are divided into five groups:

Mammals

- Have hair or fur somewhere on their bodies. Also have sweat glands.
- Have lungs for breathing and external ears.
- Are warm-blooded (able to maintain a constant body temperature).
- Most give birth to their young, though a few species lay eggs.
- Females produce milk from mammary glands to feed their young.

The embryos of mammals that give birth to their young develop inside the female's body. Females develop a placenta during pregnancy (p.113).

Birds

- Have feathers and wings (which help most birds to fly) and scaly feet.
- Have beaks for feeding and lungs for breathing.
- Are warm-blooded.
- Lay eggs to produce offspring.

Reptiles

- Most live on land.
- Have dry scaly skin which stops them from losing too much water.
- Have lungs for breathing.
- Are cold-blooded (unable to maintain a constant body temperature).
- Most lay eggs to produce offspring, but some have live births.

Fish

- Live in water and have fins to swim with.
- Have skeletons made of bone or cartilage. Most fish have scales.
- Have gills for breathing.
- Are cold-blooded.
- Most lay eggs, which are fertilised externally, but some have live births.

Amphibians

- Live on land and in water.
- Have moist, permeable skin, through which they can breathe. Adults usually have lungs. Some young amphibians have gills.
- Are cold-blooded.
- Most lay their eggs in water to be fertilised externally.

More on Features of Organisms

It's not just vertebrates that you need to know how to classify. Arthropods are a type of invertebrate that have their own features for classification — watch out, there are lot of legs coming up...

There are Four Types of **Arthropods**

1) Arthropods are invertebrates with exoskeletons and segmented bodies (bodies made of repeating parts).

2) There are four groups of arthropods:

> 1) Myriapods — have lots of legs. They have one pair of antennae. Centipedes and millipedes are myriapods.

Antennae look a bit like legs attached to the head. Arthropods use them to sense their surroundings.

> 2) Insects — have three pairs of legs and a body that is divided into three parts (a head, a thorax and an abdomen). They have one pair of antennae. They usually have wings. Beetles, ants, bees and butterflies are all insects.

> 3) Arachnids — have four pairs of legs and a body that is divided into two parts (a combined head/thorax and an abdomen). They do not have antennae or wings. Spiders, scorpions and mites are all arachnids.

> 4) Crustaceans — most live in water. They have jointed legs and some have limbs that branch into two at the ends. They have two pairs of antennae but no wings. Crabs, lobsters, shrimps and woodlice are all crustaceans.

Plants are Either **Flowering** or **Non-Flowering**

1) Most flowering plants reproduce using flowers and seeds.

2) A lot of non-flowering plants, such as ferns, reproduce with spores, though some use seeds.

3) Flowering plants can be divided into two groups. These groups are based on a structure in plant embryos called a cotyledon. The cotyledon usually forms the first leaf.

> Monocotyledons — these only have one cotyledon. Their petals usually come in multiples of three and the veins in their leaves run parallel to each other.

This lily is a monocotyledon. It has six petals.

> Dicotyledons — these have two cotyledons. They usually have multiples of four or five petals in each flower and the veins in their leaves form a branching network.

This buttercup is a dicotyledon. It has five petals.

Supplement

Four groups of arthropods and I don't like any of them...

Some of the features of the different organisms might seem obvious — but make sure you know the differences between them so that you don't get confused between your cats, catfish and caterpillars.

Dichotomous Keys

You might need to identify some organisms based on their features. Keys are a useful way of doing that.

Dichotomous Keys are Used to Identify Organisms

1) A key is a written tool that you can use to figure out what an unknown organism is.

2) A dichotomous key is a specific type of key that repeatedly divides groups of organisms into two categories.

3) To use a key you start at question 1, and the answer to that question (which you know by looking at your mystery organism) is used to narrow down your options of what it could be.

4) Sometimes keys will just have statements, rather than questions.

5) As you answer more and more questions you narrow down your options further until eventually you're just left with one possible species your organism could be.

Part of a dichotomous key is shown on the right. It can be used to identify ladybird species.	5)	Black spots on wings	go to 6
		No spots on wings	go to 11
	6)	Rings around wing spots	Eyed ladybird
		No rings around wing spots	go to 9

6) You can even construct a dichotomous key yourself:

1) First you need a sample of all the organisms the key will identify.

2) Split your sample into two groups based on one characteristic and write down two statements that describe the groups (e.g. has 6 legs, has more than 6 legs).

3) Then split each group into two using a different characteristic, writing statements for each group.

4) Keep splitting your groups until you're left with only pairs. Then link your statements together in the right order — you've now made a key.

Dichotomous keys — unlocking the door of classification...

Dichotomous keys aren't too tricky but you need to make sure you know how to use them and how to construct one yourself. If you're asked to make one in the exam, remember that each question or statement should have only two options.

Warm-Up & Exam Questions

That's it — the first section is finished. Have a go at these questions to see how much you know.
If there's anything you've forgotten, have a look back over the last few pages to remind yourself.

Warm-Up Questions

1) Define the term nutrition.
2) Define the term species.
3) What are arthropods?

Exam Questions

1   Sam is using a dichotomous key to identify some butterflies based on their wing markings.
    Part of the key is shown.

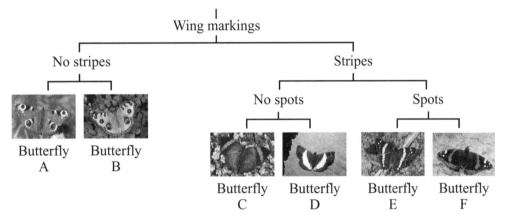

Sam is given the photograph shown below.

(a)   Using the key, describe the wing markings shown on the butterfly in the photograph.

[1]

(b)   Sam uses the key and an information sheet to identify the butterfly species in the photograph.
      It is a Red Admiral butterfly. Which of the butterflies in the key is a Red Admiral butterfly?

[1]

[Total 2 marks]

Exam Questions

2   The picture on the right shows an adult starfish. Starfish are found in oceans around the world. On the undersides of their arms they have small structures called 'tube feet', which are very sensitive to chemicals in the water, helping them to detect food. When they detect food, they move their arms to travel in the right direction. To reproduce, their arms contain glands which release eggs or sperm into the water.

(a)   Give **three** pieces of evidence from the passage that show starfish are living organisms.

[3]

(b)   Name the process by which starfish release energy from the food they eat.

[1]

(c)   Starfish carry out the process of excretion. Describe what this means.

[1]

(d)   Suggest how a very young starfish may differ from the adult starfish above.

[1]

The common starfish has the binomial name *Asterias rubens*.

(e)   What genus does it belong to?

[1]

[Total 7 marks]

3   Classification involves arranging living organisms into groups. In one system of classification, organisms are first arranged into five groups called kingdoms.

(a)   List the five kingdoms in this classification system.

[1]

Viruses are not living organisms and are not classified into their own kingdom.

(b)   Give **two** features of viruses.

[2]

[Total 3 marks]

Supplement

4   Scientists can carry out DNA analysis to determine the evolutionary relationships between organisms.

(a)   Explain how DNA sequencing can be used to determine relationships between organisms.

[2]

The table below shows the percentage similarities between the DNA sequences of humans and four other organisms.

Organism	A	B	C	D
% DNA sequence similarity to humans	18	44	92	54

(b)   Suggest which of the organisms, A-D, is most closely related to humans. Explain your answer.

[2]

[Total 4 marks]

Supplement

Cells

If you take a look down a microscope, you might see cells — the microscopic building blocks of all life.

Plant and Animal Cells have Similarities and Differences

Animal Cells

One of the big differences between plant and animal cells is the structures in the cells. Most animal cells have the following structures — make sure you know them all:

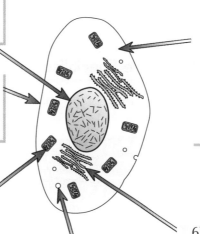

1) Nucleus — contains genetic material that controls the activities of the cell.

3) Cell membrane — holds the cell together and controls what goes in and out.

2) Cytoplasm — gel-like substance where most of the chemical reactions happen. It contains enzymes (see page 31) that control these chemical reactions. It also contains other cell structures.

4) Mitochondria — these are where most of the reactions for aerobic respiration take place (see page 78). Respiration transfers energy that the cell needs to work, so mitochondria are found in large numbers in cells with high rates of metabolism. Almost all cells except prokaryotes (e.g. bacteria) have mitochondria.

5) Vesicles — fluid-filled sacs surrounded by a membrane. They transport substances in and out of the cell, and between structures in the cell.

6) Rough endoplasmic reticulum — a system of membranes enclosing a fluid-filled space. The surface is covered with ribosomes (which are involved in protein synthesis — see p.126). Almost all cells except prokaryotes have rough endoplasmic reticulum.

Supplement

Plant Cells

Plant cells usually have all the structures that animal cells have, plus a few extra things that animal cells don't have:

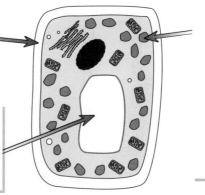

1) Rigid cell wall — made of cellulose. It supports the cell and strengthens it.

3) Vacuole — contains cell sap, a weak solution of sugar and salts. It helps to keep the cell plump and swollen.

2) Chloroplasts — these are where photosynthesis occurs, which makes food for the plant (see page 36). They contain a green substance called chlorophyll, which absorbs the light needed for photosynthesis.

Specialised Cells

The previous page shows the structure of some typical cells. However, most cells are specialised for a particular function, so their structure can vary...

Different Cells Have Different Functions

1) Multicellular organisms are organisms that contain lots of different types of cells (i.e. cells with different structures).

2) Cells that have a structure which makes them adapted to their function are called specialised cells.

3) You need to know examples of how some specialised cells are adapted to their functions. Let's take a look at palisade mesophyll cells first:

Palisade Mesophyll Cells are Specialised for Photosynthesis

1) Palisade mesophyll cells are where most of the photosynthesis happens in a plant leaf.

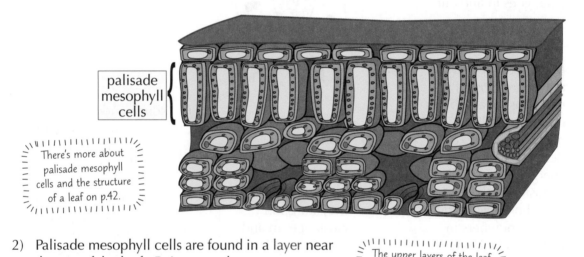

palisade mesophyll cells

There's more about palisade mesophyll cells and the structure of a leaf on p.42.

2) Palisade mesophyll cells are found in a layer near the top of the leaf. Being near the top means they can get the most light for photosynthesis.

The upper layers of the leaf are transparent so that light can pass through it to the palisade mesophyll layer.

3) The cells have lots of chloroplasts (the structures where photosynthesis takes place).

4) They're also long and thin, so more of them can be packed into the same space.

Root Hair Cells are Specialised for Absorbing Water and Minerals

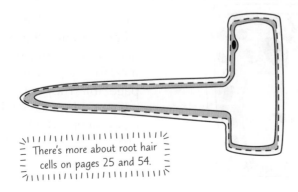

1) Root hair cells are cells on the surface of plant roots, which grow into long "hairs" that stick out into the soil.

2) This gives the plant a big surface area for absorbing water and mineral ions from the soil.

There's more about root hair cells on pages 25 and 54.

Specialised Cells

Xylem Cells are Specialised for Transporting Water

1) Xylem cells form xylem vessels (tubes). These are the water conduction vessels in a plant — they transport water around the plant.

2) Xylem vessels are strengthened with a material called lignin. This allows them to provide the plant with support.

3) The cells are long and joined end to end to form the xylem vessels.

4) The cells are hollow in the centre, so that water can flow through them.

There's more about xylem vessels on page 53.

Ciliated Cells Are Specialised for Moving Materials

1) Ciliated cells line the inner surfaces of some animal organs.

2) They have cilia (hair-like structures) on the top surface of the cell.

3) The function of these ciliated cells is to move substances — the cilia beat to move substances in one direction, along the surface of the tissue.

In the trachea and bronchi (tubes that carry air to and from your lungs), ciliated cells help to move mucus (and all of the particles from the air that it has trapped) up to the throat so it can be swallowed and doesn't reach the lungs.

There's more about ciliated cells on p.75.

Cilia

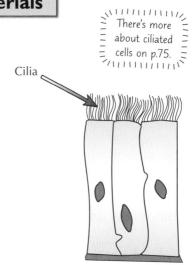

Red Blood Cells are Specialised to Transport Oxygen

1) The job of red blood cells is to transport oxygen from the lungs to all the cells in the body.

2) Their shape is a biconcave disc (a disc that's squashed in the centre) — this gives a large surface area for absorbing oxygen.

3) They contain a red pigment called haemoglobin. This substance allows red blood cells to carry oxygen.

4) They don't have a nucleus — this allows more room to carry oxygen.

There's more about red blood cells on p.63.

Specialised Cells

Nerve Cells are Specialised for Impulse Conduction

1) The function of nerve cells is to conduct (carry) impulses (electrical signals) from one part of the body to another.

2) These cells are long (to cover more distance) and have branched connections at their ends to connect to other nerve cells and form a network throughout the body.

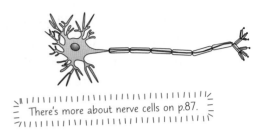

There's more about nerve cells on p.87.

Sperm and Egg Cells are Specialised for Reproduction

1) The main functions of an egg are to carry the female DNA and to nourish the developing embryo in the early stages of its development.

2) An egg cell is adapted to nourish the embryo because it is large and contains nutrients in the cytoplasm to feed the embryo.

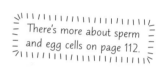

There's more about sperm and egg cells on page 112.

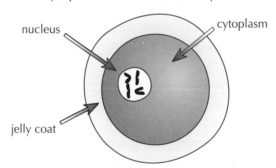

nucleus   cytoplasm

jelly coat

3) The function of a sperm is to transport the male's DNA to the female's egg. This is how it's adapted to its function:

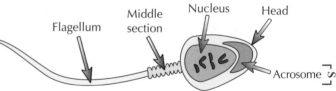

Flagellum   Middle section   Nucleus   Head

Acrosome

1) A sperm cell has a long flagellum (tail) and a streamlined head to help it swim to the egg.

2) It has enzymes in its 'head', which are needed to digest through the membrane of the egg cell. These enzymes are stored in the acrosome.

Supplement

3) It has lots of mitochondria (p.11) in the middle section to provide the energy (from respiration) needed to swim this distance.

Cells have the same basic structures but are often specialised

REVISION TIP

Make sure you know the structures of a typical animal and plant cell. Try copying out the diagrams and see if you can remember all the labels. And remember, specialised cells might look different from these typical cells and not all of them will contain all of the structures.

Levels of Organisation

Multicellular organisms contain lots of cells. These need some form of organisation.

Similar Cells are Organised into Tissues

1) You need to know the definition of a tissue:

> A tissue is a group of similar cells that work together to carry out a shared function.

Muscular tissue

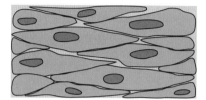

2) A tissue can include more than one type of cell.

In mammals (like humans) an example of a tissue is muscular tissue. This contracts (shortens) to move whatever it's attached to. E.g. when you breathe in, intercostal muscles between the ribs contract to move the ribs upwards (see page 74).

Tissues are Organised into Organs

You need to know the definition of an organ:

> An organ is a group of different tissues that work together to perform specific functions.

Lungs in mammals and leaves on plants are two examples of organs — they're both made up of several different tissue types. The function of the lungs is gas exchange. Leaves have several functions, including carrying out most photosynthesis.

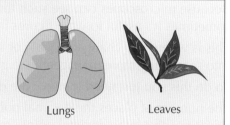

Lungs   Leaves

Organs Make Up Organ Systems

You need to know the definition of an organ system:

> An organ system is a group of organs working together to perform body functions.

For example, in mammals, the urinary system is made up of organs including the kidneys, ureters, bladder and urethra. Its function is the removal of waste from the body.

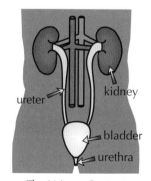

ureter   kidney

bladder
urethra

The Urinary System

Remember — cells, tissues, organs, organ systems

It's important to understand the levels of organisation in organisms. Read the page again if you need to.

Magnification

You can use microscopes to look at cells. Sometimes you need to do a bit of maths with microscope images.

Magnification is **How Many Times Bigger** the Image is

1) Microscopes use lenses to magnify images (make them look bigger).

2) If you know the real size of a specimen and have measured the size of the microscope image, you can work out the magnification of the image. This is the formula you need:

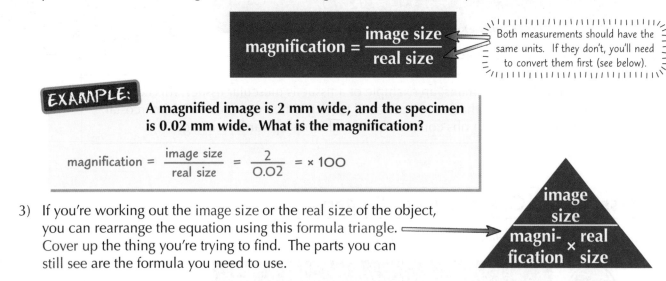

$$\text{magnification} = \frac{\text{image size}}{\text{real size}}$$

Both measurements should have the same units. If they don't, you'll need to convert them first (see below).

EXAMPLE: **A magnified image is 2 mm wide, and the specimen is 0.02 mm wide. What is the magnification?**

$$\text{magnification} = \frac{\text{image size}}{\text{real size}} = \frac{2}{0.02} = \times 100$$

3) If you're working out the image size or the real size of the object, you can rearrange the equation using this formula triangle. Cover up the thing you're trying to find. The parts you can still see are the formula you need to use.

image size

magni-fication × real size

You Might Need to **Convert Units** or Use **Standard Notation**

1) Because microscopes can see such tiny objects, sometimes it's useful to write figures in standard notation.

2) This is where you change very big or small numbers with lots of zeros into something more manageable, e.g. 0.017 can be written 1.7×10^{-2}.

3) To do this you just need to move the decimal point left or right.

4) The number of places the decimal point moves is then represented by a power of 10 — this is positive if the decimal point's moved to the left, and negative if it's moved to the right.

5) You can also use different units to express very big or very small numbers. E.g. 0.0007 m could be written as 0.7 mm.

6) The table shows you how to convert between different units. The right hand column of the table shows you how each unit can be expressed as a metre in standard notation.

To convert	Unit	To convert	In standard notation:
× 1000	Millimetre (mm)	÷ 1000	$\times 10^{-3}$ m
× 1000	Micrometre (µm)	÷ 1000	$\times 10^{-6}$ m
× 1000	Nanometre (nm)	÷ 1000	$\times 10^{-9}$ m
	Picometre (pm)		$\times 10^{-12}$ m

So 1 pm = 0.000000000001 m.

If you're taking the Core exams, you only need to be able to use millimetres in magnification calculations. If you're taking the Extended exams, you need to be able to convert between millimetres and micrometres in magnification calculations.

7) These conversions work for lots of other units too, e.g. 1 milligram (mg) = 1000 micrograms (µg).

Learn the formula for calculating magnification

You might need to use that formula triangle in the exam, so make sure you know it off by heart. You only really need to remember that image size goes at the top of the triangle, which shouldn't be too tricky, since it comes first when you put the three things in alphabetical order.

Warm-Up & Exam Questions

It's easy to think you've learnt everything in the section until you try the questions.
Don't panic if there's a bit you've forgotten, just go back over that bit until you know you really remember it.

Warm-Up Questions

1) Give two similarities and two differences between the structure of an animal cell and the structure of a plant cell.
2) Name the structures inside a cell where aerobic respiration takes place.
3) Which structure inside a cell can ribosomes be found attached to?

Exam Questions

1   The diagram on the right shows a typical plant cell.

(a)   Which label points to a chloroplast? Tick **one** box.

 A   **B**   **C**   **D**

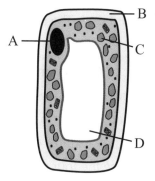

[1]

(b)   What is the function of a chloroplast?

[1]

(c)   The diagram also shows a cell wall.
What is the function of a cell wall?

[1]
[Total 3 marks]

2   The diagram on the right shows a root hair cell.
Explain how a root hair cell is specialised for its function.

[Total 2 marks]

3   A microscope is used to observe a layer of onion cells on a slide.

(a)   When the onion cell is viewed with × 100 magnification, the image of the cell is 7.5 mm wide.
Calculate the real width of the onion cell using the formula:

$$\text{magnification} = \frac{\text{image size}}{\text{real size}}$$

Give your answer in mm.

[2]

(b)   Convert your answer from **part (a)** into µm.

[1]
[Total 3 marks]

Revision Summary for Sections 1 & 2

That's the end of Sections 1 & 2 — time to put yourself to the test and find out how much you really know.
- Try these questions and tick off each one when you get it right.
- When you've done all the questions for a topic and are completely happy with it, tick off the topic.

Characteristics of Living Organisms (p.1) ☑
1) Define movement.
2) Why is respiration important?
3) True or false? Growth is only an increase in cell number.
4) What materials do plants need for nutrition? What do animals need?

Classification (p.2-3) ☑
5) True or false? Organisms can be classified based on their features.
6) How does the binomial system name organisms?
7) True or false? The more closely related two organisms are, the less recent their common ancestor.

Features of Organisms and Dichotomous Keys (p.4-8) ☑
8) Give two differences between animals and plants.
9) What are the five main groups of vertebrates?
10) Give three features of birds.
11) What are the four main groups of arthropods?
12) Flowering plants can be divided into two main groups — what are they?
13) What is a dichotomous key?

Cells and Specialised Cells (p.11-14) ☑
14) Name three structures that are found in the cytoplasm of an animal cell.
15) What is the function of the cell membrane?
16) What is the purpose of the ciliated cells that line the bronchi and trachea?
17) Draw a diagram of a nerve cell. Why is it this shape?
18) Give one way that a sperm cell is adapted for swimming to an egg cell.

Levels of Organisation (p.15) ☑
19) What is a tissue?
20) What name is given to a group of different tissues working together to perform specific functions?
21) Give one example of an organ and one example of an organ system.

Magnification (p.16) ☑
22) What is the formula for calculating magnification?
23) How would you write 0.017 using standard notation?
24) What number do you multiply by to convert from millimetres to micrometres?

Diffusion

Diffusion is really important in living organisms — it's how a lot of substances get in and out of cells. In diffusion, particles move about randomly until they end up evenly spaced.

Diffusion is Just Particles Spreading Out

1) Diffusion is simple. It's just the gradual movement of particles from places where there are lots of them to places where there are fewer of them.

 KEY TERM — Diffusion is the net movement of particles from a region of their higher concentration to a region of their lower concentration as a result of their random movement.

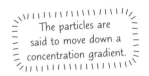 The particles are said to move down a concentration gradient.

2) Diffusion happens in both solutions and gases — that's because the particles in these substances (solutes or gas molecules) are free to move about randomly.

3) The simplest type is when different gases diffuse through each other. This is what's happening when the smell of perfume diffuses through a room:

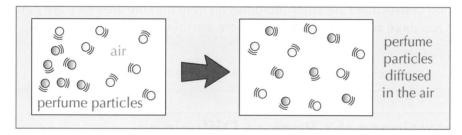

air

perfume particles

perfume particles diffused in the air

4) Diffusion is due to the molecules and ions moving about randomly because of their kinetic energy. It doesn't require any additional energy from cells to make it happen.

Cell Membranes are Pretty Clever...

1) They're clever because they hold the cell together but they let stuff in and out as well.

2) Only small molecules can diffuse through cell membranes though — things like glucose, amino acids, water and oxygen. Big molecules like starch and proteins can't fit through the membrane.

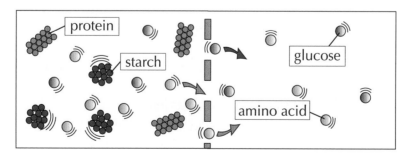

protein

starch

glucose

amino acid

• Just like with diffusion in air, particles flow through the cell membrane from where there's a higher concentration (more of them) to where there's a lower concentration (fewer of them).

• They're only moving about randomly of course, so they go both ways — but if there are a lot more particles on one side of the membrane, there's a net (overall) movement from that side.

Investigating Diffusion

You need to know about the four different factors that affect diffusion, and how you can investigate them.

The **Rate of Diffusion** Depends on **Four Main Things**

1) Surface area — the more surface there is for molecules to move across, the faster they can get from one side to the other. This means that the bigger the surface area to volume ratio of an object, the faster particles will diffuse in or out of it.

Have a look at this example using cubes. The smaller cube has a larger surface area to volume ratio.

	2 cm cube	3 cm cube
Surface area / cm²	2 × 2 × 6 = 24	3 × 3 × 6 = 54
Volume / cm³	2 × 2 × 2 = 8	3 × 3 × 3 = 27
Surface area to volume ratio	24 : 8 = <u>3 : 1</u>	54 : 27 = <u>2 : 1</u>

2) Temperature — the higher the temperature, the greater the kinetic energy of the molecules and therefore the faster their movement.

3) Concentration gradient — substances diffuse faster if there's a big difference in concentration between the area they are diffusing from and the area they are diffusing to. If there are lots more particles on one side, there are more there to move across.

4) Distance — substances diffuse more quickly when they haven't as far to move.

You Can **Investigate** the **Rate** of **Diffusion**

Phenolphthalein is a pH indicator — it's pink in alkaline solutions and colourless in acidic solutions. You can use it to investigate diffusion in agar jelly:

1) First, make up some agar jelly with phenolphthalein and dilute sodium hydroxide. This will make the jelly pink.
2) Put some dilute hydrochloric acid in a beaker.
3) Cut out a few cubes from the jelly and put them in the beaker of acid.
4) The cubes turn colourless as the acid diffuses into the jelly and neutralises the sodium hydroxide.
5) Time how long it takes for the colour to change.

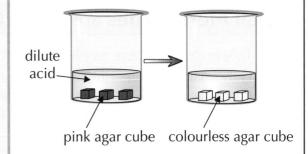

dilute acid

pink agar cube   colourless agar cube

You can modify this experiment to investigate the effect of various factors on the rate of diffusion:

- Surface area — use different sized cubes of agar jelly.
- Temperature — put the beakers of dilute acid in water baths set to different temperatures.
- Concentration gradient — use different concentrations of dilute acid.

To investigate the effect of distance on rate, you'll need to carry out a slightly different experiment:

1) Fill two identical beakers with different volumes of water, e.g. 100 cm³ and 250 cm³.
2) Once the water is still, add a couple of drops of ink to each beaker.
3) Time how long it takes for the ink to spread out completely in each beaker.

Supplement

Osmosis

If you've learnt all there is to know about diffusion, osmosis will be easy. If not, read the previous page...

Osmosis is a **Special Case** of **Diffusion**

1) Water diffuses through partially permeable membranes by osmosis.

2) A partially permeable membrane is just one with very small holes in it. So small, in fact, only tiny molecules (like water) can pass through them, and bigger molecules (e.g. sucrose) can't.

3) A cell membrane is a partially permeable membrane.

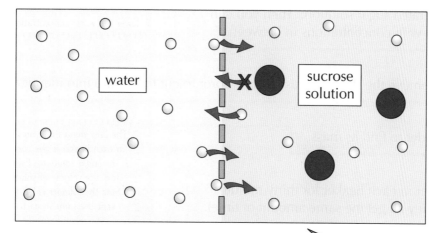

When water molecules diffuse, their net movement is from a region of their higher concentration to a region of their lower concentration — like all diffusing particles.

Net movement of water molecules

4) The water molecules actually pass both ways through the membrane during osmosis. This happens because water molecules move about randomly all the time.

5) But because there are more water molecules on one side than on the other, there's a steady net flow of water into the region with fewer water molecules, e.g. into the sucrose solution.

6) This means the sucrose solution gets more dilute. The water acts like it's trying to "even up" the concentration either side of the membrane.

Water Potential Tells You How **Concentrated** a **Solution** is

1) You can talk about osmosis in terms of water potential — water potential is the potential (likelihood) of water molecules to diffuse out of or into a solution.

2) If a solution has a high water potential, then it has a high concentration of water molecules. If it has a low water potential, then it has a low concentration of water molecules.

Pure water has the highest water potential. All solutions have a lower water potential than pure water.

3) So, you can say that:

> Osmosis is the net movement of water molecules from a region of higher water potential to a region of lower water potential, across a partially permeable membrane.

4) You could also describe osmosis as the net movement of water molecules from a dilute solution to a concentrated solution, across a partially permeable membrane.

Investigating Osmosis

You need to know how to investigate the effects of osmosis on plant tissues.

You Can **Investigate** the **Effects** of **Osmosis**

This experiment involves putting potato cylinders into different concentrations of sugar solution to see what effect different water concentrations have on them.

1) Prepare some beakers with different sugar solutions in them. One should be pure water and another should be a very concentrated sugar solution. Then you can have a few others with concentrations in between.

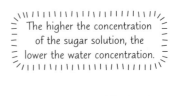
The higher the concentration of the sugar solution, the lower the water concentration.

2) Peel a potato to remove the skin, then use a cork borer to cut the potato into identical cylinders.

3) Weigh each cylinder to find its mass.

The only thing that you should change in each beaker is the concentration of the sugar solution. Everything else (e.g. the volume of solution and the time the cylinder is left for) must be kept the same in each case or the experiment won't be a fair test.

4) Leave one cylinder in each beaker for thirty minutes (make sure that they all get the same amount of time).

increasing sugar concentration

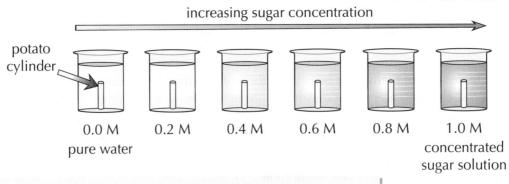

potato cylinder

| 0.0 M | 0.2 M | 0.4 M | 0.6 M | 0.8 M | 1.0 M |
| pure water | | | | | concentrated sugar solution |

5) Remove the cylinders and pat dry gently with a paper towel. This removes excess water from the surface of the cylinders.

6) Weigh each cylinder again and record the mass.

7) If the cylinders were placed in a solution with a higher concentration of water molecules than the solution inside the potato cells, they will have drawn in water by osmosis. This means they'll have increased in mass.

8) If the cylinders were placed in a solution with a lower concentration of water molecules than the solution inside the potato cells, water will have been drawn out by osmosis. This means they'll have decreased in mass.

PRACTICAL TIP

There are lots of variations on this osmosis experiment

This experiment uses sugar as a solute, but you could also do it with different solutes (e.g. salt). You could even do it with a different root vegetable, e.g. a carrot or swede (rutabaga).

Osmosis and Cells

You need to know more specifically about how osmosis affects plant cells.

Osmosis Affects **Plant Cells**

1) As you saw in the investigation on the previous page, water can be drawn into or out of plant cells by osmosis.

2) If a plant cell is placed in a solution with a higher concentration of water molecules than the solution inside the plant cell, water will move into the cell by osmosis. This will make the cell become plump and swollen.

3) A plump and swollen cell is called a turgid cell.

4) When the plant cell is full of water, the pressure of the water presses outwards on the cell wall. This helps to support the cell.

5) The pressure of the water against the inelastic (rigid) cell wall is called turgor pressure.

6) If a plant cell is placed in a solution with a lower concentration of water molecules than the solution inside the plant cell, water will move out of the cell by osmosis. This will make the cell become limp and wilted.

7) A limp and wilted cell is called a flaccid cell.

8) If the plant's really short of water, the cytoplasm inside its cells starts to shrink and the membrane pulls away from the cell wall. This process is called plasmolysis.

Plants absorb water from the soil through their root hair cells (see p.12). The water potential of the soil always tends to be higher than that of the solution inside root hair cells, which allows the plant to constantly draw in water by osmosis.

Osmosis Affects **Animal Cells** too

1) Animal cells don't have cell walls so they're more affected by their surroundings than plant cells.

2) Tissue fluid surrounds the cells and tissues in the body — it's basically just water with oxygen and glucose dissolved in it. It's squeezed out of the capillaries to supply cells and tissues with everything they need.

3) The tissue fluid will usually have a different water potential to the fluid inside a cell or tissue. This means that water will either move into the cell or tissue from the tissue fluid, or out of the cell or tissue, by osmosis.

4) The lack of cell walls means that animal cells can burst if they're surrounded by a solution with a higher water potential than them. If the water potential of the solution surrounding a cell is lower than the cell, the cell can shrivel up and die.

Water always moves into the more concentrated solution

That's why it's bad to drink sea-water. The high salt content means you end up with a much lower water potential in your blood and tissue fluid than in your cells. All the water is sucked out of your cells by osmosis and they shrivel and die. So next time you're stranded at sea, remember this...

Active Transport

Sometimes substances need to be absorbed against a concentration gradient, i.e. from a lower to a higher concentration. This is done by a process called active transport.

Active Transport Works Against a Concentration Gradient

Active transport is different from diffusion because particles are moved up a concentration gradient rather than down, and the process requires energy in addition to kinetic energy to make it work.

 KEY TERM

Active transport is the movement of particles across a cell membrane from a region of lower concentration to a region of higher concentration using energy from respiration.

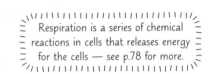
Respiration is a series of chemical reactions in cells that releases energy for the cells — see p.78 for more.

Active Transport Uses Protein Molecules

Protein molecules called carrier proteins are involved in active transport. The carrier proteins are embedded in cell membranes to help move particles across. Here's how they work:

1) A molecule that needs to move across the membrane attaches to the carrier protein.

2) The protein then changes shape, which requires energy, and moves the molecule across the membrane.

3) The molecule is released on the other side.

The diagram shows the active transport of a calcium ion:

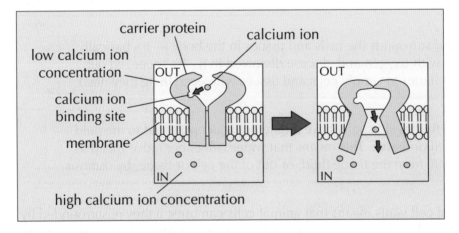

carrier protein   calcium ion

low calcium ion concentration

calcium ion binding site

membrane

OUT

OUT

IN

IN

high calcium ion concentration

 REVISION TIP

Active transport is an active process — it requires energy

Active transport involves moving substances against the concentration gradient, so it needs additional energy from respiration to make it work. Think of it like this: if you're trying to walk along a crowded street, it's hard to walk in the opposite direction to the one most people are travelling in. You have to push your way through — and that requires energy.

Supplement

Supplement

Active Transport

Active transport is important to both plants and humans — here's a page all about why.

Root Hairs Take in Minerals Using Active Transport

1) Plants need mineral ions for healthy growth.

> Water is taken into root hair cells by osmosis (see page 23).

2) The concentration of minerals is usually higher in a plant's root hair cells (see p.12) than in the soil around them.

3) This means plants can't use diffusion to take up mineral ions from the soil. If they followed the rules of diffusion, minerals would move out of the root hair cells.

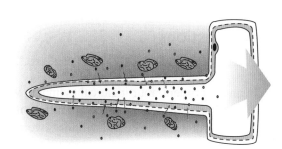

4) Instead, the cells use active transport to move minerals across their cell membranes. This allows the plant to absorb minerals from a very dilute solution, against a concentration gradient.

Active Transport is Important in Humans Too

Active transport is used by epithelial cells of the villi in the small intestine, when there is a lower concentration of glucose in the gut, but a higher concentration of glucose in the blood.

> There's more about villi on page 50.

1) When there's a higher concentration of glucose in the gut, glucose diffuses naturally into the blood.

2) BUT — sometimes there's a lower concentration of glucose in the gut than there is in the blood.

3) This means that the concentration gradient is the wrong way.

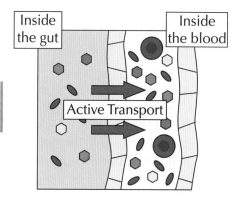

Inside the gut · Inside the blood · Active Transport

4) Active transport allows glucose to be taken across the membranes of the epithelial cells into the blood, despite the fact that the concentration gradient is the wrong way.

This means that glucose can be taken into the bloodstream when its concentration in the blood is already higher than in the gut. It can then be transported to cells, where it's used for respiration (see p.78).

The same process happens in kidney tubules (see p.84). Glucose is filtered out of the blood (along with waste products) at the start of the kidney. It's needed for respiration, so active transport allows glucose to be reabsorbed from the tubules back into the blood.

Warm-Up & Exam Questions

Question time again — Warm-Up first, then Exam (or the other way round if you want to be different).

Warm-Up Questions

1) What is the definition of osmosis? Use the term 'water potential' in your answer.
2) Give one difference between diffusion and active transport.

Exam Questions

1   In an experiment, four identical cylinders were cut from a fresh potato.
    The cylinders were then placed in different sugar solutions, as shown below.
    After 30 minutes the potato cylinders were removed and their mass measured.

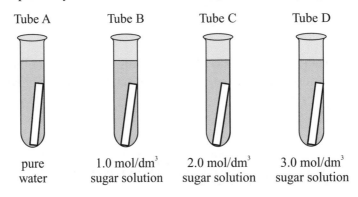

Tube A	Tube B	Tube C	Tube D
pure water	1.0 mol/dm³ sugar solution	2.0 mol/dm³ sugar solution	3.0 mol/dm³ sugar solution

(a)   Which potato cylinder would you expect to have the lowest mass after 30 minutes?
      Explain your answer.

[2]

(b)   The potato cylinder in tube A increased in mass during the 30 minutes. Explain why.

[2]

[Total 4 marks]

2   A student made up some agar jelly with cresol red solution and dilute ammonium hydroxide.
    Cresol red solution is a pH indicator that is red in alkaline solutions and yellow in acidic solutions.
    He cut the agar jelly into cubes of different sizes, and placed the cubes in a beaker of dilute
    hydrochloric acid. He measured how long it took for the cubes to change from red to yellow as the
    acid moved into the agar jelly and neutralised the ammonium hydroxide. His results are shown.

Size / mm	Time taken for cube to become yellow / s			
	Trial 1	Trial 2	Trial 3	Trial 4
5 × 5 × 5	174	167	177	182
7 × 7 × 7	274	290	284	292
10 × 10 × 10	835	825	842	838

(a)   Name the process by which hydrochloric acid moves into the cubes in this experiment.

[1]

(b)   Explain the relationship between the size of the cube and the time taken for it to become yellow.

[2]

[Total 3 marks]

Supplement

Biological Molecules

Biological molecules (molecules found in living organisms) are things like carbohydrates, proteins and fats. They're generally long, complex molecules made up from smaller basic units.

Learn the **Structure** of **Carbohydrates**, **Proteins** and **Fats**

Carbohydrates are Made Up of **Simple Sugars**

- Carbohydrate molecules contain the elements carbon, hydrogen and oxygen.
- Starch (in plants) and glycogen (in animals) are used as short-term energy stores. Cellulose is the main component of plant cell walls.
- They are all large, complex carbohydrates, which are made up of many smaller molecules of glucose (a simple sugar) joined together in a long chain.

glucose → starch

Proteins are Made Up of **Long Chains** of **Amino Acids**

- Proteins all contain carbon, nitrogen, hydrogen and oxygen atoms.
- Some proteins also contain sulfur atoms.

amino acids → proteins

Fats and **Oils** are Made Up of **Fatty Acids** and **Glycerol**

- Fats contain carbon, hydrogen and oxygen atoms.

glycerol & fatty acids → fat

Proteins Have Many **Different Functions**

When a chain of amino acids has been assembled, it folds into a unique shape which allows the protein to perform the task it's meant to do. Different sequences of amino acids result in proteins with different shapes. Here are two examples of proteins and how their shape lets them do their task:

ENZYMES — act as biological catalysts to speed up chemical reactions in the body (see page 31). In order to speed up a reaction, a part of the enzyme called the active site has to bind to the substrate (reacting molecule). The shape of the enzyme affects the shape of its active site, which determines what substrate it can bind to and what chemical reaction it can catalyse.

ANTIBODIES — are part of the immune system and help the body fight pathogens (see page 70). A part of the antibody called the binding site binds to molecules on the surface of pathogens called antigens. The shape of the antibody affects the shape of its binding site, which determines which antigen it can bind to and which pathogen it can help fight.

Supplement ... *Supplement*

Biological molecules are the basic units of Biology

Since all living organisms are made up of carbohydrates, proteins and fats, you'll come across all of these molecules again during your course. This makes them very likely to come up somewhere in your exams — so make sure you learn everything you need to here before you move on.

Testing for Biological Molecules

You need to know how you can test for biological molecules using different chemicals.

You Can Test for **Sugars** Using **Benedict's Solution**

There are lots of different types of sugar molecules. Due to their chemical properties, many sugars (e.g. glucose) are called reducing sugars. You don't need to know exactly what reducing sugars are, but you do need to know how to test for them:

1) Add Benedict's solution (which is blue) to a sample and heat it in a water bath that's set to 75 °C.

2) If the test's positive it will form a coloured precipitate (solid particles suspended in the solution).

3) The higher the concentration of reducing sugar, the further the colour change goes — you can use this to compare the amount of reducing sugar in different solutions.

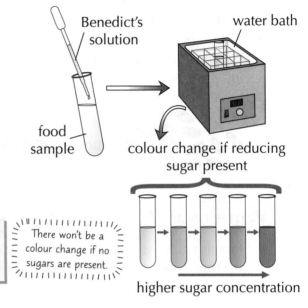

Benedict's solution

water bath

food sample

colour change if reducing sugar present

The colour of the precipitate changes from:

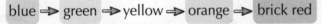

blue ⇒ green ⇒ yellow ⇒ orange ⇒ brick red

There won't be a colour change if no sugars are present.

higher sugar concentration

The **Biuret Test** is Used for **Proteins**

If you needed to find out if a substance contained protein you'd use the biuret test.

1) First, add a few drops of potassium hydroxide solution to make the solution alkaline.

2) Then add some copper(II) sulfate solution (which is bright blue).

3) If there's no protein, the solution will stay blue.

4) If protein is present, the solution will turn purple.

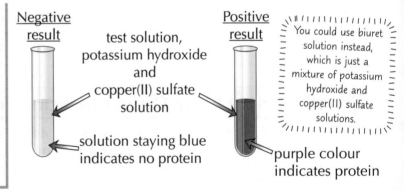

Negative result

test solution, potassium hydroxide and copper(II) sulfate solution

solution staying blue indicates no protein

Positive result

You could use biuret solution instead, which is just a mixture of potassium hydroxide and copper(II) sulfate solutions.

purple colour indicates protein

Starch is Tested for with **Iodine**

Just add iodine solution to the test sample.

1) If starch is present, the sample changes from browny-orange to a dark, blue-black colour.

2) If there's no starch, it stays browny-orange.

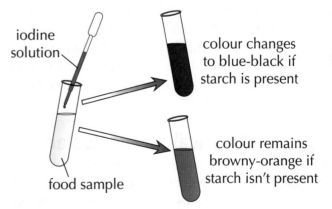

iodine solution

colour changes to blue-black if starch is present

colour remains browny-orange if starch isn't present

food sample

Testing for Biological Molecules

There are a couple more tests coming up on this page — for fats and oils, and vitamin C.

Use the **Ethanol Emulsion Test** for **Fats** and **Oils**

To find out if there are any fats or oils in a sample:

1) Shake the test substance with ethanol for about a minute until it dissolves, then pour the solution into water.

2) If there are any fats or oils present, they will precipitate out of the liquid and show up as a milky emulsion.

3) The more fat there is, the more noticeable the milky colour will be.

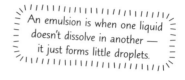
An emulsion is when one liquid doesn't dissolve in another — it just forms little droplets.

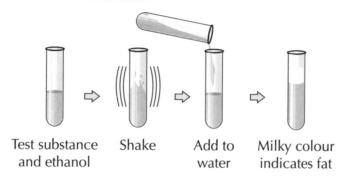

Test substance and ethanol   Shake   Add to water   Milky colour indicates fat

Use the **DCPIP Test** for **Vitamin C**

To find out how much vitamin C is in a food sample you'd use DCPIP solution.

1) Add DCPIP solution drop by drop to a food sample containing vitamin C (e.g. juice).
2) DCPIP solution changes from blue to colourless when vitamin C is present.
3) Keep adding DCPIP until the blue colour no longer disappears when it's mixed with the sample. (Vitamin C reacts with DCPIP solution, making it colourless. The colour stops changing when all the vitamin C has been used up.)
4) The higher the volume of DCPIP solution added before the blue colour stops disappearing, the more vitamin C the food sample contains.

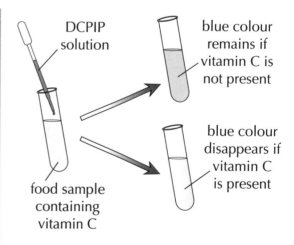

DCPIP solution — blue colour remains if vitamin C is not present — blue colour disappears if vitamin C is present — food sample containing vitamin C

Make sure you think about all of the hazards...

Iodine solution is an irritant to the eyes, and the chemicals used in the biuret test are dangerous, so wear safety goggles when carrying out these tests. If you spill any of the chemicals on your skin, wash them off straight away. Be careful around the water bath in the Benedict's test, too.

Water and DNA

Water and DNA are essential for life. Water is needed by living organisms to stay alive. DNA is needed to build proteins, which are required for the cells in living organisms to function.

Water is Important as a Solvent

Water is a major component of the body and cells. It is a solvent, which means that some substances dissolve in it to form a solution. Most chemical reactions take place in solution. Here are some examples of why water is an important solvent:

TRANSPORT — water allows soluble molecules, such as urea (a waste product produced from the breakdown of proteins), glucose and amino acids, to be transported around the body in the blood.

DIGESTION — digestive enzymes need to be in solution to work properly. Water helps the body to digest food by acting as a solvent for the enzymes.

Water also acts as a solvent for the products of digestion, which allows them to diffuse into the bloodstream.

EXCRETION — your body uses water to transport metabolic waste products (such as urea and toxins) out of the body through, e.g. sweating and urination (weeing).

DNA is a Double Helix

1) A DNA molecule has two strands coiled together in the shape of a double helix (two spirals).

2) Each strand contains chemicals called bases. There are four different bases (shown in the diagram as different colours) — A, C, G and T.

3) The two strands are held together by cross-links that are formed by pairs of bases.

4) The bases always pair up in the same way — it's always A-T and C-G.

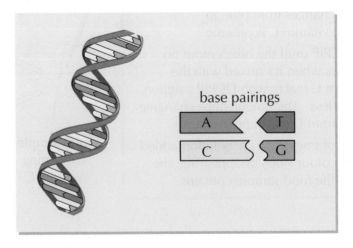

base pairings

A — T

C — G

Every living organism has DNA

DNA contains all the instructions needed to make living organisms. If you're doing the Extended course, one of the things you'll need to learn is how DNA's double helix structure is held together by four bases.

Enzymes

Life would not be possible without chemical reactions. And enzymes are essential for chemical reactions.

Enzymes are **Proteins** that Act as **Catalysts**

1) Living things have thousands of different chemical reactions going on inside them all the time. These reactions need to be carefully controlled — to get the right amounts of substances in the cells.

2) You can usually make a reaction happen more quickly by raising the temperature. This would speed up the useful reactions but also the unwanted ones too... not good. There's also a limit to how far you can raise the temperature inside a living creature before its cells start getting damaged.

3) Catalysts allow reactions to take place faster without needing to increase the temperature.

 A catalyst is a substance which increases the rate of a reaction, without being changed or used up in the reaction.

4) So living things produce enzymes:

 An enzyme is a protein that functions as a biological catalyst.

5) Enzymes reduce the need for high temperatures and we only have enzymes to speed up the useful chemical reactions in the body. These reactions are called metabolic reactions. Without enzymes, metabolic reactions would not be fast enough to sustain life.

An **Enzyme's Shape** Lets it **Catalyse Reactions**

1) Chemical reactions usually involve things either being split apart or joined together.

2) A substrate is a molecule that is changed in a reaction.

3) An enzyme has a shape that is complementary to (matches) the shape of the substrate molecules that bind to it.

4) When the substrate molecule binds to an enzyme, it is changed to a product and then released.

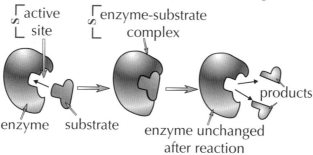

enzyme   substrate   enzyme unchanged after reaction

Supplement

1) The part of an enzyme where the substrate binds is known as the active site.

2) The active site has to be complementary in shape to its substrate for the substrate to fit.

3) This means that enzymes are specific — they usually only speed up one reaction.

4) When a substrate binds to an enzyme, a temporary enzyme-substrate complex forms.

5) The substrate is then converted to products.

Enzymes speed up chemical reactions

A substrate fits into an enzyme just like a key fits into a lock. You've got to have the correct key for a lock and the right substrate for an enzyme. If the substrate doesn't fit, the enzyme won't catalyse the reaction.

More on Enzymes

Enzymes need just the right conditions if they're going to work properly.

Enzymes Like it **Warm** but **Not Too Hot**

Supplement

1) Like with any reaction, a higher temperature increases the rate at first, up to an optimum temperature where the enzyme is most active.

2) After the optimum temperature, the rate of reaction decreases.

3) As the temperature increases, the enzymes and substrate have more kinetic (movement) energy, so they move about more and there are more effective collisions forming enzyme-substrate complexes.

4) But if it gets too hot, some of the bonds holding the enzyme together break. This changes the shape of the enzyme's active site, so the substrate won't fit any more.

5) When this happens the enzyme is said to be denatured.

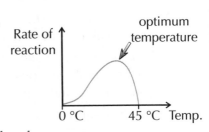

Enzymes Also Need the **Right pH**

Supplement

1) Enzymes have an optimum pH that they work best at. If the pH is above or below the optimum, the rate of reaction decreases.

2) When the pH is too high or too low, the pH affects the bonds holding the enzyme together. This changes the shape of the active site and denatures the enzyme.

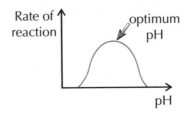

You can **Investigate Factors** that Affect **Enzyme Activity**

One way of investigating how temperature affects enzyme activity is by measuring the rate at which starch is broken down by the enzyme amylase (p.49). Here's how to do it using iodine solution (p.28) and the apparatus shown below:

1) Put a drop of iodine solution into each well on the spotting tile.

2) Every ten seconds, drop a sample of the mixture into a well using a pipette. When the iodine solution remains browny-orange (i.e. starch is no longer present) record the total time taken.

3) Repeat with the water bath at different temperatures to see how it affects the time taken for the starch to be broken down. Remember to control all of the variables each time.

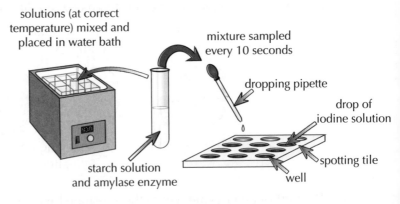

You can adapt this experiment to investigate the effect of pH on enzyme activity. Follow the same method but instead of changing the temperature, add different buffer solutions (solutions with constant pH) with different pH levels to different tubes containing the starch-amylase mixture.

If only enzymes could speed up revision...

Make sure you can describe the effect of changes in temperature and pH on enzyme activity. If the temperature or pH is too high or too low, the enzyme will stop working and no product will appear.

Warm-Up & Exam Questions

The best way to check whether you've learnt something is to test yourself. Have a go at these questions.

Warm-Up Questions

1) Which smaller molecule is cellulose made from?
2) Name the smaller basic units that make up the following molecules: a) a fat, b) a protein.
3) What solution is used to test for reducing sugars?
4) Some iodine solution is added to a sample and the colour changes
   from browny-orange to blue-black. What does this indicate?
5) What is an enzyme?
6) What is the name for the part of an enzyme that a substrate joins onto?
7) How does the shape of an enzyme affect its function?
8) Why don't enzymes work well when the temperature is too hot?

Exam Questions

1 The elements below make up different biological molecules.
1. carbon
2. hydrogen
3. nitrogen
4. oxygen

Which of these elements make up proteins?

☐ **A** 1, 2, 3 and 4

☐ **B** 1, 2 and 4 only

☐ **C** 1 and 4 only

☐ **D** 1 and 3 only

[Total 1 mark]

2 Which row in the following table best describes enzymes?

	are affected by pH	speed up reactions	get used up during reactions	all have the same shape
☐ **A**	✓	✓		
☐ **B**			✓	
☐ **C**	✓	✓		✓
☐ **D**		✓	✓	✓

[Total 1 mark]

Exam Questions

3 The enzyme amylase is involved in the breakdown of starch into simple sugars.

A student investigated the effect of temperature on the activity of amylase in starch solution.
The student used the following method:

1. Amylase and starch solution were added to test tubes **X**, **Y** and **Z**.
2. The test tubes were placed in water baths of different temperatures, as shown in the table below.

Test tube	Temp / °C
X	45
Y	60
Z	75

3. Spotting tiles were prepared with a drop of iodine solution in each well.
   Iodine solution is a browny-orange colour but it turns blue-black in the presence of starch.
4. Every 30 seconds, a drop of the solution from each of the test tubes was added to a separate well on a spotting tile.
5. The resulting colour of the solution in the well was recorded in the table below.

Time / s	30	60	90	120	150
Tube **X**	Blue-black	Blue-black	Blue-black	Browny-orange	Browny-orange
Tube **Y**	Blue-black	Browny-orange	Browny-orange	Browny-orange	Browny-orange
Tube **Z**	Blue-black	Blue-black	Blue-black	Blue-black	Blue-black

(a) Name **one** piece of equipment that could be used to add iodine solution to each well.

[1]

(b) State the temperature at which the rate of reaction was greatest. Explain your answer.

[2]

(c) Suggest an explanation for the results in tube **Z**.

[1]

(d) Suggest **two** variables that should be controlled in this experiment.

[2]

[Total 6 marks]

4 Describe the structure of a DNA molecule.

[Total 4 marks]

5 Outline **three** processes in which water acts as a solvent in organisms.

[Total 3 marks]

Revision Summary for Sections 3 & 4

That's nearly all for Sections 3 & 4 — try these summary questions to put your knowledge to the test.
*   Try these questions and tick off each one when you get it right.
*   When you've done all the questions for a topic and are completely happy with it, tick off the topic.

Movement In and Out of Cells (p.19-25) ☐

1) What is diffusion?

2) A solution of pure water is separated from a concentrated sucrose solution by a partially permeable membrane. In which direction will molecules flow, and what substance will these molecules be?

3) Describe how surface area affects the movement of substances in and out of cells.

4) Describe an experiment that shows diffusion taking place.

5) How is osmosis similar to diffusion?

6) Describe an experiment using plant tissue that shows osmosis taking place.

7) What is turgor pressure?

8) What is plasmolysis?

9) What happens when animal cells are placed in a solution with a higher water potential than theirs?

10) How is active transport different from diffusion in terms of:
    a) energy requirements,
    b) concentration gradients?

11) Give one example of when active transport is used by organisms.

Biological Molecules (p.27-30) ☐

12) Name the three main chemical elements that are found in carbohydrates.

13) Name one biological molecule made up of glucose molecules.

14) What type of biological molecules are made up of fatty acids and glycerol?

15) Describe how you could use biuret solution to test for proteins.

16) What test could you use to see if there are fats in a sample?

17) Why is water essential for organisms?

18) What are the four bases in a DNA molecule?

19) How do the bases in a DNA molecule pair up?

Enzymes (p.31-32) ☐

20) What does a biological catalyst do?

21) Do enzymes and substrate molecules have more or less kinetic energy when the temperature increases?

22) What happens to the frequency of effective collisions between enzyme and substrate molecules when the temperature increases?

23) What does it mean when an enzyme has been 'denatured'?

24) What happens to an enzyme's rate of reaction when the pH is too high or too low?

25) Briefly describe an experiment to show how temperature can affect enzyme activity.

Photosynthesis

Plants can make their own food — which sounds easier than going out to the shops. Here's how they do it...

Photosynthesis Needs Sunlight

1) Basically, photosynthesis is the process that produces 'food' in plants. The 'food' it produces is glucose.

2) You need to learn the proper definition for photosynthesis though:

 KEY TERM

> Photosynthesis is the process that plants use to manufacture carbohydrates (glucose) from raw materials (carbon dioxide and water) using energy from light.

3) Photosynthesis happens in the leaves of all green plants — this is largely what the leaves are for.

4) More specifically, it happens inside the chloroplasts, which are found in leaf cells and in other green parts of a plant. Chloroplasts contain a pigment called chlorophyll, which absorbs sunlight.

5) Chlorophyll transfers light energy from the Sun into chemical energy in molecules, such as glucose.

6) The word equation for photosynthesis is shown below:

$$\text{carbon dioxide} + \text{water} \xrightarrow[\text{chlorophyll}]{\text{LIGHT}} \text{glucose} + \text{oxygen}$$

7) If you're taking the Extended course, you also need to learn the balanced chemical equation:

$$6CO_2 + 6H_2O \xrightarrow[\text{chlorophyll}]{\text{LIGHT}} C_6H_{12}O_6 + 6O_2$$

Plants Use Glucose in Five Main Ways...

For respiration — This transfers energy from glucose (see p.78) which enables the plants to convert the rest of the glucose into various other useful substances.

Making cellulose — Glucose is converted into cellulose for making strong plant cell walls (see p.11).

Making amino acids — Glucose is combined with nitrate ions (absorbed from the soil) to make amino acids, which are then made into proteins.

Stored as fats or oils — Glucose is turned into fats and oils for storing in seeds.

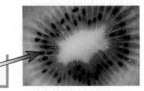

Stored as starch — Glucose is turned into starch and stored in roots, stems and leaves, ready for use when photosynthesis is happening less, like in the winter.

 REVISION TIP

Make sure you really know the photosynthesis equation

Keep trying to write it out from memory (without peeking at the book) until you can do it by heart.

Rate of Photosynthesis

Photosynthesis can happen at different rates (speeds) depending on the environmental conditions.

Limiting Factors Affect the Rate of Photosynthesis

Supplement

1) The rate of photosynthesis varies. It all depends on what the limiting factor is at that moment in time.

 KEY TERM A limiting factor is something present in the environment in such short supply that it restricts life processes.

Life processes are the characteristics of living organisms (p.1).

Supplement

2) Limiting factors that affect photosynthesis include light intensity, temperature and CO_2 concentration.

3) The limiting factor depends on the environmental conditions. E.g. in winter, low temperatures might be the limiting factor. At night, light is likely to be the limiting factor.

Not Enough Light Slows Down the Rate of Photosynthesis

Chlorophyll uses light energy to carry out photosynthesis. It can only photosynthesise as quickly as the light energy is arriving.

1) If the light intensity is increased, the rate of photosynthesis will increase steadily, but only up to a certain point.

2) Beyond that, it won't make any difference.

3) Then it'll be the temperature or the CO_2 level which is the limiting factor.

S

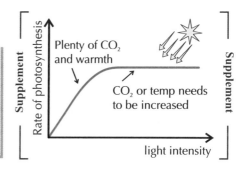

Plenty of CO_2 and warmth

CO_2 or temp needs to be increased

Rate of photosynthesis

light intensity

Supplement

Too Little CO₂ Slows Down the Rate of Photosynthesis

CO_2 is one of the raw materials needed for photosynthesis — only 0.04% of the air is CO_2, so it's limited as far as plants are concerned.

1) As with light intensity, increasing the concentration of CO_2 will only increase the rate of photosynthesis up to a point. After this, it won't make any difference.

2) This shows that CO_2 is no longer the limiting factor.

3) As long as light and CO_2 are in plentiful supply then the factor limiting photosynthesis must be temperature.

S

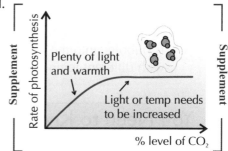

Plenty of light and warmth

Light or temp needs to be increased

Rate of photosynthesis

% level of CO_2

Supplement

The Temperature Has to be Just Right

As temperature increases, the rate of photosynthesis increases up to a point — then it rapidly decreases.

1) Temperature affects the rate of photosynthesis — because it affects the enzymes involved.

2) If the temperature is too high (over about 45 °C), the plant's enzymes will be denatured (destroyed), causing the rapid decrease in the rate of photosynthesis.

3) Usually though, if the temperature is the limiting factor it's because it's too low, and things need warming up a bit.

Supplement

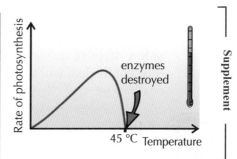

enzymes destroyed

Rate of photosynthesis

45 °C Temperature

Investigating Photosynthesis

Oxygen and glucose are products of photosynthesis (see p.36). Glucose can be stored by plants as starch.
You can test for oxygen and starch to investigate photosynthesis.

Oxygen Production Shows the Rate of Photosynthesis

Canadian pondweed can be used to measure the effect of light intensity on the rate of photosynthesis.
The rate at which the pondweed produces oxygen corresponds to the rate at which it's photosynthesising
— the faster the rate of oxygen production, the faster the rate of photosynthesis.

Here's how the experiment works:

1) The apparatus is set up according
to the diagram. The gas syringe
should be empty to start with.
Sodium hydrogencarbonate may be
added to the water to make sure the
plant has enough carbon dioxide
(it releases CO_2 in solution).

2) A source of white light is placed at a
specific distance from the pondweed.

3) The pondweed is left to
photosynthesise for a set amount
of time. As it photosynthesises,
the oxygen released will collect in the capillary tube.

O_2 bubble   ruler   syringe

light source

water in
capillary tube

clamp

small O_2 bubbles

Canadian pondweed

water (+ sodium
hydrogencarbonate)

ruler to vary
distance from plant

The rate of photosynthesis can also be given as
the volume of gas produced over a set time.

4) At the end of the experiment, the syringe is used to move the gas bubble in the tube up alongside a
ruler and the length of the gas bubble is measured. This is proportional to the volume of O_2 produced.

5) For this experiment, any variables that could affect the results should be controlled,
e.g. the temperature the pondweed is left to photosynthesise at and the length of time it's left for.

6) The experiment is then repeated with the light source placed at different distances from the pondweed.

The apparatus above can be altered to measure the effect of
temperature and CO_2 on photosynthesis, e.g. the test tube of
pondweed is put into a water-bath at a set temperature and CO_2
is bubbled into the test tube (then the experiment's repeated
with different temperatures of water or concentrations of CO_2).

You should find that as you move
the light source closer to the plant,
increase the temperature, or increase
the CO_2 concentration, that the rate of
photosynthesis increases (up to a point).

You Need to Know How to Test a Leaf for Starch

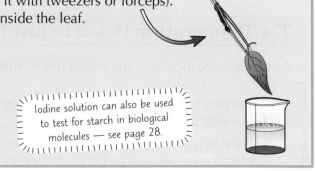

1) Start by holding the leaf in boiling water (hold it with tweezers or forceps).
This stops any chemical reactions happening inside the leaf.

2) Now put the leaf in a boiling tube with some
ethanol and heat it in an electric water-bath
until it boils — this gets rid of any chlorophyll
and makes the leaf an almost white colour.

3) Finally, rinse the leaf in cold water and add
a few drops of iodine solution — if starch is
present the leaf will turn blue-black.

Iodine solution can also be used
to test for starch in biological
molecules — see page 28.

PRACTICAL TIP

Make sure you stay safe during these investigations

For example, ethanol is highly flammable, so keep it away from naked flames, e.g. Bunsen burners.

Investigating Photosynthesis

The Starch Test Shows Whether Photosynthesis is Taking Place

If a plant can't photosynthesise, it can't make starch. You can use this principle
to show that chlorophyll, light and CO_2 are needed for photosynthesis. Here's how...

Chlorophyll

You can show that chlorophyll is needed for
photosynthesis using variegated (green and white) leaves.
Only the green parts of the leaf contain chlorophyll.

1) Take a variegated leaf from a plant that's been
   exposed to light. Make sure you record which
   bits are green and which bits aren't.

2) Test the leaf for starch as on the previous page —
   only the bits that were green turn blue-black.

3) This suggests that only the parts of the
   leaf that contained chlorophyll are able
   to photosynthesise and produce starch.

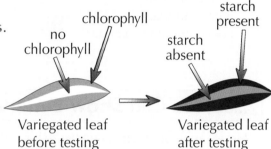

Variegated leaf before testing   Variegated leaf after testing

The white parts of the leaf go yellow/orange
because the brown iodine solution stains them.

Light

1) To show that light is needed for photosynthesis
   you need a plant that's been grown without
   any light, e.g. in a cupboard for 48 hours.
   This will mean that it has used up its starch stores.

2) Cut a leaf from the plant and test it for starch
   — the leaf won't turn blue-black.

3) This shows that light is needed for
   photosynthesis, as no starch has been made.

Even though the
plant is kept in
the dark, you need
to make sure it's
warm enough to
photosynthesise and
that there's plenty of
CO_2 — or it won't
be a fair test.

CO_2

1) You can show that CO_2 is needed for photosynthesis
   with the apparatus shown on the right.

2) The soda lime will absorb CO_2 out of the air in the jar.

3) If you leave the plant in the jar for a while and then
   test a leaf for starch, it won't turn blue-black.

4) This shows that no starch has been made in the leaf,
   which means that CO_2 is needed for photosynthesis.

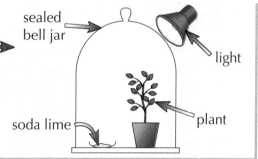

sealed bell jar   light   plant   soda lime

- For these experiments, it's important to use controls to make sure that only the factors
  being investigated (chlorophyll, light or CO_2) are affecting the results. This is why a
  variegated leaf is used in the first investigation — the green parts of the leaf are the control.

- For the other two investigations, the control should use identical plants that are kept
  in the same conditions, but they should also be provided with light and CO_2 respectively.

EXAM TIP

You might have to describe experiments like this in the exam

If you're asked to describe an experiment, make sure you do it step-by-step, as if
you're guiding someone who's never done it before through how to carry it out.

Investigating Gas Exchange in Plants

If you're not convinced about CO_2 being needed for photosynthesis, here's how you can see it for yourself...

Hydrogencarbonate Indicator Shows CO_2 Concentration...

A solution of hydrogencarbonate indicator in air with a normal CO_2 concentration is orange.

If the CO_2 concentration of the indicator increases, it becomes more yellow.

If the CO_2 concentration of the indicator decreases, it becomes purple.

...So You Can Show Differences in Net Gas Exchange in Plants

Here's an experiment using hydrogencarbonate indicator to show how light affects gas exchange:

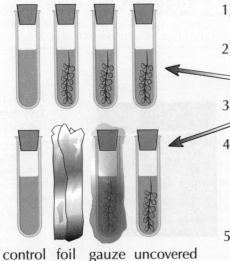

control   foil   gauze   uncovered

1) Add the same volume of hydrogencarbonate indicator to four boiling tubes.

2) Put similar-sized, healthy-looking pieces of Canadian pondweed into three of the tubes. Keep the fourth tube empty as a control. Seal the tubes with rubber bungs.

3) Completely wrap one tube in aluminium foil, and a second tube in gauze.

4) Place all the tubes in bright light. This will let plenty of light on to the uncovered pondweed, and a little light onto the pondweed covered in gauze. The pondweed covered in foil will get no light — assuming you've wrapped it up properly.

5) Leave the tubes for an hour, then check the colour of the indicator.

Results

1) There shouldn't be any change in the colour of the control tube.

2) You'd expect the indicator in the darkened tube (with the foil) to go yellow. Respiration (which produces CO_2 — see p.78) will still take place but there will be no photosynthesis, so the CO_2 concentration in the tube will increase.

3) You'd expect the indicator in the shaded tube (with the gauze) to stay a similar colour. With a little photosynthesis and some respiration taking place, roughly equal amounts of CO_2 will be taken up and produced by the pondweed, so the CO_2 concentration in the tube won't change very much.

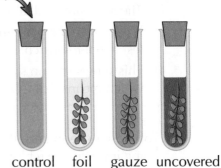

control   foil   gauze   uncovered

4) You'd expect the indicator in the well-lit (uncovered) tube to go purple. There will be some respiration, but lots of photosynthesis, leading to net uptake of CO_2 by the pondweed. This will lower the CO_2 concentration in the tube.

Make sure the colour change is really clear

When checking for colour changes, it's a good idea to hold the boiling tube against a clear white background, such as a white tile. This helps make the colour change really clear and easy to spot.

Supplement

Improving Plant Growth

Growing plants outdoors can be very difficult, especially on a large scale — it's almost impossible to control the weather and other conditions. But there's a way around that...

The Rate of **Photosynthesis** Affects **Plant Growth**

1) As you saw on page 37, a plant's rate of photosynthesis is affected by the amount of light, the amount of carbon dioxide (CO_2) and the temperature.

2) Since plants have to photosynthesise in order to make food for themselves and grow, these three factors need to be carefully controlled in order to improve plant growth.

You Can **Create** the **Ideal Conditions** for **Photosynthesis**

Photosynthesis can be helped along by artificially creating the ideal conditions in glasshouses (big greenhouses) or polytunnels (big tube-like structures made from plastic).

1) Keeping plants enclosed in a glasshouse makes it easier to control the environmental conditions.

2) It allows plant growers to supply artificial light to help give plants the optimum light intensity for growth. Artificial lighting can also be used after sunset to give the plants more time to photosynthesise.

3) Glasshouses trap the Sun's heat to keep the plants warm. In winter, heaters can also be used to help keep the temperature at the optimum level for the plants to grow.

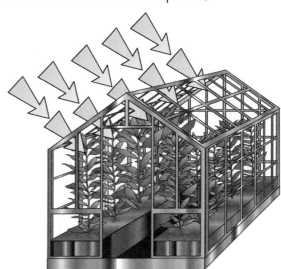

4) The level of carbon dioxide in glasshouses can also be increased, e.g. by using a paraffin heater. As the paraffin burns, it produces carbon dioxide as well as heat. Increasing the level of carbon dioxide is known as carbon dioxide enrichment.

5) By increasing the temperature and CO_2 concentration, as well as the amount of light available, the rate of photosynthesis can be increased. This means the plants will be able to grow bigger and faster.

Growing plants indoors and carefully controlling the conditions in glasshouses also allows plants that grow naturally in tropical countries (e.g. hot, sunny countries like Brazil) to be grown in temperate countries (e.g. cooler, cloudier countries like the UK), and vice versa.

You can use glasshouses to control the growing environment

Plant growers use glasshouses to make sure plants get the right amount of carbon dioxide, light and heat. They can alter the conditions using paraffin heaters (to supply extra CO_2 and warmth) and artificial light. This ensures nothing becomes a limiting factor for photosynthesis, which means a lovely plant grows.

Supplement

Supplement

Leaf Structure and Mineral Requirements

It's important that leaves are able to carry out photosynthesis and that plants get the minerals they need.

Leaves are Designed for **Making Food** by **Photosynthesis**

You need to know all the different parts of a typical leaf shown on the diagram:

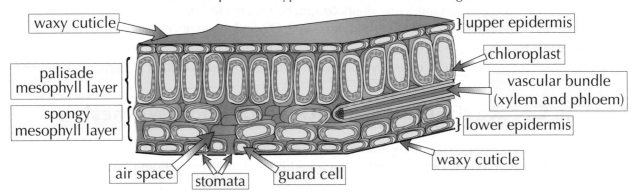

waxy cuticle — upper epidermis}
chloroplast
palisade mesophyll layer
vascular bundle (xylem and phloem)
spongy mesophyll layer
lower epidermis}
air space
stomata
guard cell
waxy cuticle

Leaves are **Adapted** for **Efficient Photosynthesis**

1) Leaves are broad, so there's a large surface area exposed to light.

2) Most of the chloroplasts are found in the palisade mesophyll layer.
   This is so that they're near the top of the leaf where they can get the most light.

3) The upper epidermis is transparent so that light can pass through it to the palisade mesophyll layer.

4) Leaves of dicotyledonous plants (see p.7) have a network of vascular bundles — these are the transport vessels xylem and phloem (p.53). They deliver water and other nutrients to the leaf and take away the glucose produced by photosynthesis. They also help to support the leaf structure.

5) The waxy cuticle on the top and bottom helps to reduce water loss by evaporation.

6) There are air spaces inside the leaf. These let gases like CO_2 and O_2 move easily between cells. They also increase the surface area for gas exchange and so make photosynthesis more efficient.

7) The lower surface is full of little holes called stomata. They're there to let CO_2 (necessary for photosynthesis — see p.36) and O_2 (produced by photosynthesis) diffuse in and out of the leaf.

Supplement

Plants Need **Mineral Ions** For **Growth**

1) Plants need certain elements so they can produce important compounds.

2) They get these elements from mineral ions in the soil.

3) If there aren't enough of these mineral ions in the soil, plants suffer deficiency symptoms.

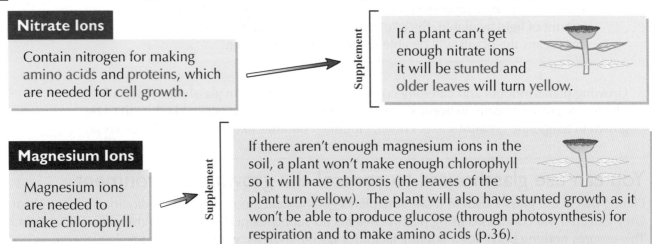

Nitrate Ions

Contain nitrogen for making amino acids and proteins, which are needed for cell growth.

If a plant can't get enough nitrate ions it will be stunted and older leaves will turn yellow.

Magnesium Ions

Magnesium ions are needed to make chlorophyll.

If there aren't enough magnesium ions in the soil, a plant won't make enough chlorophyll so it will have chlorosis (the leaves of the plant turn yellow). The plant will also have stunted growth as it won't be able to produce glucose (through photosynthesis) for respiration and to make amino acids (p.36).

Warm-Up & Exam Questions

Before we move on to human nutrition, test that you've understood everything you need
to know about plant nutrition by answering the questions below and on the next page.

Warm-Up Questions

1) What is the name for the pigment inside chloroplasts that absorbs light?
2) What do plants need nitrate ions for?
3) What could you measure to show the rate of photosynthesis?
4) What is meant by the term 'limiting factor'?
5) What colour does hydrogencarbonate indicator turn if the carbon dioxide level decreases?
6) Why might a farmer want to increase the rate of photosynthesis in her greenhouse of tomatoes?

Exam Questions

1 Photosynthesis produces glucose using light.

(a) Complete the word equation for photosynthesis.

$$\text{carbon dioxide} + \text{.....................................} \xrightarrow[\text{chlorophyll}]{\text{light}} \text{glucose} + \text{.....................................}$$

[1]

(b) Plants use some of the glucose they produce to make a substance which strengthens
their cell walls. Which of the following strengthens cells walls? Tick **one** box.

☐ **A** cellulose ☐ **B** oils ☐ **C** starch ☐ **D** fats

[1]

[Total 2 marks]

2 A student investigated the effect of limiting factors on the rate of photosynthesis of his plant.

The results are shown in the graph.

```
              0.1% CO₂
              0.07% CO₂
              0.04% CO₂
```

(a) Describe the effect that increasing the concentration of CO_2 has on the rate of photosynthesis
as light intensity increases.

[2]

(b) Explain why all the lines on the graph level off eventually.

[1]

[Total 3 marks]

Exam Questions

3   The diagram shows a cross-section through a typical leaf. Some of the structures in the leaf are labelled **A** to **E**.

The table below contains descriptions of how the structures labelled in the diagram make the leaf well-adapted for efficient photosynthesis.

Complete the table by matching the letters in the diagram to the correct description. The first one has been done for you.

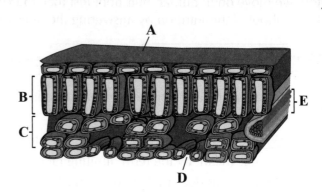

Description of structure	Letter
contains air spaces to aid gas exchange	C
delivers water and nutrients to the leaf	
helps to reduce water loss by evaporation	
where most of the chloroplasts in the leaf are located, to maximise the amount of light they receive	
allows carbon dioxide to diffuse directly into the leaf	

[Total 4 marks]

4   The diagram below shows a variegated leaf. It is partly green and partly white. Chlorophyll is present in the green parts of the leaf but not the white parts.

A student did an experiment in which part of the leaf was covered with black paper, as shown in the diagram below. The leaf was then exposed to light for four hours and was then tested for starch.

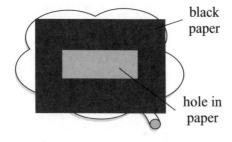

(a)   Complete the diagram by shading in the part(s) of the leaf that you would expect to contain **starch**.

[1]

(b)   Explain your answer to **(a)**.

[2]

[Total 3 marks]

Human Diet

Your body needs the right fuel or it won't work properly — that means eating a balanced diet.

You Need to **Eat Different Foods** to Get **Different Nutrients**

Nutrient		Found in...	Function(s)
Carbohydrates		Pasta, rice, sugar	Provide energy.
Fats		Butter, oily fish	Provide energy, act as an energy store, provide insulation and provide protection of the organs.
Proteins		Meat, fish, beans	Needed for growth and repair of tissue, and to provide energy in emergencies.
Vitamins	C	Fruit, e.g. oranges	Needed for tissue repair, is important for the immune system, and prevents scurvy (see next page).
	D	Eggs, oily fish	Needed for calcium absorption. *Vitamin D is also made by your body when your skin is exposed to sunlight.*
Mineral salts	Calcium	Milk, cheese	Needed to make bones and teeth.
	Iron	Red meat, beans	Needed to make haemoglobin for healthy blood.
Water		Food and drink	Just about every bodily function relies on water — we need a constant supply to replace water lost through urinating, breathing and sweating.
Fibre (roughage)		Wholemeal bread, fruit	Aids the movement of food through the gut.

A **Balanced Diet** Supplies **All** Your **Essential Nutrients**

1) A balanced diet gives you all the essential nutrients you need — in the right proportions.
2) The six essential nutrients are carbohydrates, proteins, fats, vitamins, minerals and water.
3) You also need fibre (or roughage) to keep the gut in good working order.

Energy Requirements **Vary** in Different People

You get energy from the food you eat, but the amount of energy you need isn't a set thing — it's different for everyone. The energy a person needs depends on things like...

- Activity level — Active people need more energy than people who are less active.
- Age — Children and teenagers need more energy than older people. They need energy to grow and they're generally more active.
- Gender — In general, men are bigger and have more muscle than women. The bigger you are, the more energy you need, so men tend to need more energy than women.
- Pregnancy — Pregnant and breast-feeding women need more energy than other women. They've got to provide the energy their babies need to develop and grow.

There is no one perfect diet that's right for everyone

It depends on each person's energy requirements, and this varies based on things like age and activity level.

Malnutrition in Humans

Not getting the right nutrition can have serious consequences on the human body.

Malnutrition Can Increase the Risk of Disease

1) Malnutrition just means 'poor nutrition' and it can refer to overnutrition (getting more nutrients than are needed) or undernutrition (not getting enough nutrients).

2) Both overnutrition and undernutrition can lead to an increased risk of disease.

Overnutrition

- Obesity — Eating too much can lead to obesity (excess body fat). Obesity is linked to health issues such as high blood pressure and coronary heart disease. It's also a risk factor for some cancers.

  Obesity is defined as being more than 20% over the maximum recommended body mass.

- Coronary Heart Disease — Too much saturated fat in your diet can increase your blood cholesterol level. Too much of a certain type of cholesterol (known as LDL or 'bad' cholesterol) in the blood can cause fatty deposits to form on the inside wall of arteries, which can lead to coronary heart disease. This restricts blood flow to the heart and can lead to a heart attack, which can be fatal.

Undernutrition

- Starvation — When you simply aren't eating enough, the body isn't being provided with the energy and nutrients that it needs to function properly. It can lead to issues such as fatigue and poor resistance to infection. Prolonged starvation can lead to organ damage and death.

- Constipation — When you aren't eating enough fibre (roughage) or drinking enough fluids (e.g. water), it can prevent faeces (poo) from passing through the rectum. This means that waste isn't being passed from the body as it should and so builds up. This can cause the rectum and large intestine to swell, resulting in severe pain and vomiting if untreated.

- Scurvy — A lack of vitamin C can lead to scurvy. It causes bleeding gums, poor wound healing and pain, especially in the legs.

- Vitamin D deficiency — This is caused by not eating enough food containing vitamin D (e.g. eggs) or by not getting enough sunlight. Vitamin D is important for calcium absorption, which is needed for bone formation and strength. Therefore vitamin D deficiency can lead to bone deformation, bone pain, weak or brittle bones, and dental problems. Vitamin D deficiency also causes fatigue and muscle weakness.

- Iron deficiency — This is caused by not eating enough food containing iron (e.g. red meat). Iron is used to make haemoglobin in the blood. Haemoglobin is what allows the blood to carry oxygen, so an iron deficiency means that the blood isn't able to carry enough oxygen. This leads to symptoms such as tiredness, shortness of breath and pale skin.

- Kwashiorkor — When you don't eat enough protein, the amount of protein in the blood is reduced. This makes the water potential of the blood higher than normal. This causes fluid from the blood to move into the tissues of the body, which causes swelling.

- Marasmus — A form of severe malnutrition, marasmus occurs when the body isn't taking in enough energy (similar to starvation above). This can lead to emaciation (being extremely thin), fatigue and poor resistance to infection.

  Kwashiorkor and marasmus are known as protein-energy deficiency diseases.

Supplement

Eating a healthy, balanced diet that is rich in fruit and vegetables can reduce your risk of getting many of these conditions.

The Alimentary Canal

Digestion takes place in the alimentary canal — it's where the food you eat gets broken down into smaller food molecules ready to be taken into your body cells (or passed out of the body as faeces — yuk).

Your **Alimentary Canal** Runs Through Your Body

You need to know the names and functions of the alimentary canal's main parts, plus a few of the organs associated with it.

The alimentary canal is another name for the gut.

Mouth

1) Salivary glands in the mouth produce amylase enzyme (p.49) in the saliva.
2) Teeth (next page) break down food.

Oesophagus

The muscular tube that connects the mouth and stomach.

Liver

Where bile is produced (see page 50).

Gall bladder

Where bile is stored (see page 50).

Large intestine

1) Also called the colon.
2) Where excess water is absorbed from the food.

Rectum

1) The last part of the large intestine.
2) Where the faeces (made up mainly of indigestible food) are stored before they are passed out through the anus.

Tongue

Stomach

1) Churns the food up with its muscular walls.
2) Produces the protease enzyme, pepsin.
3) Produces gastric juice (which contains hydrochloric acid) for two reasons:

• To kill bacteria in food. It does this because it has a low (acidic) pH which denatures the enzymes in the harmful microorganisms.
• To give an acid pH for the enzyme pepsin to work. The optimum pH is 2.

Pancreas

Produces protease, amylase and lipase enzymes. Releases these into the small intestine.

Small intestine

1) Produces protease (trypsin), amylase and lipase enzymes to complete digestion.
2) Where nutrients are absorbed out of the alimentary canal into the body.
3) Where most of the water is absorbed into the body.
4) It has two parts — the duodenum and the ileum.

Look, cover, write, check...

Copy out the diagram and then try and label all the parts correctly without looking at the page.

Mechanical Digestion

The first step in digestion is mechanical — tearing, cutting and grinding down food into smaller pieces.

Teeth Do the Work First

1) After you've ingested food, teeth do the first part of mechanical digestion.

2) Here's the definition of ingestion that you need to know:

Ingestion is the taking of substances (e.g. food and drink) into the body through the mouth.

3) And here's the definition of mechanical digestion that you need to know:

Mechanical digestion is the breakdown of food into smaller pieces without chemical change to the food molecules.

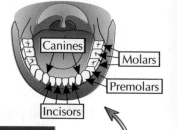

4) You also need to know what the different types of teeth are, what they do and where they're found:

Incisors and canines have sharp biting surfaces.

Incisors are used for biting and cutting into food.

Canines are used for gripping and tearing food.

Premolars and molars have flat biting surfaces.

Premolars are used for tearing and crushing food.

Molars are used for crushing and grinding food.

You Need to Know the Structure of a Typical Tooth

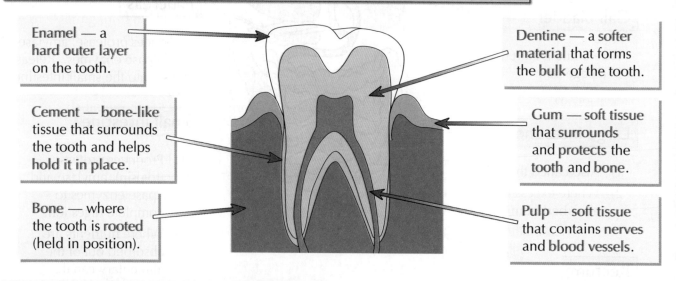

Enamel — a hard outer layer on the tooth.

Cement — bone-like tissue that surrounds the tooth and helps hold it in place.

Bone — where the tooth is rooted (held in position).

Dentine — a softer material that forms the bulk of the tooth.

Gum — soft tissue that surrounds and protects the tooth and bone.

Pulp — soft tissue that contains nerves and blood vessels.

Proper Tooth Care is Important

1) Without proper tooth care, dental decay can occur.

2) Over time, a coating of bacteria and food forms on teeth. The bacteria use sugars in the food for respiration (p.78), and produce acid. This acid dissolves enamel and dentine, damaging teeth.

3) Regular brushing clears the coating of bacteria and food from teeth, preventing acid production.

4) Restricting the amount of sugar in the diet reduces the amount of sugar available to the bacteria. This also reduces the amount of acid produced, helping to prevent dental decay.

Chemical Digestion

Chemical digestion involves the breakdown of food using enzymes.

Enzymes Break Down Food in Chemical Digestion

1) Starch, proteins and fats are BIG molecules. They're too big to pass through the walls of the alimentary canal. They're also insoluble.

2) Simple sugars, amino acids, glycerol and fatty acids are much smaller molecules. They're soluble and can pass easily through the walls of the alimentary canal.

 KEY TERM Chemical digestion is the breakdown of large, insoluble molecules into small, soluble molecules.

3) The digestive enzymes break down the BIG molecules into the smaller ones.

4) You need to know about three digestive enzymes — where they're secreted from and what they do:

Amylase Breaks Down Starch into Simple Sugars

starch → amylase enzyme → simple sugars

Starch is a carbohydrate.

Amylase is made in three places: 1) The salivary glands 2) The pancreas 3) The small intestine

Amylase breaks down starch to a sugar called maltose. Maltose is broken down further by maltase to glucose. This happens on the membranes of the epithelium lining of the small intestine.

Proteases Break Down Proteins into Amino Acids

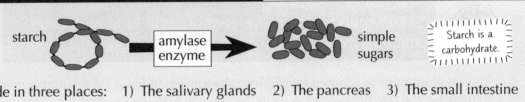

proteins → protease enzymes → amino acids

Proteases are made in three places: 1) The stomach 2) The pancreas 3) The small intestine

The protease in the stomach is called pepsin, and the one in the small intestine is called trypsin.

Lipases Break Down Fats into Glycerol and Fatty Acids

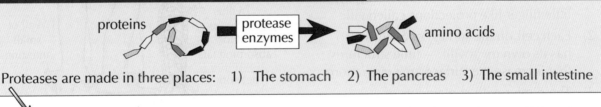

fat → lipase enzymes → glycerol and fatty acids

Lipases are made in two places: 1) The pancreas 2) The small intestine

Make sure you really know this stuff before moving on

The next two pages are about what happens to these smaller food molecules after chemical digestion has happened. So if you're not completely confident with this page, the next two might be a bit hard to follow.

Chemical Digestion and Absorption

There's just a bit more on chemical digestion, then it's on to how these small food molecules are absorbed.

Supplement

Bile **Neutralises** the Stomach Acid and **Emulsifies** Fats

1) Bile is produced in the liver. It's stored in the gall bladder before it's released into the duodenum in the small intestine.

2) The hydrochloric acid in the stomach makes the pH too acidic for enzymes in the small intestine to work properly. Bile is alkaline — it neutralises the acidic mixture of food and stomach acid, and makes conditions alkaline. The enzymes in the small intestine work best in these conditions.

3) Bile also emulsifies fats (breaks the fat into tiny droplets). This gives a much bigger surface area of fat for the enzyme lipase to work on — which makes its digestion faster.

Most **Absorption** Happens in the **Small Intestine**

1) Digested food and water are absorbed into the blood in the small intestine. (Some water is also absorbed in the colon (large intestine) but most of it is absorbed in the small intestine.)

Absorption is the movement of small food molecules and ions through the wall of the intestine into the blood.

2) The small intestine is adapted for efficient absorption. It has a large surface area to increase the rate of absorption — in the same way that a large surface area increases the rate of diffusion (see page 20).

Villi Increase the **Surface Area** of the **Small Intestine**

1) The small intestine has a big surface area for absorption, because its walls are covered in millions and millions of tiny little finger-like projections called villi.

2) Each cell on the surface of a villus also has its own microvilli — little structures that increase the surface area even more.

3) These microvilli contain lots of mitochondria (p.11) which provide energy from respiration (p.78). This is used for active transport (pages 24-25), to absorb molecules into the blood capillaries.

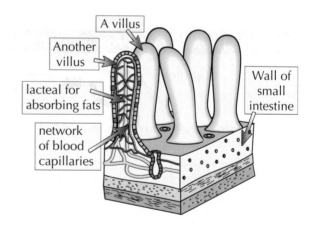

4) The network of blood capillaries is needed so that the absorbed molecules can be transported round the body. A good blood supply allows for quick absorption.

5) Villi have a single permeable layer of surface cells which also allows for quick absorption.

6) The lacteals are tubes in the villi that absorb digested fats. Here's how they work:

- Fats move from the small intestine into the lacteals in the villi.
- Lacteals contain fluid called lymph that transports fats away from the small intestine.
- The lacteals merge to form larger vessels, before the lymph (and the fats it contains) empties into the blood.
- The fats can then be transported around the body in the blood.

Assimilation and Egestion

Eating food provides the body's cells with the molecules that they need to function. Any food that isn't digested or absorbed is removed from the body. This page is about both of these things.

All Food that You Eat Ends up Assimilated or Egested

1) When the digested food molecules and water have been absorbed into the blood, they are assimilated.

 Assimilation is the movement of digested food molecules (and water) into the cells of the body where they are used, becoming part of the cells.

2) Any food that isn't fully digested or absorbed is egested.

 Egestion is the passing out of food that has not been digested or absorbed, as faeces, through the anus.

Diarrhoea is Watery Faeces

1) Normally, faeces are quite solid. However, sometimes watery faeces are produced — this is known as diarrhoea.
2) This occurs when water can't be absorbed from the intestines, or when extra water is secreted into them.
3) The loss of water can lead to dehydration. It also causes the body's levels of salt, glucose and other important minerals to decrease. This can affect proper functioning of the body and can also cause the body to lose even more water.
4) If diarrhoea continues for a long time it can result in serious dehydration and may even lead to death.
5) Dehydration can be treated with oral rehydration therapy (ORT).
6) ORT involves drinking water that contains relatively large amounts of dissolved salt, glucose and other important minerals. This helps to bring the body's levels of water, salt, glucose and other important minerals back up. ORT needs to be given regularly until diarrhoea stops.

Cholera is a Bacterial Disease that Causes Diarrhoea

Cholera is a disease caused by a bacterium. It causes diarrhoea, dehydration and loss of salts from blood. Here's how cholera causes these effects:

Supplement

1) The bacterium produces a toxin that causes the secretion of chloride ions into the small intestine. This reduces the water potential of the small intestine.
2) This reduced water potential causes water to move from the blood into the small intestine by osmosis (p.21), leading to diarrhoea and dehydration.
3) Chloride ions and other salts are then lost from the body due to the diarrhoea.

Supplement

 Phew, lots to remember here
To help you remember it all, try drawing a flow chart that shows all the different steps including digestion, absorption, assimilation and egestion. Then look at it until you have learnt it all.

Warm-Up & Exam Questions

We've covered plant nutrition, now it's time for questions on human nutrition — then Section 5 is done.

Warm-Up Questions

1) Give **two** factors that affect the energy requirements in people.
2) Name the **three** parts of the alimentary canal that produce protease enzymes.
3) What are canine teeth used for?
4) Which enzyme digests: (a) starch   (b) protein   (c) fats?
5) What are the products of the digestion of: (a) starch   (b) protein   (c) fats?
6) Briefly describe the structure of a villus.
7) What is the definition of egestion?

Exam Questions

1   The diagram shows part of the alimentary canal.

    (a)   Label the place where bile is produced.

[1]

    (b)   State why bile needs to have an alkaline pH.

[1]

    (c)   Outline how bile helps with the digestion of fats.

[2]

[Total 4 marks]

2   Malnutrition occurs when a person is either getting too many nutrients or not enough nutrients.

    (a)   Fatigue and emaciation (being extremely thin) are
        symptoms of which disease caused by malnutrition?

[1]

    (b)   Outline **one** other disease that may result from malnutrition.

[2]

[Total 3 marks]

3   Dentists often recommend using interdental brushes or floss to clean between teeth.
This helps to remove food from hard-to-reach places, such as between the gums and the teeth.

    (a)   Explain how removing this food will prevent tooth decay.

[2]

    (b)   Gum disease can result in the gums pulling away from the teeth, leaving the
        bone and cement exposed. If left untreated, this could result in tooth loss.
        Suggest how gum disease could lead to tooth loss.

[2]

[Total 4 marks]

Transport in Plants

Water and food need to be transported throughout a plant. Flowering plants have two types of transport vessel — xylem and phloem. Both types of vessel go to every part of the plant, but they are totally separate.

Xylem Tubes Take Water UP

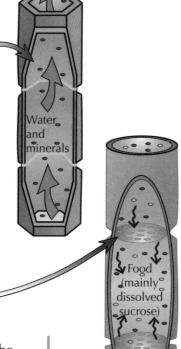

1) Xylem tubes are made of dead cells joined end to end with no end walls between them and a hole down the middle. They're strengthened with a material called lignin.

2) They carry water and mineral ions from the roots to the stem and leaves. They also provide support for the plant.

Water and minerals

Phloem Tubes Transport Food

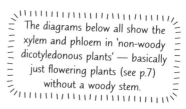

1) Phloem tubes are made of columns of elongated living cells with small pores in the end walls to allow stuff to flow through.

2) They transport food substances (mainly sucrose) made in the leaves to the rest of the plant for immediate use (e.g. in growing regions) or for storage. The transport goes in both directions.

Food (mainly dissolved sucrose)

You Can Identify Xylem and Phloem From Their Position

Xylem and phloem are always located in the same places in a stem, root or leaf, which allows you to identify them from cross-sections.

1) In a stem, the xylem and phloem are near the outside.

2) In a root, the xylem is in the centre surrounded by phloem to provide support.

3) In a leaf, xylem and phloem make up a network of veins.

The diagrams below all show the xylem and phloem in 'non-woody dicotyledonous plants' — basically just flowering plants (see p.7) without a woody stem.

Stem cross-section

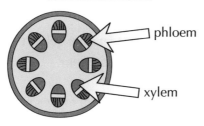

phloem

xylem

Root cross-section

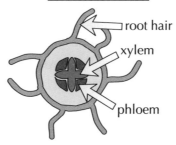

root hair

xylem

phloem

Leaf cross-section

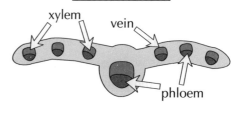

xylem

vein

phloem

REVISION TIP

Xylem vessels carry water, phloem vessels carry sucrose

Make sure you don't get your phloem mixed up with your xylem. To help you to learn which is which, you could remember that ph_loem transports substances in b_oth directions, but xylem only transports things upwards — x_y to the sky. It might just get you a mark or two in the exam...

Water Uptake

Water from the soil enters the plant through the roots, then continues up through the plant. You can see the pathway that water takes in an experiment.

Root Hairs Take In Water and Mineral Ions

1) You might remember from page 12 that the cells on the surface of plant roots grow into "hairs", which stick out into the soil.

2) Each branch of a root will be covered in millions of these microscopic hairs.

3) The hairs give the plant roots a much larger surface area, which increases the rate of absorption of water by osmosis (see p.21) and mineral ions by active transport (see p.24).

Water Follows a Pathway Through The Plant

Water in the soil travels from the root hairs to the leaves through xylem vessels in the stem. The diagram below shows the pathway water takes:

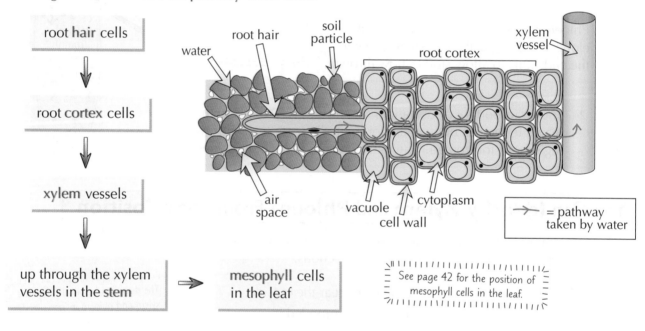

See page 42 for the position of mesophyll cells in the leaf.

You Can Investigate the Pathway of Water in a Plant

1) Place a plant stem (e.g. a celery stalk) into a beaker of water containing a stain, like coloured dye.

2) As water moves up the stem, you'll see the dye travel up the stem, staining the xylem.

3) If the plant stem has leaves, you'll see the dye reach the leaves too.

Plants take up water through root hair cells

Make sure you know the pathway that water follows through the roots, stems and leaves of a plant, and that you are able to describe how to investigate the pathway of water through the above-ground parts of a plant (the stem and the leaves), in case it comes up in the exams.

Transpiration

If you don't water a house plant for a few days it starts to wilt (droop). Plants need water.

Transpiration is the **Loss of Water** from the Plant

You need to know this definition of transpiration:

Transpiration is the loss of water vapour from plant leaves by evaporation of water at the surface of the mesophyll cells followed by the diffusion of water vapour through the stomata.

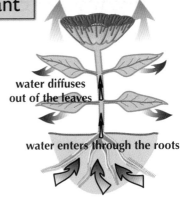

water diffuses out of the leaves

water enters through the roots

Most transpiration happens at the leaves.

A **Transpiration Pull** Moves Water **Up** the Plant

1) Evaporation and diffusion of water from the leaves at the 'top' of the xylem creates a slight shortage of water in the leaf.
2) More water is drawn up from the rest of the plant through the xylem vessels to replace it.
3) Water molecules are cohesive (they stick together) so when some are pulled into the leaf others follow. This means the whole column of water molecules in the xylem, from the leaves down to the roots, moves upwards.
4) This in turn means more water is drawn up from the roots, and so there's a constant transpiration pull of water through the plant.

Leaf Structure Increases **Water Loss**

1) Transpiration is just a side-effect of the way leaves are adapted for photosynthesis (see p.42).
2) Mesophyll cells in the leaf have a large surface area.
This means that a lot of water can evaporate in a short period of time.
3) The interconnecting air spaces in the leaf mean that water vapour can diffuse through the leaf.
4) Because there's more water inside the plant than in the air outside, the water escapes from the leaves through the stomata by diffusion.

Stomata are tiny holes in the leaf's surface. They're able to open and close to control water loss.

Wilting Happens When There is a **Lack** of **Water**

1) Watering a plant increases the water potential (see p.21) of the soil around it.
This means that all the plant cells draw in water by osmosis until they become turgid (plump and swollen). The contents of the cell push against the cell wall, creating a turgor pressure that helps to support the plant tissues (see p.23).
2) If there's no water in the soil, a plant starts to wilt (droop).
This is because the cells become flaccid — they start to lose water.
The plant doesn't totally lose its shape though, because the inelastic cell wall keeps things in position. It just droops a bit.

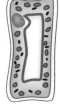

Turgid Cell   Flaccid Cell

Transpiration involves evaporation and diffusion

A big tree loses about a thousand litres of water from its leaves every single day. That's as much water as the average person drinks in a year, so the roots have to be very effective at drawing in water from the soil.

Supplement (left margin)
Supplement (right margin)

The Rate of Transpiration

Here's another page on transpiration for you. But this time it's all about the rate of transpiration.

A **Potometer** can be Used to **Estimate Transpiration Rate**

1) You can estimate the rate of transpiration by measuring the uptake of water by a plant.

2) This is because you can assume that water uptake by the plant is directly related to water loss by the leaves (transpiration).

3) Set up the apparatus as in the diagram, and then record the starting position of the air bubble.

4) Start a stopwatch and record the distance moved by the bubble per unit time, e.g. per hour.

5) The set up below will be your control — you can vary an environmental condition, e.g. the temperature or the humidity, run the experiment again and compare the results to the control to see how the change affected the transpiration rate.

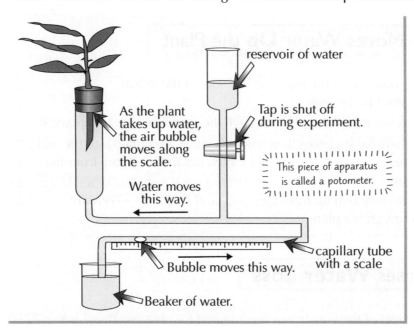

As the plant takes up water, the air bubble moves along the scale.

reservoir of water

Tap is shut off during experiment.

This piece of apparatus is called a potometer.

Water moves this way.

Bubble moves this way.

capillary tube with a scale

Beaker of water.

6) You can increase or decrease the temperature by putting the apparatus in a room that's warmer or colder than where you did the control experiment.

7) You can increase the humidity of the air around the plant by spraying a little water into a clear plastic bag before sealing it around the plant.

Transpiration Rate is Affected by **Temperature** and **Humidity**

Temperature

1) The warmer it is, the faster transpiration happens.

2) When it's warm the water particles have more kinetic energy to evaporate and diffuse out of the stomata.

There's more on how temperature and concentration gradients affect the rate of diffusion on p.20.

Humidity

1) The more humid (full of water) the air around a leaf, the slower transpiration happens.

2) If the air is humid there's a lot of water in it already, so there's not much of a concentration gradient between the inside and the outside of the leaf.

3) Diffusion happens fastest if there's a really high concentration in one place, and a really low concentration in the other.

Translocation

So now you know how plants transport water, it's time to learn how plants move the substances they make around. They do this by a process called translocation.

Translocation Happens in the Phloem

Translocation is the movement of sucrose and amino acids in the phloem from sources to sinks.

1) Translocation moves solutes like sucrose and amino acids through the phloem to where they're needed in a plant.

2) Translocation always moves solutes from 'sources' to 'sinks'.

3) The source of a solute is the place where it's made (the region of production). The solute is at a high concentration there.

4) The sink is an area where solutes are used up (so they are at a lower concentration there). A sink could be:

- a region where sucrose and amino acids are stored.
- a region where sucrose and amino acids are used in respiration or growth.

Supplement

Supplement

Plant Organs Can Be Both Sources and Sinks

Some parts of a plant can act as sources or as sinks at different times during the life of the plant:

When plants are growing, the leaves are actively photosynthesising and producing lots of sucrose — they are sources.

Photosynthesis makes glucose, which is then converted to sucrose before it is transported around the plant.

Reproductive structures (e.g. flowers and fruits) and growing stems act as sinks when plants are growing, because they use the sucrose up. Places where sucrose is stored, like roots, tubers and bulbs also act as sinks.

During winter, when some plants lose their leaves, storage sites like roots, tubers and bulbs become the sources of sucrose.

Amino acids are made in the roots or the shoots (sources) then transported to developing roots, leaves, flowers and seeds (sinks).

The newly growing leaves act as sinks. Once they mature they will become sources once again.

Translocation moves substances from sources to sinks

Make sure you understand the difference between a source and a sink. A source is the place where sucrose and amino acids are made and a sink is a part of a plant where sucrose and amino acids are used up. Parts of a plant can act as both a source and a sink throughout a plant's life, as the plant grows and develops.

Warm-Up & Exam Questions

That's the end of transport in plants. Before moving onto transport in animals, test that you've understood everything you need to know about plant transport by answering the questions below.

Warm-Up Questions

1) Outline the pathway taken by water through a plant.
2) What is transpiration?
3) What is the difference between a source and a sink?
4) Explain why wilting occurs.

Exam Questions

1   Aphids are insects. They feed on liquid which they extract from a plant's transport vessels, using their sharp mouthparts to pierce the stem. This liquid contains dissolved sucrose.

  (a)   Name the process by which sucrose is transported around the plant.

[1]

  (b)   Name the type of transport vessel that the aphids extract their liquid food from.

[1]

  (c)   Which letter (**A** or **B**) points to the position of the transport vessel you named in **(b)** on the diagram on the right?

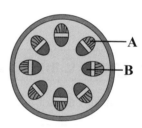

[1]

[3 marks]

2   A student investigated the effect of temperature on transpiration in basil plants. She put groups of three plants in two different conditions. She weighed the plants before and after the experiment and calculated the % loss in mass for each plant. Her results are shown in below.

plant	% loss in mass	
	Group A: 20 °C	Group B: 25 °C
1	5	10
2	5	11
3	4	9
mean	4.7	

  (a)   Calculate the mean % loss in mass for the three plants in Group **B**.

[2]

  (b)   Explain why the plants in Group **B** lost a greater percentage of their mass than the plants in Group **A**.

[3]

  (c)   Explain how humidity can affect the rate of transpiration.

[2]

[7 marks]

Circulatory System — The Heart

The heart plays a major role in the circulatory system. It's needed to pump blood through the blood vessels.

The **Circulatory System** Moves **Blood** Through the **Body**

Blood vessels are the tubes that blood flows through (p.62).

1) The circulatory system is a system of blood vessels with a pump (the heart) and valves to make sure that blood always flows in one direction.

2) Fish have a single circulatory system — deoxygenated blood from the fish's body passes through the heart, which then pumps it right round the body again in a single circuit (via the gills where it picks up oxygen). Blood only goes through the heart once in each full circuit it makes of the body.

3) Mammals have a double circulatory system. This means that the heart pumps blood around the body in two circuits:

   - In the first circuit, the heart pumps deoxygenated blood to the lungs to take in oxygen. Oxygenated blood then returns to the heart.

   - In the second circuit, the heart pumps oxygenated blood around all the other organs of the body to deliver oxygen to the body cells. Deoxygenated blood then returns to the heart.

4) There are advantages of a double circulatory system over a single one:

   - Returning blood to the heart after it has picked up oxygen at the lungs means it can be pumped out around the body at a much higher pressure.

   - This means that blood can be pumped around the body much faster, so more oxygen can be delivered to the cells. This is important for mammals because they use up a lot of oxygen maintaining their body temperature.

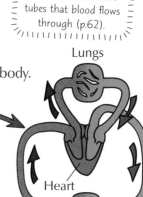

Lungs

Heart

Rest of Body

Supplement

The Heart **Pumps Blood** Through the **Blood Vessels**

In mammals, blood is pumped away from the heart into arteries and returns to the heart in veins.

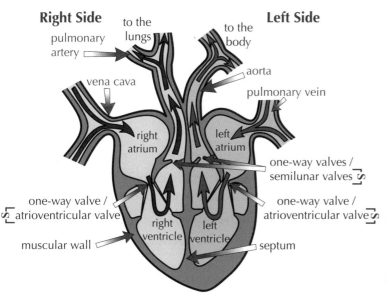

Right Side — to the lungs — **Left Side** — to the body

pulmonary artery

vena cava

aorta

pulmonary vein

right atrium

left atrium

one-way valves / semilunar valves

one-way valve / atrioventricular valve

one-way valve / atrioventricular valve

muscular wall

right ventricle

left ventricle

septum

Blue = deoxygenated blood. Red = oxygenated blood.

1) The right atrium of the heart receives deoxygenated blood from the body through the vena cava (a large vein).

2) The left atrium receives oxygenated blood from the lungs via the pulmonary vein.

3) The atria pump blood into the ventricles.

4) The right ventricle pumps deoxygenated blood to the lungs via the pulmonary artery.

5) The left ventricle pumps oxygenated blood to the body via the aorta (an artery).

6) The muscular walls of the atria and ventricles contract to pump the blood.

7) Valves prevent the backflow of blood.

8) The septum separates the left and right sides of the heart, so oxygenated and deoxygenated blood remain separate.

Supplement

The left ventricle has a much thicker wall than the right ventricle. It needs more muscle because it has to pump blood around the whole body at high pressure, whereas the right ventricle only has to pump it to the lungs. The muscular walls of the atria are not as thick as those of the ventricles, as they only have to pump blood to the ventricles.

Supplement

Section 6 — Transport in Plants and Animals

Circulatory System — The Heart

Different factors, like exercise affect the heart rate. Changes in heart rate can be monitored.

There are **Different** Ways to **Monitor** the **Activity** of the **Heart**

1) By listening to it. The opening and closing of heart valves make a "lub dub" sound. A stethoscope can be used to listen to the heart sounds, to check that the heart is functioning normally.

2) By measuring the pulse rate (see below). This gives an idea of how quickly the heart is beating compared to what is expected.

3) By using an electrocardiogram (ECG). The heart's activity is controlled by electrical impulses. In an ECG, sensors are attached to a person's skin that detect these electrical impulses. These impulses are recorded by a machine, so that anything unusual can be detected.

You Can Investigate The **Effect** of **Physical Activity** on **Pulse Rate**

1) Each contraction of the ventricles creates a surge of blood in the arteries. This is your pulse.

2) To measure your pulse rate, put two fingers on the inside of your wrist or your neck and count the number of pulses in 1 minute.

3) You can investigate how physical activity affects your pulse rate. E.g. you could take your pulse after:

- sitting down for 5 minutes,
- then after 5 minutes of gentle walking,
- then again after 5 minutes of slow jogging,
- then again after running for 5 minutes.

4) You could then plot your results in a bar chart.

5) Your pulse rate will increase the more intense the exercise is.

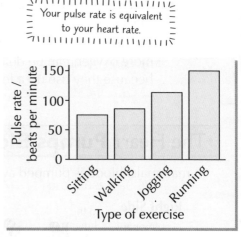

Your pulse rate is equivalent to your heart rate.

Physical Activity Increases **Heart Rate**

See pages 78-79 for more on respiration.

1) When you exercise, your muscles need more energy, so you respire more.

2) This means you need to get more oxygen into the cells and remove more carbon dioxide. For this to happen the blood has to flow faster, so your heart rate increases. Here's how:

- Exercise increases the amount of carbon dioxide (CO_2) in the blood.
- High levels of blood CO_2 are detected by receptors in two of the arteries.
- These receptors send impulses to the brain.
- The brain sends impulses to the heart, causing it to contract more frequently and with more force.

Supplement

Physical activity causes the pulse rate to increase

Measuring pulse rate is one way that the activity of the heart can be monitored. Make sure you can describe how to do this, and know how physical activity affects pulse rate. If you're doing the Extended course, you'll need to explain the effect that physical activity has on heart rate too.

Coronary Heart Disease

Coronary heart disease is a big problem. The good news is there are lots of ways to treat it.

Several Factors can Lead to **Coronary Heart Disease**

1) The coronary arteries supply blood to the heart muscle. Coronary heart disease (CHD) is when the coronary arteries get blocked by layers of fatty material building up.

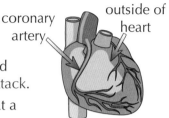
coronary artery
outside of heart

2) This causes the arteries to become narrow, so blood flow is restricted and there's a lack of oxygen to the heart muscle — this can lead to a heart attack.

3) Risk factors are things that are linked to an increase in the likelihood that a person will develop a certain disease during their lifetime. There are many risk factors for coronary heart disease. They include:

- Eating a diet high in saturated fat and salt
- High levels of stress
- Smoking
- The genes you inherit
- Getting older
- Being male rather than female

Both men and women can get coronary heart disease, but it's more likely if you're male.

Diet and **Exercise** can Help to Prevent **Coronary Heart Disease**

Diet

- High blood pressure and a high level of cholesterol can cause fatty deposits to form in arteries.
- Reducing the amount of saturated fat in your diet will help to reduce the cholesterol level (p.46). Reducing the amount of salt in your diet may help to reduce blood pressure.
- So a diet low in saturated fat and salt is likely to reduce the risk of fatty deposits occurring and therefore help to prevent coronary heart disease.
- Eating plenty of fruits and vegetables is also thought to help protect the heart against CHD.

Exercise

Another risk factor for coronary heart disease is being inactive. Regular exercise can lower blood pressure and reduce the risk of coronary heart disease.

Coronary Heart Disease can be **Treated** with **Drugs** or **Surgery**

1) Sometimes the build up of fatty materials damages blood vessels. Blood cells can build up at the site of damage and cause a blood clot to form (see p.64). Blood clots can block arteries, which can cause a heart attack. Taking aspirin daily can thin the blood, which helps to prevent blood clots from forming in the arteries, lowering the risk of a heart attack.

2) There are different types of surgery that can be used to treat coronary heart disease:

- Angioplasty is where a small balloon is inserted into a narrowed coronary artery and inflated. This opens up the artery again, allowing blood to pass through.
- Stents are tubes that are inserted inside arteries. They keep them open, making sure blood can pass through to the heart muscles, lowering the risk of a heart attack.
- If part of a blood vessel is blocked, a piece of healthy vessel taken from elsewhere can be used to bypass the blocked section. This is known as coronary bypass surgery.

Coronary heart disease is associated with blood flow

Factors like age and family history can increase the risk of coronary heart disease but they can't be changed. It is possible to control and modify lifestyle-related risk factors, like diet, smoking and stress.

Supplement

Circulatory System — Blood Vessels

Blood is carried round the body in a set of 'tubes' called blood vessels. Here's a page on the different types.

Arteries Carry Blood Under Pressure

1) Arteries carry blood from the heart to the rest of the body.

2) The walls are thick compared to the size of the hole down the middle (the "lumen"). They contain thick layers of muscle and elastic fibres.

3) The walls need to be thick to withstand the high pressure of blood in the arteries. They need to be elastic so they can stretch and recoil with each surge of blood as the heart beats.

4) The arteries branch into smaller blood vessels called arterioles, which control the amount of blood flowing to the tissues.

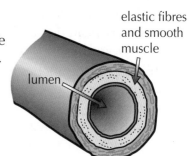

elastic fibres and smooth muscle

lumen

Capillaries are Really Small

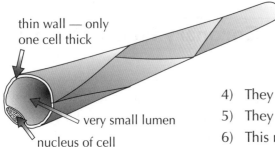

thin wall — only one cell thick

very small lumen

nucleus of cell

1) Arterioles branch into capillaries.

2) Capillaries are really tiny — too small to see.

3) They carry the blood really close to every cell in the body to exchange substances with them.

4) They supply glucose and oxygen, and take away wastes like CO_2.

5) They have permeable walls that are usually only one cell thick.

6) This means that substances can diffuse in and out at an increased rate because the distance over which diffusion happens is reduced.

Veins Take Blood Back to the Heart

1) Their walls are not as thick as artery walls and they have a bigger lumen than arteries.

2) Veins also have one-way valves inside them.

3) The blood is at lower pressure in the veins so the walls don't need to be as thick.

4) They have a bigger lumen than arteries to help the blood flow despite the lower pressure.

5) The valves help keep the blood flowing in the right direction despite the lower pressure.

6) Venules are very small veins, that come from capillaries and join together to form veins.

7) Veins are sometimes connected directly to arteries by blood vessels called shunt vessels. This means the blood doesn't need to travel from the arteries to the veins via the capillaries.

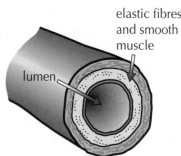

elastic fibres and smooth muscle

large lumen

valve

Learn The Blood Vessels That Go To and From These Organs

Organ	Main blood vessel to...	Main blood vessel from...
Heart	vena cava	aorta
	pulmonary vein	pulmonary artery
Lungs	pulmonary artery	pulmonary vein
Kidney	renal artery	renal vein

There's more on the vena cava, aorta and pulmonary blood vessels on p.59. There's more on the renal artery and renal vein on p.83.

Circulatory System — Blood

Blood acts as a huge transport system — it is a tissue that contains different cells.

Red Blood Cells Carry Oxygen

1) The job of red blood cells is to carry oxygen from the lungs to all the cells in the body.

2) They have a biconcave disc shape to give a large surface area for absorbing oxygen.

3) They don't have a nucleus — this allows more room to carry oxygen.

4) They contain a red pigment called haemoglobin, which binds to oxygen in the lungs and releases it in body tissues, allowing it to be transported around the body to cells.

White Blood Cells Defend Against Infection

1) White blood cells are usually larger than red blood cells. Unlike red blood cells, white blood cells do have a nucleus.

2) White blood cells help to defend against infection by:

   • Phagocytosis — surrounding and digesting disease-causing organisms.

   • Producing antibodies — proteins that attach to disease-causing organisms and help to destroy them.

3) Phagocytes are white blood cells that carry out phagocytosis.

4) Lymphocytes are white blood cells that produce antibodies against microorganisms.

Supplement

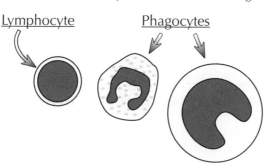

Lymphocyte   Phagocytes

There's more on white blood cells and how they work on page 70.

Make Sure You Can Identify Blood Cells Under A Microscope

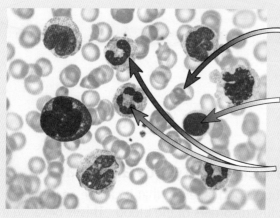

Most of the cells are red blood cells. They're easy to spot because they don't have a nucleus. The rest are white blood cells — they do have a nucleus.

This is a lymphocyte. The nucleus takes up most of the cell and there's very little cytoplasm to be seen.

These are different types of phagocytes. One has a 'multi-lobed' nucleus (a nucleus with several interconnected parts). The other has a kidney-bean shaped nucleus.

Supplement

Circulatory System — Blood

Blood doesn't just contain red blood cells and white blood cells — it also contains platelets and plasma.

Platelets Help Blood Clot

1) These are small fragments of cells.
2) They have no nucleus.
3) When you damage a blood vessel, platelets clump together to 'plug' the damaged area. This is known as blood clotting.
4) Lack of platelets can cause excessive bleeding and bruising.

Blood Clotting Involves Proteins Too

1) Your blood contains a soluble protein called fibrinogen.
2) When you damage a blood vessel, it triggers a series of reactions that convert fibrinogen into another protein called fibrin.
3) Fibrin is made up of insoluble fibres. These tangle together and form a mesh in which platelets and red blood cells get trapped — this forms the blood clot.
4) Clotting stops you losing too much blood from a wound and stops pathogens (disease-causing organisms) from getting in.

Plasma is the Liquid That Carries Everything in Blood

This is a pale, straw-coloured liquid which carries just about everything, including:
1) Red and white blood cells and platelets.
2) Nutrients like glucose and amino acids. These are the soluble products of digestion which are absorbed from the gut and taken to the cells of the body.
3) Carbon dioxide from the organs to the lungs.
4) Ions.
5) Hormones.

Blood — red blood cells, white blood cells, platelets and plasma

Sometimes, when you're ill, you might have a sample of your blood taken so that it can be analysed. Blood tests can be used to diagnose loads of things — not just disorders of the blood. This is because the blood transports so many chemicals produced by so many organs... and it's easy to take a sample of blood.

The Lymphatic System

The lymphatic system helps to circulate body fluids and protect us from infection and disease.

Supplement

Materials are **Transferred** between **Capillaries** and **Tissue Fluid**

1) The network of capillaries in an area of tissue is called a capillary bed.
2) Capillaries allow substances to leave the blood plasma, e.g. oxygen, water and nutrients.
3) These substances make up a fluid called tissue fluid. It surrounds the cells in tissues.
4) Unlike blood, tissue fluid doesn't contain red blood cells or big proteins, because they're too large to be pushed out through the capillary walls.
5) Cells take in oxygen and nutrients from the tissue fluid, and release carbon dioxide into it.

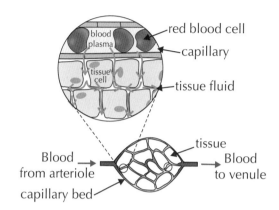

Excess Tissue Fluid **Drains** into the **Lymphatic Vessels**

1) Some of the tissue fluid re-enters the capillaries at the venule end of the capillary bed, but some excess tissue fluid is left over.
2) This extra fluid eventually gets returned to the blood through the lymphatic system — a network of tubes that helps to circulate body fluids.
3) The lymphatic system is made up of lymphatic vessels.

The lymphatic system is also part of the immune system (p.70).

- The smallest lymphatic vessels are the lymphatic capillaries.
- Excess tissue fluid passes into lymphatic vessels. Once inside, it's called lymph.
- Valves in the lymphatic vessels stop the lymph going backwards.
- Lymph gradually moves towards the main lymphatic vessels in the thorax (chest cavity). Here, it's returned to the blood, near the heart.

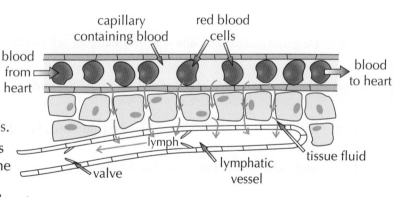

Lymph Nodes Help the **Body** to **Fight Infection**

1) The lymph flows through glands called lymph nodes as it travels through the lymphatic vessels.
2) The lymph nodes filter anything harmful, e.g. pathogens or toxins out of the lymph.
3) They also contain lots of lymphocytes (see p.63) to help destroy pathogens.

The lymphatic system contains lymph vessels and lymph nodes

Like the circulatory system, the lymphatic system runs throughout your body. But instead of carrying blood, the lymphatic system carries a fluid called lymph through lymphatic vessels and lymph nodes.

Warm-Up & Exam Questions

That's Section 6 finished. Have a go at these questions to see how much you know.

Warm-Up Questions

1) What is the circulatory system?
2) State three ways that the activity of the heart can be monitored.
3) What do veins do?
4) Describe the purpose of platelets in blood.
5) Give three things that are carried in blood plasma.

Exam Questions

1   Blood is a tissue that transports important substances around the body.
     The cell shown below transports oxygen around the body.

View   Cut through
from above   view

   (a)   What type of cell is shown?

                                                                                [1]

   (b)   Describe and explain **one** way in which this cell is adapted for carrying oxygen.

                                                                                [2]

   (c)   Name another type of blood cell, and state its function.

                                                                                [2]

   (d)   Blood cells are carried in the bloodstream inside blood vessels.
         Capillaries are one type of blood vessel.
         State and explain **two** ways that the structure of a capillary enables it to carry out its function.

                                                                                [4]
                                                                      [Total 9 marks]

2   Doctors are assessing the heart of a patient with coronary heart disease.

   (a)   What is coronary heart disease?

                                                                                [1]

   (b)   State **two** possible risk factors for coronary heart disease.

                                                                                [2]

   (c)   Describe how aspirin can be used to treat coronary heart disease.

                                                                                [1]
                                                                      [Total 4 marks]

Exam Questions

---

3 The diagram below shows the human heart, as seen from the front.
The left ventricle has been labelled.

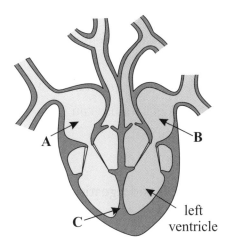

(a) Name the parts labelled **A**, **B** and **C**.

[1]

(b) Describe the passage of deoxygenated blood from the body
through the heart to reach the lungs.

[4]

(c) Explain why the wall of the left ventricle is thicker than the wall of the right ventricle.

[2]

(d) Give the function of the valves in the heart.

[1]

(e) The human heart is part of a double circulatory system. Give **one** advantage for
humans of having a double circulatory system instead of a single circulatory system.

[1]

[Total 9 marks]

4 Platelets help the blood to clot at a wound.

(a) Give **two** reasons why it is important for blood to clot at a wound.

[2]

(b) Describe the process of blood clotting.

[2]

[Total 4 marks]

5 The lymphatic system helps the body to protect itself from infection.

(a) How does the lymphatic system help to protect the body from infection?

[2]

(b) State **one** other function of the lymphatic system.

[1]

[Total 3 marks]

Supplement

Supplement

Revision Summary for Sections 5 & 6

That's the end of Sections 5 and 6 — time to put yourself to the test and find out how much you really know.
- Try these questions and tick off each one when you get it right.
- When you've done all the questions for a topic and are completely happy with it, tick off the topic.

Photosynthesis and Gas Exchange in Leaves (p.36-42) ☐

1) What is photosynthesis? ☑
2) Explain how a) light, b) CO_2 concentration and c) temperature limit the rate of photosynthesis. ☑
3) Briefly describe a test to show that chlorophyll is needed for photosynthesis to take place. ☑
4) What colour does hydrogencarbonate indicator turn if the CO_2 concentration increases? ☑
5) Give one reason why keeping plants in a glasshouse can improve plant growth. ☑
6) Where are the stomata located in a typical leaf? ☑
7) What do plants need magnesium ions for? ☑

Diet, Digestion, Absorption, Assimilation and Egestion (p.45-51) ☐

8) Why is having a balanced diet important? ☑
9) Why does the stomach produce gastric juice? ☑
10) What are incisor teeth used for? ☑
11) What is the role of digestive enzymes in chemical digestion? ☑
12) How do the villi in the small intestine help absorption? ☑
13) What is assimilation? ☑
14) How does the cholera bacterium cause diarrhoea? ☑

Transport in Plants, Water Uptake, Transpiration and Translocation (p.53-57) ☐

15) What is the function of xylem? ☑
16) Is the xylem or the phloem found in the centre of root cells? ☑
17) Explain how water moves upwards through a plant. ☑
18) Describe how you'd use a potometer to estimate the rate of transpiration. ☑
19) What is translocation? ☑
20) Name a part of a plant that can be both a source and a sink. ☑

The Circulatory System and The Heart (p.59-61) ☐

21) Do fish have a single or a double circulatory system? ☑
22) Do arteries take blood to or from the heart? ☑
23) Why do the ventricles have thicker muscular walls than the atria? ☑
24) Describe how you can investigate the effect of physical activity on pulse rate. ☑

Blood Vessels, Blood and The Lymphatic System (p.62-65) ☐

25) Which blood vessels have valves? ☑
26) How are arteries adapted to carry out their function? ☑
27) What are a) arterioles, b) shunt vessels? ☑
28) What are the names of the two main blood vessels associated with the lungs? ☑
29) Give one structural difference between red blood cells and white blood cells. ☑
30) Describe how materials are transferred between capillaries and tissue fluid. ☑
31) What do lymph nodes contain? ☑

Fighting Disease

Here's a page all about what causes disease and how disease can be spread — scary stuff.
Thankfully, you also need to know about the barriers in the human body that help to protect us.

Some **Diseases** are **Caused** by **Pathogens**

 KEY TERM   A pathogen is a disease-causing organism.

1) Pathogens can be bacteria, viruses, fungi or protoctists.
2) They cause transmissible (infectious) diseases in other organisms (called hosts).

 KEY TERM   A transmissible disease is a disease where the pathogen can be passed from one host to another.

Pathogens Can Be **Spread Through**...

...**Direct** Contact...

Pathogens spread through direct contact are spread directly from one organism to another.

For example, some pathogens are spread through contact with a host's blood or other body fluids, e.g. mucus or saliva.

Some pathogens are spread in the droplets of mucus and saliva released when a person coughs or sneezes.

...Or **Indirect** Contact

Pathogens spread through indirect contact are spread from one organism to another via an intermediate. For example:

- Some pathogens can be picked up by touching contaminated surfaces.
- Some pathogens are picked up by eating contaminated food.
- Some animals (insects in particular) can spread pathogens.
- Some pathogens are breathed in as they are carried in the air.

A surface that's been contaminated with a pathogen has the pathogen living on it.

Barriers **Stop Pathogens Entering** the **Body**

The human body has mechanical (physical) and chemical defences against pathogen entry.

Mechanical Barriers

1) The skin acts as a barrier to pathogens. If it gets damaged, blood clots quickly to seal cuts and keep microorganisms out.
2) Hairs in your nose trap particles from the air that could contain pathogens.

These mechanical and chemical barriers are non-specific — they work against many different types of pathogens.

Chemical Barriers

1) Cells in your trachea and bronchi (airways in the lungs) produce mucus, which traps pathogens.
2) The stomach produces acid, which kills most pathogens that are swallowed.

Fighting Disease — Immune System

Sometimes, pathogens do make it into your body — this page is all about what happens next.

Your **Immune System** Deals with **Pathogens**

1) Once pathogens have entered your body they'll reproduce rapidly unless they're destroyed. That's the job of your immune system, and white blood cells are the most important part of it.

2) White blood cells have two different methods for defence that you need to know about: phagocytosis and antibody production.

Phagocytosis

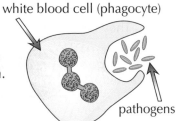

white blood cell (phagocyte)

pathogens

1) Some white blood cells detect things that are 'foreign' to the body, e.g. pathogens. They then engulf (surround) the pathogens and digest them.

2) This process is called phagocytosis. The white blood cells are called phagocytes.

Production of **Antibodies**

Some white blood cells make proteins called antibodies. Antibodies are used to destroy pathogens. Here's how they work:

1) Every pathogen has unique molecules (called antigens) on its surface. These antigens have specific shapes.

2) When some types of white blood cell (called lymphocytes) come across a foreign antigen, they will start to produce antibodies. The antibodies have specific shapes to fit the antigens.

3) The antibodies lock on to the antigens on the invading pathogens, which either causes the direct destruction of pathogens or marks them out for destruction by phagocytes.

4) The antibodies produced are specific to that antigen — they won't lock on to any others.

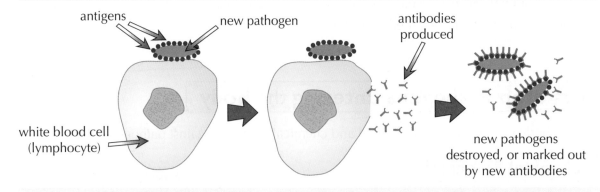

antigens — new pathogen — antibodies produced

white blood cell (lymphocyte)

new pathogens destroyed, or marked out by new antibodies

5) Memory cells are also produced in response to the antigen. These are white blood cells that stay in the body and remember a specific antigen. They can produce antibodies very quickly if the same antigen enters the body again — so the pathogen can be destroyed before you get sick. This gives you long-term active immunity against the pathogen.

KEY TERM

Active immunity is the defence against a pathogen by the production of antibodies in the body.

Active immunity can be gained after infection by a pathogen or by vaccination (see p.71).

Supplement

Preventing the Spread of Disease

We don't always have to deal with the problem of disease once it's happened — we can prevent it happening in the first place. Here are a few ways to prevent the spread of disease.

The **Spread** of **Disease** Can Be **Reduced**

There are several measures that can be taken to control the spread of disease.

Certain foods also need thorough cooking to kill bacteria.

1) Hygienic food preparation — preparing food in hygienic (clean) conditions can reduce the spread of pathogens from work surfaces, chopping boards, etc. to food.

2) Good personal hygiene — simple hygiene measures, such as washing your hands after going to the toilet, can prevent the spread of disease.

3) Waste disposal — not letting rubbish build up, and having systems in place to safely dispose of things like soiled bandages and used needles, can prevent the spread of disease.

4) Sewage treatment — having a good system for the treatment of sewage (which prevents sewage from contaminating drinking water) will reduce the spread of water-borne pathogens.

Vaccination Can **Enhance** the **Defences** of the Body

The body's defences can be enhanced through vaccination.
Vaccination triggers the body to produce antibodies against a specific pathogen.

1) Vaccination usually involves injecting dead or inactive pathogens into the body.

2) Even though the pathogens are harmless, they carry antigens which trigger an immune response by lymphocytes, which produce antibodies to help destroy the pathogens.

3) The antigens also trigger the production of memory cells.
These give long-term active immunity against the pathogen.

Example:

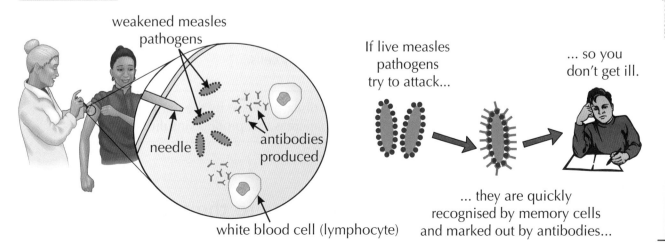

weakened measles pathogens

needle

antibodies produced

white blood cell (lymphocyte)

If live measles pathogens try to attack...

... they are quickly recognised by memory cells and marked out by antibodies...

... so you don't get ill.

Preventing the Spread of Disease

Here's some more information about preventing the spread of disease — plus, how passive immunity works and what happens when the immune system goes wrong.

Vaccination Can be Used to Control the Spread of Disease

1) Individuals who have been vaccinated against a disease are immune — they won't develop the infection and pass it on to someone else.

2) When lots of people in a population have been vaccinated, it also helps to protect individuals that have not been vaccinated — they are less likely to catch the disease because there are fewer people to catch it from.

Some Immunity Can be Passive

1) You can also become immune to a disease without producing your own antibodies. This is known as passive immunity.

 KEY TERM

Passive immunity is the short-term defence against a pathogen by antibodies made by a different organism.

For example, a baby gets passive immunity from the antibodies it receives from its mother through the placenta and in breast milk. This is important because the immune systems of infants are not fully functional at birth, so they are at a greater risk of infection than older children and adults.

2) Passive immunity is short-term because the antibodies given do not remain in the blood long-term and memory cells are not produced. This means there is a risk of being infected by the same disease later on.

Immune Defences Can Go Wrong

1) Some diseases are caused by the immune system targeting the wrong cells.

2) Instead of targeting foreign antigens, white blood cells start to target and destroy healthy body cells.

For example, Type 1 diabetes is a disease caused by the immune system targeting the cells in the pancreas that produce insulin.

Memory cells speed up the next response to the pathogen

Vaccination has helped to save millions of lives — and it's all because of antibodies and memory cells.

Supplement

Warm-Up & Exam Questions

It's easy to think you've learnt everything until you try some questions. Don't panic if there's a bit you've forgotten, just go back over that bit until it's firmly fixed in your brain.

Warm-Up Questions

1) What are the unique molecules found on the surface of pathogens called?
2) What is meant by a transmissible disease?
3) How does the skin defend against the entry of pathogens?
4) What is meant by passive immunity?

Exam Questions

1   There are many defences that help to prevent pathogens from entering the body.

(a)   Describe the role of hairs in the nose.

[1]

(b)   Describe a chemical defence of the body against pathogens found in food.

[1]
[Total 2 marks]

2   The methods used to prevent the spread of a disease depend on how the disease is transmitted.
It is important for chefs to wash their hands thoroughly before cooking. Suggest why.

[Total 1 mark]

3   The human immune system fights pathogens using a number of different mechanisms.

(a)   Name and describe the mechanism for destroying pathogens which is shown in the diagram.

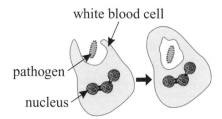

white blood cell

pathogen

nucleus

[2]

(b)   Describe the role of antibodies in the immune response.

[3]
[Total 5 marks]

4   Child A and child B are born to different women on the same day.
Child A is vaccinated with the rubella vaccine, but child B is not.
Three years later the two children are exposed to the rubella virus.
Explain why child B becomes ill but child A does not.

[Total 5 marks]

The Gas Exchange System

Your gas exchange system is found in your chest. It contains the lungs (the gas exchange organs).

The **Gas Exchange System** has Lots of Parts

1) The lungs are protected by the ribs.

2) Intercostal muscles run between the ribs.

3) There are actually three layers of intercostal muscles. You need to know about two of them — the internal and external intercostal muscles.

4) The air you breathe in goes through the larynx and then the trachea.

5) The trachea is a hollow tube surrounded by C-shaped rings of cartilage. This makes it strong, but also allows it to move.

6) The trachea splits into two tubes called bronchi (each one is a bronchus), one going to each lung. The bronchi split into smaller tubes called bronchioles.

7) The bronchioles end at small sacs called alveoli where gas exchange takes place (see next page). The alveoli are surrounded by capillaries.

8) All of the structures mentioned above are separated from the lower part of the body by a muscle called the diaphragm.

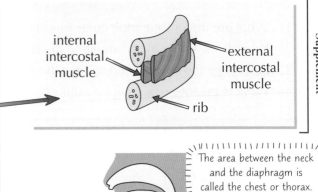

internal intercostal muscle

external intercostal muscle

rib

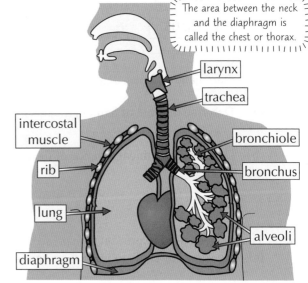

The area between the neck and the diaphragm is called the chest or thorax.

larynx

trachea

intercostal muscle

rib

lung

diaphragm

bronchiole

bronchus

alveoli

Ventilation is the Process of...

...**Breathing In** (Inspiration)...

1) The external intercostal muscles and diaphragm contract. The internal intercostal muscles relax.

2) This causes the ribs to move upwards and outwards.

3) This increases the volume of the thorax.

4) This decreases the pressure inside the thorax, drawing air in.

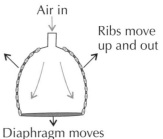

Air in

Ribs move up and out

Diaphragm moves down as it contracts

...and **Breathing Out** (Expiration)

1) The internal intercostal muscles contract. The external intercostal muscles and diaphragm relax.

2) This causes the ribs to move downwards and inwards.

3) This decreases the volume of the thorax.

4) This increases the pressure inside the thorax, so air is forced out.

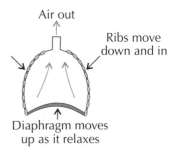

Air out

Ribs move down and in

Diaphragm moves up as it relaxes

Gas Exchange

Gas exchange isn't too tricky — it's just a simple trade of gases between the air and your blood. You also need to know the differences between the air breathed in and air breathed out.

Gas Exchange Happens in the Lungs

1) The job of the lungs is to transfer oxygen to the blood and to remove waste carbon dioxide from it.

2) To do this the lungs contain millions of little air sacs called alveoli where gas exchange takes place.

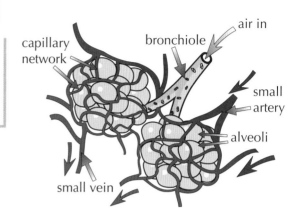

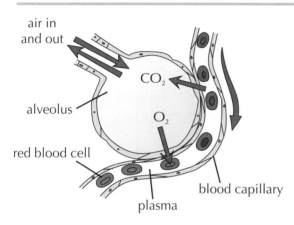

Blue = blood with carbon dioxide.
Red = blood with oxygen.

3) The alveoli form a specialised gas exchange surface. This means they have features to maximise the diffusion of oxygen and CO_2. They have:

- A large surface area (about 75 m^2 in humans).
- A very thin surface.
- A good blood supply.
- Good ventilation with air.

Gas exchange surfaces in other organisms tend to have similar features.

The Composition of Inspired and Expired Air is Different

The proportions of some gases in the air you breathe in are different from the proportions you breathe out.

	Oxygen / %	Carbon Dioxide / %	Water Vapour
Inspired Air	21	0.04	% Varies
Expired Air	16	4	Saturated (the air holds as much water as it can)

This is because aerobic respiration uses up oxygen and produces carbon dioxide and water — so there's less oxygen and more carbon dioxide and water vapour in expired air than inspired air.

There's more about respiration on page 78.

The Gas Exchange System Has to be Protected

1) Your airways are lined with cells that have a protective role.

2) Goblet cells produce a sticky substance called mucus to coat the inner lining of the trachea and bronchi.

3) The mucus catches any pathogens and particles before they reach the lungs.

4) Ciliated cells are covered in tiny hair-like structures called cilia. These waft the mucus up to the back of the throat where it can be swallowed.

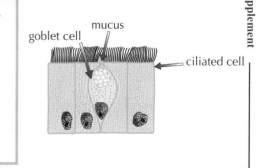

Investigating Breathing

Time for some investigating. On this page there's a test to show that the composition of inspired and expired air is different, and an investigation into how exercise affects your breathing rate.

You Can Show the **Release** of **Carbon Dioxide** in Your Breath

1) You can do an experiment with limewater to show that carbon dioxide (CO_2) is released when we breathe out.

2) Limewater is a colourless solution which turns cloudy in the presence of carbon dioxide.

- Set up two boiling tubes as in the diagram on the right. Put the same amount of limewater in each.
- Put your mouth around the mouthpiece and breathe in and out several times.
- As you breathe in, air from the room is drawn in through boiling tube A. This air contains very little carbon dioxide so the limewater in this boiling tube remains colourless.
- When you breathe out, the air you expire bubbles through the limewater in boiling tube B. This air contains CO_2 produced during respiration, so the limewater in this boiling tube turns cloudy.

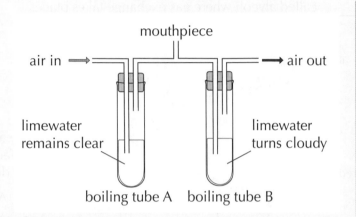

You Can Investigate the **Effect** of **Exercise** on **Breathing Rate**

1) When you exercise, your muscle cells need more oxygen (O_2) and produce more CO_2. So an increase in your breathing rate helps to deliver more O_2 to the cells and to remove the waste CO_2.

2) There's a simple experiment you can do to see what happens to breathing rate when you exercise:

- Firstly, sit still for five minutes. Then, for one minute, count the number of breaths you take.
- Now do four minutes of exercise (running, skipping...) and as soon as you stop count your breaths for a minute.
- Repeat the steps above, and work out your mean (average) results for resting and after exercise.
- You could also ask two other people to do the same so you get three sets of results to compare.

3) Your results should show that exercise increases breathing rate.

4) Exercise also increases the depth of breathing. When you breathe deeply, you inspire and expire a greater volume of air. This can be measured with a piece of equipment called a spirometer.

5) This all happens because the brain detects the increased concentration of CO_2 in the blood and increases the rate and depth of breathing so that more CO_2 is removed.

Supplement

You should always carry out repeats in an investigation

You should carry out repeats (at least three) and calculate a mean in order to help improve the precision of your results. To calculate a mean, just add all your repeat results together (ignoring any anomalous results) and then divide the total by the number of repeats. Lovely.

Warm-Up & Exam Questions

The questions on this page are great practice for the exam. I'd give them a go if I were you...

Warm-Up Questions

1) True or False? Expired air has a greater proportion of oxygen than inspired air.
2) What solution can be used to test for the presence of carbon dioxide?
3) What effect does physical activity have on breathing rate?
4) In the gas exchange system, what function do the ciliated cells have?

Exam Questions

1 A diagram of the human gas exchange system is shown below.

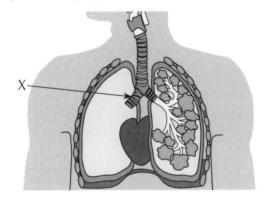

(a) Label the diaphragm and a rib on the diagram.

[2]

(b) A structure of the respiratory system is labelled X on the diagram. Name structure X.

[1]

(c) Name the structures in the respiratory system where gas exchange takes place.

[1]

(d) Give **two** ways in which these gas exchange structures are specialised for their function.

[2]

[Total 6 marks]

2 The statements below describe the events that take place when you breathe in.
Which of the options (**A-D**) shows the events in the correct order? Tick **one** box.

Event	Number
Pressure in thorax decreases	1
The external intercostal muscles and diaphragm contract, and the internal intercostal muscles relax	2
Air is drawn into the lungs	3
Thorax volume increases	4

☐ A 2, 1, 4, 3

☐ B 3, 4, 1, 2

☐ C 2, 4, 1, 3

☐ D 3, 2, 4, 1

[Total 1 mark]

Section 8 — Gas Exchange and Respiration

Respiration

You need energy to stay alive and to do all of the things that you love doing (like revising). Energy comes from the food you eat, and it's transferred by respiration.

Respiration Involves Many Reactions

1) Respiration is the process of transferring energy from the breakdown of nutrient molecules, e.g. glucose (a sugar). It goes on in every cell in your body continuously.
2) Respiration transfers the energy that cells need to do just about everything.
3) It involves a series of different chemical reactions, which are controlled by enzymes.
4) There are two types of respiration, aerobic and anaerobic.

Respiration Transfers Energy for All Kinds of Things

Here are seven examples of how humans use the energy transferred by respiration:

1) To allow the muscles to contract (so we can move about).
2) To build proteins from amino acids in protein synthesis.
3) For cell division, e.g. when replacing damaged cells with new cells.
4) To move molecules by active transport.
5) So that we can grow.
6) For passing nerve impulses along neurones.
7) To maintain (keep) a constant body temperature.

Aerobic Respiration Needs Plenty of Oxygen

1) Aerobic just means "with oxygen" and it's the most efficient way to transfer energy from glucose.
2) Here's the definition you need to learn:

 KEY TERM   Aerobic respiration is the series of chemical reactions in cells that uses oxygen to break down nutrient molecules to release energy.

3) This type of respiration goes on all the time in plants and animals. Here's the word equation:

glucose + oxygen $\longrightarrow$ carbon dioxide + water

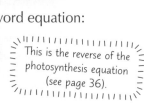 This is the reverse of the photosynthesis equation (see page 36).

Supplement

4) And here's the balanced chemical equation:

$$C_6H_{12}O_6 + 6O_2 \longrightarrow 6CO_2 + 6H_2O$$

Respiration releases energy

It's important to understand what respiration is and what it is used for. You're going to struggle to follow the next couple of pages if you don't. Read this page again if you need to, until you're sure you've got it.

Anaerobic Respiration

Now that you've learnt about aerobic respiration, it's time to learn about anaerobic respiration too.

Anaerobic Respiration is Used if There's Not Enough Oxygen

1) When you do vigorous (hard) exercise and your body can't supply enough oxygen to your muscles, they start doing anaerobic respiration as well as aerobic respiration. Here's the definition you need:

 Anaerobic respiration is the series of chemical reactions in cells that breaks down nutrient molecules to release energy without using oxygen.

2) Here's the word equation for anaerobic respiration in muscle cells:

 glucose ⟶ lactic acid

3) Anaerobic respiration transfers much less energy per glucose molecule than aerobic respiration.

4) So, anaerobic respiration is only useful in emergencies, e.g. during exercise when it allows you to keep on using your muscles for a while longer.

Supplement

Anaerobic Respiration Leads to an Oxygen Debt

1) Your muscles contract more frequently when you exercise, so you need more energy from respiration. This means you need to get more oxygen into your muscles for aerobic respiration.

2) Your breathing rate and breathing depth increase to get more oxygen into the blood, and your heart rate increases to get the blood (and the oxygen in it) around the body faster.

3) When you do really vigorous exercise your body can't supply oxygen to your muscles quickly enough for aerobic respiration alone, so they start respiring anaerobically as well. This causes lactic acid (see above) to build up in muscle cells and in the blood.

4) After respiring anaerobically, when you stop exercising you'll have an "oxygen debt".

5) An oxygen debt is the amount of extra oxygen your body needs to get rid of the lactic acid.

6) In other words you have to "repay" the oxygen that you didn't get to your muscles in time, because your lungs, heart and blood couldn't keep up with the demand earlier on:

- The blood that enters your muscles transports the lactic acid to the liver. The lactic acid is then broken down using oxygen, in aerobic respiration.

- Heart rate stays high after exercise to transport lactic acid in the blood from muscles to the liver. Breathing rate and depth stay high to supply oxygen for aerobic respiration of lactic acid.

Supplement

Anaerobic Respiration in Yeast is Slightly Different

1) Yeast can respire without oxygen too, but they produce alcohol and carbon dioxide, not lactic acid.

2) Here's the word equation for anaerobic respiration in yeast:

 *Yeast are single-celled microorganisms.*

 glucose ⟶ alcohol + carbon dioxide

Supplement

3) And here's the balanced chemical equation:

 $C_6H_{12}O_6 \longrightarrow 2C_2H_5OH + 2CO_2$

 Aerobic and anaerobic respiration produce different products
Make sure you know the differences between aerobic and anaerobic respiration for your exam. Learn the products of each type, which transfers the most energy and which type requires oxygen.

Investigating Respiration

You can do an experiment to investigate the uptake of oxygen by respiring organisms, such as arthropods and germinating seeds.

You Can Measure the Uptake of Oxygen by Respiring Organisms

In aerobic respiration, organisms use up oxygen from the air. Here's an experiment which uses woodlice, a water bath and a piece of equipment called a respirometer. Instead of woodlice, you could use other arthropods (p.7) or germinating seeds.

1) Some soda lime granules are added to two test tubes. The soda lime absorbs the CO_2 produced by the respiring woodlice in the experiment.

Safety goggles and gloves must be worn when handling soda lime to protect the eyes and skin.

2) A ball of cotton wool is placed above the soda lime in each tube. Woodlice are placed on top of the cotton wool in one tube. Glass beads with the same mass as the woodlice are used in the control tube. (There's more on controls on page 182.)

3) The respirometer is then set up as shown in the diagram.

4) The syringe is used to set the coloured fluid in the tube to a known level.

5) The apparatus is then left for a set period of time in a water bath set to e.g. 15 °C.

6) During this time, there'll be a decrease in the volume of the air in the test tube containing the woodlice. This is because the woodlice use up oxygen in the tube as they respire. (The CO_2 they produce is absorbed by the soda lime so it doesn't affect the experiment.)

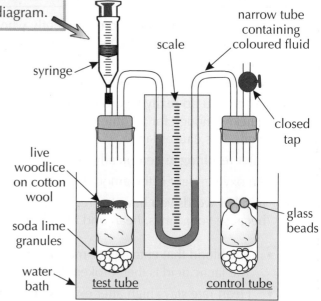

7) The decrease in volume reduces the pressure in the tube, causing the coloured fluid to move towards the test tube containing the woodlice.

8) The liquid moves because oxygen is taken up by the woodlice. You can use the distance moved by the liquid to calculate the volume of oxygen taken in by the woodlice.

Supplement

You can also use this equipment to investigate the effect of temperature on the rate of respiration of arthropods or germinating seeds. Repeat steps 1-8 with the water bath set at different temperatures, e.g. 20 °C and 25 °C. This will allow you to see how changing the temperature affects the rate of respiration.

PRACTICAL TIP

Learn how to investigate respiration in respiring organisms

If you're given a method to follow in order to carry out an investigation, take your time and read each of the steps carefully before you begin — you might not get the right results if you don't.

Warm-Up & Exam Questions

You know the drill by now — work your way through the Warm-Up questions, then the Exam Questions.

Warm-Up Questions

1) Give two examples of how humans use the energy transferred by respiration.
2) What is produced by aerobic respiration in plants?
3) What is the balanced chemical equation for aerobic respiration?
4) State one way that the body clears the oxygen debt caused by vigorous exercise.
5) What is the balanced chemical equation for anaerobic respiration in yeast?

Exam Questions

1   Respiration is a process carried out by all living cells.
    It can take place aerobically or anaerobically.

  (a)   State the purpose of respiration.

                                                                    [1]

  (b)   Give **two** differences between aerobic and anaerobic respiration in animals.

                                                                    [2]

  (c)   Write the word equation for aerobic respiration.

                                                                    [2]
                                                          [Total 5 marks]

2   In the human body, respiration may be aerobic or anaerobic at different times.

  (a)   Write down the word equation for anaerobic respiration in humans.

                                                                    [1]

  (b)   Glennon runs a 200 m race.
        (i) What type(s) of respiration will Glennon use when she is relaxing before the race?

                                                                    [1]

        (ii) What type(s) of respiration will Glennon use towards the end of the race?

                                                                    [1]
                                                          [Total 3 marks]

3   Outline an experiment that can be performed to measure the volume of oxygen taken up by
    respiring organisms.

                                                          [Total 3 marks]

4   A student investigated the effect of temperature on the rate
    of respiration in germinating seeds using a respirometer.
    The results are shown in the graph on the right.

    Describe how temperature affected the rate of respiration.

                       [Total 3 marks]

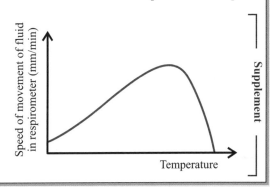

Revision Summary for Sections 7 & 8

That's the end of Sections 7 & 8 — time to see how much you can remember.
- Try these questions and tick off each one when you get it right.
- When you've done all the questions for a topic and are completely happy with it, tick off the topic.

Fighting Disease (p.69-70) ☑

1) What is a pathogen?
2) State two ways that pathogens can be spread.
3) How do cells in the lining of the trachea and bronchi defend against pathogens?
4) What is an antibody?

Preventing the Spread of Disease (p.71-72) ☑

5) State two ways that the spread of disease can be reduced.
6) How do vaccines prepare the immune system against infection by a particular pathogen?
7) State an example of a disease caused by the immune system destroying healthy body cells.

The Gas Exchange System (p.74-75) ☑

8) Name the key structures of the gas exchange system.
9) Name one of the functions of cartilage in the trachea.
10) What causes air to be forced out of the lungs when you breathe out normally?
11) Why do the alveoli have a very thin surface?
12) What is the percentage of carbon dioxide in: a) inspired air,   b) expired air?
13) Why is the composition of expired air different from the composition of inspired air?
14) What is the function of the goblet cells in the trachea?

Investigating Breathing (p.76) ☑

15) Describe an investigation that shows carbon dioxide is released on expiration.
16) What effect does physical activity have on depth of breathing?
17) Explain why physical activity affects breathing rate.

Respiration (p.78-79) ☑

18) Glucose is one reactant in aerobic respiration. What is the other?
19) What is produced by anaerobic respiration in muscle cells?
20) Which type of respiration releases the most energy per glucose molecule?
21) What is produced by anaerobic respiration in yeast?
22) In what organ is lactic acid broken down using aerobic respiration?

Investigating Respiration (p.80) ☑

23) When using a respirometer to measure the oxygen consumption of respiring organisms, what is the purpose of the soda lime in the respirometer?
24) What equipment can you use to change the temperature when investigating the effect of temperature on the rate of respiration?

Excretion

Excretion means getting rid of waste products from metabolic reactions. Read on to find out more...

Excretion is an **Important Process**

Supplement

1) Many metabolic reactions in the body produce unwanted substances as well as useful ones. For example, aerobic respiration produces carbon dioxide as a waste product.

2) The waste products of metabolic reactions need to be removed (excreted) from the body. For example, carbon dioxide is excreted through the lungs when you breathe out.

3) Excretion is important because the build-up of waste products like carbon dioxide and urea (see below) is toxic and can harm body cells.

The **Kidneys** are **Excretory Organs**

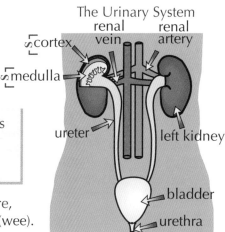

The Urinary System

1) The kidneys are part of the urinary system. The kidneys are involved in removing these things from the body:

   • Urea, which is produced in the liver from excess amino acids
   • Excess salts
   • Excess water

2) Kidneys work by filtering stuff out of the blood under high pressure, and then reabsorbing the useful things. The end product is urine (wee).

3) The outer part of the kidney is called the cortex and the inner part is called the medulla. Blood is carried to the kidneys by the renal arteries and removed by the renal veins.

The **Volume** and **Concentration** of **Urine** Varies

1) When the body is dehydrated (short of water) the kidneys reabsorb more water into the blood. This means a smaller volume of more concentrated (darker) urine is produced to help conserve the water in the body.

2) You become dehydrated when you lose more water than you take in. One of the ways you lose water is through sweating, so if you sweat a lot on a hot day or when you're exercising, and your water intake is too low, you'll become dehydrated. Your kidneys will then reabsorb more water and produce less urine.

3) When the water content of the blood is too high, more water is excreted via the kidneys and a larger volume of more dilute (paler) urine is produced. So if your water intake is higher than you need, and you're not losing much through sweating, your kidneys will reabsorb less water and produce more urine.

Urea is Produced as a Result of **Deamination**

1) We get amino acids from the breakdown of proteins during digestion.

2) These amino acids are then converted into new proteins. For example, the liver converts amino acids into proteins found in the blood plasma, such as fibrinogen (see page 64), as well as other proteins, such as enzymes. The amino acids are said to have been 'assimilated' (see page 51) into our bodies.

3) As well as being involved in the assimilation of amino acids, the liver is also involved in the breakdown of excess amino acids (ones that aren't needed to make proteins) so they can be removed from the body. It does this through the process of deamination.

KEY TERM Deamination is the removal of the nitrogen-containing part of amino acids to form urea.

Excretion — The Kidneys

Blood is filtered in the kidneys in the kidney tubules. These are positioned across the kidney cortex and medulla. Here's what happens as blood passes through the kidney tubules...

1) Filtration:

1) Blood from the renal artery flows through the glomerulus — a bundle of capillaries at the start of the tubule (see diagram below).
2) A high pressure is built up which squeezes water, urea, salts and glucose out of the blood and into the capsule.
3) The membranes of the glomerulus act like filters, so big molecules like proteins and blood cells are not squeezed out. They stay in the blood.

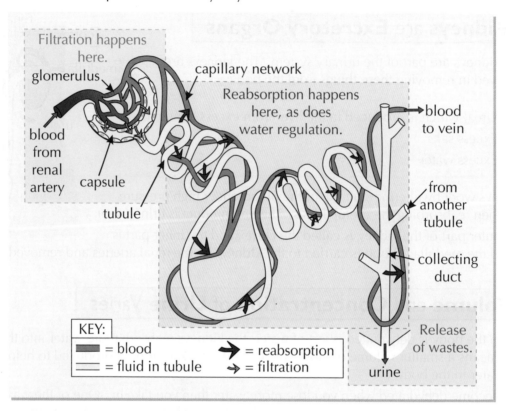

2) Reabsorption:

It's called selective reabsorption because only some substances are reabsorbed.

As the fluid flows along the tubule, useful substances are selectively reabsorbed back into the blood:

1) All the glucose is reabsorbed so that it can be used in respiration. The reabsorption of glucose involves the process of active transport (see p.24) against the concentration gradient.
2) Some salts are reabsorbed. Excess salts aren't.
3) Most water is reabsorbed. This happens by osmosis (see p.21) and leads to urea becoming more concentrated in the fluid.

3) Release of Wastes:

The remaining substances (including excess water, excess salts and urea) form urine. This continues out of the tubule, through the ureter and down to the bladder, where it is stored before being released via the urethra.

The kidneys remove urea and control salt and water levels

Remember the three subheadings on this page — they're key to understanding how the kidneys work.

Treatments for Kidney Failure

If someone's kidneys stop working, there are two treatments — dialysis or a transplant.

Dialysis Machines **Filter** the Blood

Dialysis machines are sometimes called kidney machines.

1) People with kidney failure have to have dialysis done regularly to keep the concentrations of dissolved substances in the blood at normal levels, and to remove waste substances.

2) In a dialysis machine the person's blood flows between partially permeable membranes, surrounded by dialysis fluid. The membranes are permeable to things like salts and waste substances, but not big molecules like proteins (just like the membranes in the kidney).

3) The dialysis fluid has the same concentration of salts and glucose as healthy blood.

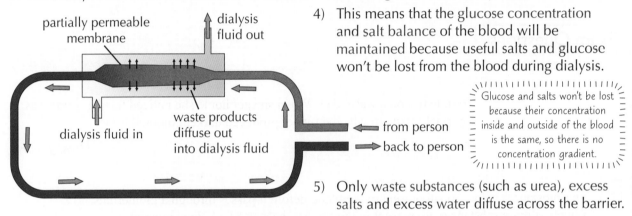

partially permeable membrane

dialysis fluid out

dialysis fluid in

waste products diffuse out into dialysis fluid

from person

back to person

4) This means that the glucose concentration and salt balance of the blood will be maintained because useful salts and glucose won't be lost from the blood during dialysis.

Glucose and salts won't be lost because their concentration inside and outside of the blood is the same, so there is no concentration gradient.

5) Only waste substances (such as urea), excess salts and excess water diffuse across the barrier.

6) Many patients with kidney failure have to have a dialysis session three times a week. Each session takes 3-4 hours, so dialysis takes up a lot of time.

7) Plus, dialysis may cause blood clots or infections.

8) Being on a dialysis machine is not a pleasant experience and it is expensive for the NHS to run.

9) However, dialysis can buy a patient with kidney failure time until a donor organ is found.

Supplement

Kidney Transplants are a **Cure**, but can be **Rejected**

1) At the moment, the only cure for kidney failure is to have a kidney transplant.

2) Healthy kidneys are usually transplanted from people who have died suddenly.

3) Kidneys can also be transplanted from people who are still alive (as we all have two of them) but there is a small risk to the person donating the kidney.

4) Whoever the donor kidney comes from, there is a risk that the donor kidney will be rejected by the patient's immune system. Two things can be done to try to reduce the risk of this happening:

- The patient is treated with drugs to suppress their immune system. They must take these drugs for the rest of their life.

- Donor kidneys are matched by blood type (and a few other things) to the patient — however, this means a potentially long waiting time for a suitable kidney.

5) Despite these drawbacks, transplants are cheaper (in the long run) than dialysis and they can put an end to the hours patients have to spend on dialysis.

REVISION TIP

Dialysis or transplant? Both have their downsides...

You need to be able to write about the advantages and disadvantages of kidney transplants in comparison with dialysis. Draw yourself a table with 'Advantages' in the header for one column, and 'Disadvantages' in the other. Then cover up the page and try to fill in the table from memory.

Warm-Up & Exam Questions

Think you know everything there is to know about excretion in humans? Time to put it to the test...

Warm-Up Questions

1) Where is urea produced?
2) Through which organ is the waste product carbon dioxide excreted?
3) What is deamination?
4) What is the glomerulus?
5) Why is excretion of carbon dioxide necessary?

Exam Questions

1 A runner went for a 10 mile run on a warm day. When she got home she noticed that her urine was darker in colour than normal. Explain why the runner produced darker coloured urine.

[Total 4 marks]

2 The substances below are all present in the blood before it passes through a glomerulus. Which of these substances are present in the fluid at the start of a kidney tubule?

1. glucose
2. urea
3. proteins
4. water

☐ **A** 1 and 2   ☐ **B** 1, 2 and 3

☐ **C** 1, 2 and 4   ☐ **D** 1, 2, 3 and 4

[Total 1 mark]

3 A hospital patient has kidney failure. She has dialysis three times a week.

(a) Explain how the dialysis machine removes urea from the patient's blood.

[2]

(b) Explain why the patient does not lose glucose from her blood during dialysis.

[2]

The patient is on the waiting list to receive a kidney transplant.

(c) Suggest **one** reason why this form of treatment may be preferable to dialysis.

[1]

(d) Give **one** disadvantage of kidney transplants.

[1]

[Total 6 marks]

Supplement

The Nervous System

The nervous system allows humans to react to their surroundings, coordinate their behaviour and regulate body functions. This page is all about how it works.

There are **Two Parts** to the **Nervous System**

1) The nervous system contains neurones (nerve cells) which go to all parts of the body.

2) The nervous system is split into the central and peripheral nervous systems:

- The central nervous system (CNS) consists of the brain and the spinal cord.
- The peripheral nervous system is made up of all the neurones outside of the CNS.

The **CNS Coordinates** a **Response**

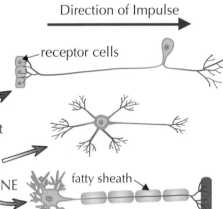

Direction of Impulse

1) The body has lots of sensory receptors — groups of cells that can detect a change in your environment (a stimulus).

receptor cells

2) When a stimulus is detected by receptors, the information is converted to a nerve impulse (an electrical signal) and sent to the CNS along SENSORY NEURONES.

3) The CNS coordinates the response (in other words, it decides what to do about the stimulus and tells something to do it). Impulses travel through the CNS along RELAY (CONNECTOR) NEURONES.

4) The CNS sends information along a MOTOR (EFFECTOR) NEURONE to an effector (muscle or gland). The effector then responds accordingly — e.g. a muscle may contract or a gland may secrete a hormone (see p.92).

fatty sheath

effector cells

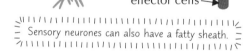

Sensory neurones can also have a fatty sheath.

Neurones are **Connected** by **Synapses**

 KEY TERM | A synapse is a junction between two neurones.

1) A synapse consists of the ends of two neurones, separated by a synaptic cleft (a gap).

2) The end of the neurone before the cleft holds vesicles (p.11) filled with neurotransmitters (chemicals).

3) The end of the neurone after the cleft has neurotransmitter receptor molecules in its membrane.

4) This is how a nerve impulse is passed across a synapse:

- The nerve impulse reaches the end of the neurone before the synaptic cleft and triggers the release of neurotransmitters from the vesicles into the synaptic cleft.
- The neurotransmitters diffuse (see p.19) across the synaptic cleft to bind with receptor molecules in the membrane on the next neurone.
- This causes the electrical impulse to continue in the next neurone.

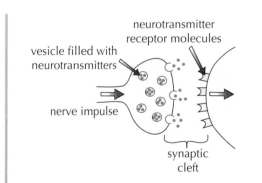

neurotransmitter receptor molecules

vesicle filled with neurotransmitters

nerve impulse

synaptic cleft

5) Because the receptors are only on one side of the synaptic cleft, synapses make sure that impulses can only travel in one direction.

6) Many drugs, such as heroin, act upon synapses (see p.102).

Reflex Actions

Neurones transmit information very quickly to and from the brain, and your brain quickly decides how to respond to a stimulus. But reflex actions are even quicker...

Reflex Actions Help Prevent Injury

1) Reflex actions are rapid, automatic responses to certain stimuli that don't involve the conscious part of the brain — it basically means your body reacts without you having to think about what to do.

2) The response of an effector is coordinated with a stimulus — this means that the response of an effector to a particular stimulus will always be the same.

> For example, if someone shines a bright light in your eyes, your pupils automatically get smaller so that less light gets into your eyes — this stops them from getting damaged (see p.90).

3) Reflex actions are involuntary actions.

4) Involuntary actions do not involve conscious decisions. They are much faster than voluntary actions and always produce the same response to certain stimuli. For example, if you touch a hot plate, you move your hand away quickly without thinking.

5) Voluntary actions involve a conscious decision, so take a longer time and produce different responses. For example, walking towards a piece of cake that you want to eat.

6) The passage of nerve impulses in a reflex action (from receptor to effector) is called a reflex arc.

Supplement (items 3-5)

The Reflex Arc Goes Through the Central Nervous System

1) The neurones in reflex arcs go through the spinal cord or through an unconscious part of the brain.

2) When a stimulus (e.g. a bee sting) is detected by receptors, impulses are sent along a sensory neurone to the CNS.

3) When the impulses reach a synapse between the sensory neurone and a relay neurone, the impulses cross the synapse and are sent along the relay neurone.

4) When the impulses reach a synapse between the relay neurone and a motor neurone, the same thing happens and the impulses are sent along the motor neurone.

5) The impulses then travel along the motor neurone to the effector (in this example it's a muscle).

6) The muscle then contracts and moves your hand away from the bee.

5. Impulses travel along a motor neurone, via a synapse.

4. Impulses travel along a relay neurone, via a synapse.

6. When impulses reach the muscle, it contracts.

3. Impulses travel along a sensory neurone.

2. Sting detected by pain receptors.

1. Bee stings finger.

Relay neurones connect sensory neurones to motor neurones.

Don't get all twitchy — just learn it...

Reflex actions bypass your conscious brain completely when a quick response is essential — your body just gets on with things. If you had to stop and think first, you'd end up in a lot more pain (or worse).

The Eye

If you can read this, you're using your eyes. And that's great because you need to know all about them.

The **Eye** is a **Sense Organ**

 KEY TERM — Sense organs are groups of receptor cells that respond to specific stimuli (e.g. light, sound, touch, temperature and chemicals).

Different receptors in your body detect different stimuli. Receptors in your eyes detect light.

Learn the Eye with All Its Labels

1) The CORNEA is the transparent outer layer found at the front of the eye. It refracts (bends) light into the eye.

2) The IRIS contains muscles that allow it to control the diameter of the PUPIL (the hole in the middle) and therefore how much light enters the eye.

3) The LENS focuses the light onto the RETINA (which contains light receptors, some of which are sensitive to light of different colours).

4) The OPTIC NERVE carries impulses from the receptors on the retina to the brain.

5) Where the optic nerve leaves the eye is called the BLIND SPOT — there aren't any light receptors, so it's not sensitive to light.

6) The FOVEA is a specific area of the retina which contains cone cells (see below).

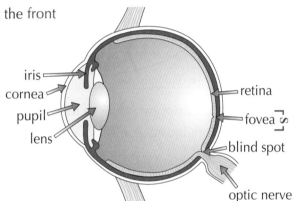

The **Retina** Contains **Two Types** of **Receptor**

The retina is covered in two different types of receptor — rods and cones.

Rods

- Rods are mainly found in the peripheral parts (outside edges) of the retina.
- Rods are very sensitive to light, so work well in dim light (e.g. at night).
- There is one kind of rod, which gives information in black and white (not colour vision).

Cones

- Cones are mainly found packed together in the fovea.
- Cones are less sensitive to light than rods (they work best in bright light).
- There are three kinds of cones which give information in different colours for colour vision.

Supplement

Learn that diagram of the eye...

 REVISION TIP — It'll help if you sketch the diagram out roughly, close this book and then try to label your sketch. If your artistic skills aren't great, you could even trace it, then label the traced version.

The Eye

This page is all about reflex actions in the eye. If you've forgotten anything about reflex actions, have a look back over page 88.

The **Pupil Reflex** — Adjusting for **Bright Light**

1) Very bright light can damage the retina — so you have a reflex action to protect it.

2) When light receptors in the eye detect a high light intensity (very bright light), a reflex action is triggered that reduces the diameter of the pupil (makes it smaller). This reduces the amount of light that can enter the eye.

3) The opposite process happens in a low light intensity (dim light) — the diameter of the pupil increases (it is made wider), which increases the amount of light that can enter the eye.

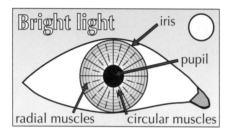 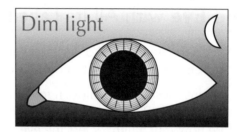

4) The iris contains two types of muscles to control pupil diameter — the radial and circular muscles.

5) These work by antagonistic action — when one muscle contracts, the other muscle relaxes.

- To make the pupil wider, the radial muscles in the iris contract and the circular muscles relax.
- To make the pupil smaller, the circular muscles in the iris contract and the radial muscles relax.

Focusing on Near and Distant Objects — Another **Reflex Action**

The eye focuses light on the retina by changing the shape of the lens — this is known as accommodation.

To Look at **Near Objects**:

1) The ciliary muscles contract, which slackens the suspensory ligaments.
2) The lens becomes fat (more curved).
3) This increases the amount by which it refracts (bends) light.

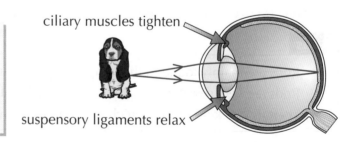

To Look at **Distant Objects**:

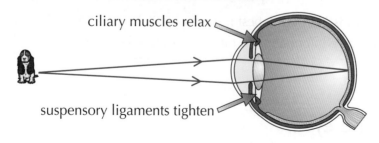

1) The ciliary muscles relax, which allows the suspensory ligaments to pull tight.
2) This makes the lens go thin (less curved).
3) So it refracts light by a smaller amount.

Supplement

Supplement

Warm-Up & Exam Questions

Welcome to the first set of questions in this section. Having a go at some questions is one of the best ways of figuring out just what you know. Time to get started...

Warm-Up Questions

1) Name the two parts of the body which make up the central nervous system.
2) In what form is information transmitted along neurones?
3) Give an example of a reflex action.

Exam Questions

1   A man picked up a plate without realising it was hot, then immediately dropped it. The diagram below shows the reflex arc for this incident.

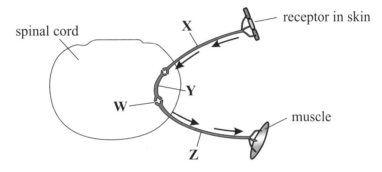

(a)   Name the **three** types of neurone labelled **X**, **Y** and **Z**.

[3]

(b)   What name is given to the small gap between neurones, marked **W** on the diagram?

[1]

(c)   State what the effector is in this reflex arc and describe its response.

[2]

[Total 6 marks]

2   The diagram below shows a cross section through the eye.

(a)   Name the parts labelled **A** and **B**.

[2]

(b)   Describe the function of the iris.

[1]

(c)   (i)   Name the **two** types of light receptor found on the retina.

[2]

(ii)   Name the part of the retina that has the greatest number of colour-sensitive light receptors.

[1]

(d)   Describe how information about light entering the eye is passed to the brain.

[2]

[Total 8 marks]

Hormones

On page 87 you learnt how information is passed around the body via neurones.
The body also uses hormones as a way to communicate, which is what this page is all about.

Hormones Are **Chemical Messengers** Sent in the **Blood**

Hormones are chemical substances, produced by glands and carried by
the blood, which alter the activity of one or more specific target organs.

1) Hormones control things in organs and cells that need constant adjustment.
2) The glands that produce and secrete hormones are called endocrine glands.
   These glands make up your endocrine system.

Endocrine Glands Are Found in **Different Places** in the Body

You need to know about four endocrine glands, and which hormones they secrete:

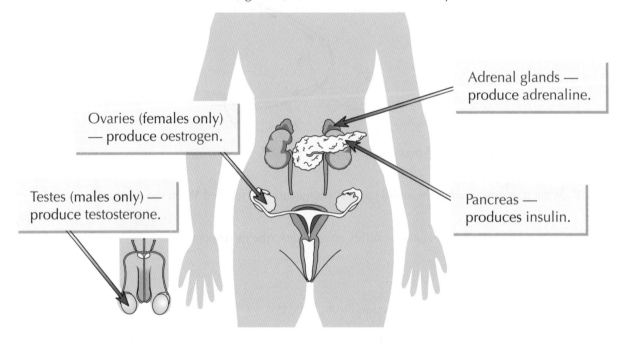

Ovaries (females only)
— produce oestrogen.

Adrenal glands —
produce adrenaline.

Testes (males only) —
produce testosterone.

Pancreas —
produces insulin.

These **Hormones** Have Different **Functions**

The function of adrenaline
is on the next page.

1) Insulin helps to regulate the blood glucose level (see page 95)
   by stimulating the liver to turn glucose into glycogen for storage.

2) Oestrogen is the main female sex hormone. It is involved in the
   menstrual cycle (see pages 116-117) and promotes the development
   of secondary sexual characteristics, e.g. breast development.

3) Testosterone is the main male sex hormone. It controls sperm production and promotes
   the development of secondary sexual characteristics, e.g. growth of hair on the chest.

Hormones

Adrenaline Prepares You for 'Fight or Flight'

1) Adrenaline is a hormone released by the adrenal glands (see previous page).

2) Adrenaline prepares the body for 'fight or flight' — in other words, standing your ground in the face of a threat (e.g. a predator) or running away.

3) When your brain detects a stressful, dangerous or exciting situation, it sends nerve impulses (see p.87) to the adrenal glands, which secrete adrenaline. This gets the body ready for action.

> Examples of situations when adrenaline is released include extreme sports (such as skydiving or bungee jumping), at the start of a race or test, or during an emergency.

4) Adrenaline causes an increase in breathing and pulse rate. It also causes the pupils to widen, heightens sensitivity and makes a person more alert.

5) Increasing the breathing and pulse rate increases the supply of oxygen and glucose to cells, which increases metabolic activity. Here's how:

- Adrenaline causes the heart muscle to contract more frequently and with more force, so heart rate and pulse rate increase.
- This increases blood flow to the muscles, so the cells receive more oxygen and glucose for increased respiration.
- Adrenaline also causes the liver to break down its glycogen stores (see p.95) to release glucose.
- This increases the blood glucose level, so there's more glucose in the blood to be transported to the cells.

Hormones and Nerve Impulses Work Differently

Hormones and nerve impulses do similar jobs — they both carry information and instructions around the body. But there are some important differences between them that you need to know too:

Nerve Impulses

1) Very fast message.
2) Act for a very short time.

Hormones

1) Slower message.
2) Act for a long time.

If you're not sure whether a response is nervous or hormonal, have a think about the speed of the reaction and how long it lasts:

1) If the Response is Really Quick, It's Probably Nervous

1) Some information needs to be passed to effectors really quickly (e.g. pain signals, or the pupil reflex).
2) It's no good using hormones to carry the message — they're too slow.

2) But if a Response Lasts For a Long Time, It's Probably Hormonal

> For example, when you eat food, insulin is released in response to increased blood glucose levels (see page 95). This lasts until the blood glucose concentration has returned to normal.

Supplement

Homeostasis

Homeostasis involves balancing body functions to keep everything at the level it is supposed to be at.

Homeostasis — it's all about **Balance**

1) Conditions in your body need to be kept steady so that cells can function properly.
   This involves balancing inputs (stuff going into your body) with outputs (stuff leaving). For example...

> Body temperature — you need to get rid of excess body heat
> when you're hot, but keep heat in when the environment is cold.

2) Homeostasis is what keeps conditions balanced. Here's the definition:

> **KEY TERM** Homeostasis is the maintenance of a constant internal environment.

Supplement

3) Homeostasis controls the internal environment within set limits, so conditions stay roughly constant.
   Set limits are ranges that are best for the body, e.g. body temperature stays between 36.1 and 37.2 °C.

4) Conditions are kept steady using negative feedback systems. This means that when the body's
   receptors detect that a condition has gone above or below its normal level, they trigger a response to
   bring the level back to normal again.

Internal Body Temperature Must Be Kept Constant

1) It's important to maintain the right core body temperature.

2) Body temperature is monitored by blood temperature receptors and skin temperature
   receptors. The brain coordinates a response (see p.87) based on signals from these
   receptors and activates the necessary effectors to keep the body temperature just right.

3) There are different mechanisms that are used to change body temperature:

Mechanisms to REDUCE body temperature:

Hairs lie flat — a layer of hair provides insulation
by trapping air. When it's hot, erector muscles relax
so the hairs lie flat. Less air is trapped, so the skin
is less insulated and heat can be lost more easily.

Sweating — more sweat
is secreted from sweat
glands when the body's
too hot. The water in
sweat evaporates from
the surface of the skin
and takes heat from
the body. The skin
is cooled.

Mechanisms to INCREASE body temperature:

Hairs stand up — erector muscles contract
when it's cold, which makes the hairs stand up.
This traps an insulating layer of air near the
surface of the skin and so prevents heat loss.

Much less sweat — less sweat
is secreted from sweat glands
when it's cold, reducing the
amount of heat loss.

Shivering — when it's cold, muscles
contract in spasms. This makes
the body shiver and more heat is
produced from increased respiration.

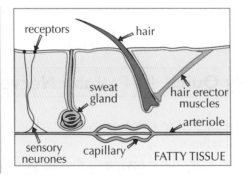

receptors · hair · sweat gland · hair erector muscles · arteriole · sensory neurones · capillary · FATTY TISSUE

Supplement

Vasodilation — when it's hot, arterioles (p.62)
near the surface of the skin dilate (this is called
vasodilation). More blood flows through the
capillaries (p.62) in the surface of the skin.
This means more heat is lost from the skin
and the temperature is lowered.

Supplement

Vasoconstriction — when it's cold, arterioles
near the surface of the skin constrict (this is
called vasoconstriction) so less blood flows
through the capillaries in the surface layers
of the skin. This reduces heat loss.

Controlling Blood Glucose

Insulin and glucagon are hormones that control how much glucose there is in your blood.

Insulin and Glucagon Control Blood Glucose Concentration

1) Eating foods containing carbohydrates puts glucose into the blood from the small intestine.
2) The normal metabolism of cells removes glucose from the blood.
3) Excess glucose can be stored as glycogen in the liver and in the muscles.
4) Changes in blood glucose concentration are monitored and controlled by the pancreas, using the hormones insulin and glucagon, as shown:

Blood glucose concentration too HIGH — INSULIN is secreted by the pancreas:

Blood glucose concentration too LOW — GLUCAGON is secreted by the pancreas:

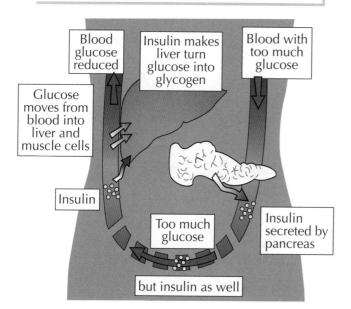

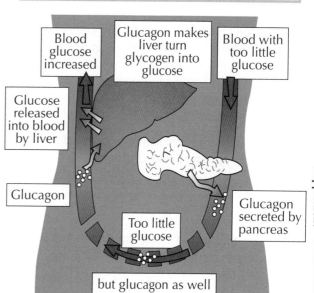

Type 1 Diabetes — Caused by a Lack of Insulin

Remember, insulin reduces blood glucose level.

1) Type 1 diabetes is a condition where the pancreas produces little or no insulin.
2) Symptoms of Type 1 diabetes include frequent urination, increased thirst and hunger, and weight loss. If untreated, a person's blood glucose can rise to a level that can kill them.
3) A person with Type 1 diabetes will need to be treated with insulin therapy — this usually involves injecting insulin under the skin, from where it will enter the bloodstream.
4) Injections are often done at mealtimes to make sure that glucose is removed from the blood quickly once the food has been digested. This stops the level of glucose in the blood from getting too high.
5) As well as insulin therapy, people with Type 1 diabetes also need to think about:
   • Not eating too many simple carbohydrates, i.e. sugars (which cause the blood glucose level to rise rapidly).
   • Taking regular exercise — this helps to remove excess glucose from the blood.

And people used to think the pancreas was just a cushion...

This stuff can seem a bit confusing at first, but you could have a go at remembering it like this: if blood glucose is <u>in</u>creasing, <u>in</u>sulin's added. If blood glucose is almost <u>gone</u>, gluca<u>gon</u>'s added.

Warm-Up & Exam Questions

Here are some more questions — they make for great practice.

Warm-Up Questions

1) What is a hormone?
2) State the sources of the following hormones: (a) oestrogen, (b) testosterone, (c) adrenaline.
3) What is homeostasis?

Exam Questions

1 Changes in the skin are an important part of temperature regulation. The diagram shows a cross-section through the skin of a person who is cold.

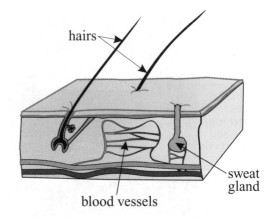

hairs

blood vessels

sweat gland

(a) Explain the response of the hairs when a person is cold.

[2]

(b) Explain the response of sweat glands when a person is cold.

[2]

[Total 4 marks]

2 Responses to stimuli can be either nervous or hormonal. Describe the differences between responses brought about by hormones and those brought about by the nervous system.

[Total 2 marks]

3 The diagram shows how the blood glucose concentration is regulated in humans.

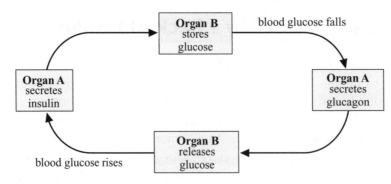

Organ B stores glucose

blood glucose falls

Organ A secretes glucagon

Organ A secretes insulin

Organ B releases glucose

blood glucose rises

(a) Identify organs **A** and **B** in the diagram.

[2]

(b) With reference to the diagram, explain what goes wrong with the regulation of blood glucose level in people with Type 1 diabetes.

[3]

(c) Describe what the hormone glucagon does.

[1]

[Total 6 marks]

Section 10 — Coordination and Response

Tropic Responses

Plants don't just grow randomly. They grow in response to the things going on around them.

A **Tropism** is a **Response** to a **Stimulus**

There are two types of tropism that you need to know about:

 KEY TERM

Phototropism is a response in which parts of a plant grow towards or away from the direction from which light is coming.

 KEY TERM

Gravitropism is a response in which parts of a plant grow towards or away from gravity.

Shoots grow towards light and upwards against gravity, and roots grow away from light and downwards with gravity.

You Need to Know **How** This **Works** in **Shoots**

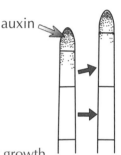

auxin

1) Auxin is a plant hormone that chemically controls growth near the tips of shoots.
2) It is produced in the tips and spreads through the plant from there.
   The distribution (spread) of auxin is unequal, in response to light and gravity.
3) Auxin stimulates cell elongation in the cells just behind the tips.
4) If the shoot tip is removed, no auxin is available and the shoot may stop growing.
5) Phototropism and gravitropism are both examples of the chemical control of plant growth.

Shoots Grow **Towards Light** (**Positive** Phototropism)

1) When a shoot tip is exposed to light, more auxin accumulates (builds up) on the side that's in the shade than the side that's in the light.
2) This stimulates the cells to elongate faster on the shaded side, so the shoot bends towards the light.

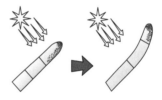

Shoots Grow **Away From Gravity** (**Negative** Gravitropism)

1) When a shoot grows sideways, gravity produces an unequal distribution of auxin, with more on the lower side of the tip.
2) This stimulates the cells of the lower side to elongate faster, bending the shoot upwards.

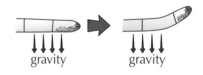

gravity   gravity

Synthetic Plant **Hormones** can be Used as **Weedkillers**

1) Selective weedkillers have been developed from auxins. They disrupt the normal growth patterns of certain plants (e.g. weeds), which kills them. They leave grasses and crops untouched.
2) 2,4-D is a synthetic plant hormone that is an example of a selective weedkiller.

Tropisms allow plants to react to their surroundings

By responding to stimuli in their environment, plants increase their chances of survival. For example, by growing towards the light, plants increase the amount of light they receive for photosynthesis.

Investigating Plant Growth Responses

Here are two investigations you need to know about that demonstrate plant growth responses.

You can **Investigate Plant Growth Responses**

You can investigate phototropism in the growth of shoots like this...

1) Put 10 seeds into three different Petri dishes, each lined with moist filter paper. (Remember to label your dishes, e.g. A, B, C.)

2) Put the dishes in a dark place and shine a lamp onto one of the dishes from above and two of the dishes from different directions.

3) Leave your seeds alone for one week until you can observe their responses — you'll find the seedlings grow towards the light.

> It needs to be dark to make sure that the light on each dish is only coming from one direction.

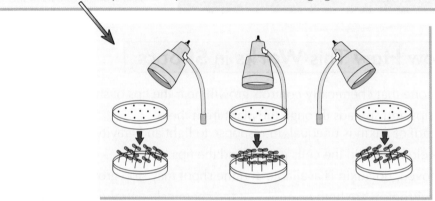

You can also investigate gravitropism in plant growth...

1) Place four seedlings on damp cotton wool in separate Petri dishes.

2) Store each Petri dish vertically in a dark place, each with their shoots and roots pointing in different directions.

3) Leave your seeds alone for one week and you should find that the shoots of each seedling grow upwards and that the roots of each seedling grow downwards.

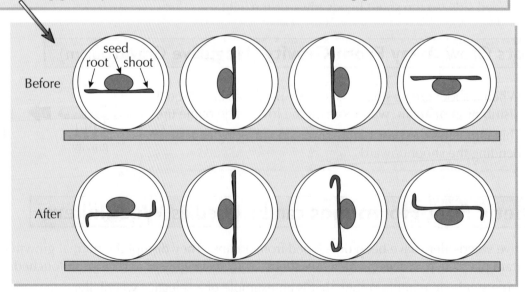

Record your results using scientific drawings

PRACTICAL TIP
Labelled diagrams are a really good way to show the results of experiments like this. There's more about scientific drawings on page 187. Make sure your drawings are neat and useful — don't do any sketching or shading and label your drawing using straight, uncrossed lines.

Warm-Up & Exam Questions

You could skim through this page in a few minutes, but there's no point unless you check over any bits you don't know and make sure you understand everything. It's not quick, but it's the only way.

Warm-Up Questions

1) What is phototropism?
2) Name the plant hormone responsible for both phototropism and gravitropism.
3) Where is this plant hormone made?
4) Explain what causes plant shoots to grow towards the light.

Exam Questions

1 A gardener frequently uses products containing synthetic plant hormones in her garden.

(a) The gardener has a problem with weeds in her lawn.
She uses a selective weedkiller that targets the weeds without affecting the growth of the lawn.
Explain how selective weedkillers work.

[1]

(b) Name the synthetic plant hormone likely to be present in the weedkiller.

[1]

[Total 2 marks]

2 A student placed some germinating beans on the surface of some
damp soil and left them in the dark for five days. The appearance of
the beans before and after the five day period is shown in the diagram.

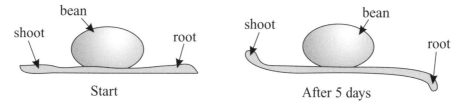

Start   After 5 days

Both the shoot and the root have undergone a gravitropic response after 5 days.

(a) Describe the gravitropic response of the shoot.

[1]

(b) Explain the mechanism behind this response.

[2]

(c) The student wants to compare his findings with beans grown in the light.
He puts some new germinating beans on damp soil and shines a light on them.
Describe what the student would expect to see happen to the shoots.
Explain why this would happen.

[3]

[Total 6 marks]

Revision Summary for Sections 9 & 10

Nice work — you've finished Sections 9 & 10. Time to find out how much you know with some questions.
- Try these questions and tick off each one when you get it right.
- When you've done all the questions for a topic and are completely happy with it, tick off the topic.

Excretion in Humans (p.83-85) ☑

1) Name three things excreted by the kidneys. ☐
2) What is urea formed from? ☐
3) Describe what is meant by amino acid assimilation. ☐
4) What is reabsorbed by the tubule in the kidney? ☐

The Nervous System, Reflexes and The Eye (p.87-90) ☐

5) What is a nerve impulse? ☐
6) How does an impulse travel across a synapse? ☐
7) Explain how synapses ensure impulses travel in only one direction. ☐
8) Give an example of a drug that acts upon synapses. ☐
9) State a difference between a voluntary and involuntary action. ☐
10) What is a sense organ? ☐
11) Describe the function of the cornea. ☐
12) Describe the pupil reflex. Why is it needed? ☐
13) How does accommodation of the eye work? ☐

Hormones, Homeostasis and Controlling Blood Glucose (p.92-95) ☐

14) Where is insulin made? ☐
15) Describe testosterone's role in the body. ☐
16) What is the role of the hormone adrenaline? What effects does it have on the body? ☐
17) Explain how negative feedback helps to maintain a stable internal environment. ☐
18) Explain why we shiver when we get cold. ☐

Tropic Responses and Investigating Plant Growth (p.97-98) ☐

19) What is gravitropism? ☐
20) What is auxin? ☐
21) Describe an experiment to investigate the effect of phototropism on some shoots. ☐

Medicinal Drugs

Drugs can be used for lots of different reasons. Those that are used to help treat infections, cure diseases or reduce symptoms are known as medicinal drugs. These types of drugs are really important for health.

Drugs Have Effects **Inside the Body**

Before we get started, make sure you know the definition of a drug:

> A drug is any substance taken into the body that modifies (changes) or affects chemical reactions in the body.

Antibiotics are a Useful Type of **Medicinal Drug**

1) Antibiotics (e.g. penicillin) can be used to treat bacterial infections.

2) These drugs work by actually killing (or preventing the reproduction of) the bacteria causing the problem, without killing your own body cells.

3) Different antibiotics kill different types of bacteria, so it's important to be treated with the right one.

4) The use of antibiotics has greatly reduced the number of deaths from transmissible diseases (p.69) caused by bacteria.

5) But, antibiotics don't destroy viruses (e.g. flu or cold viruses).

- Antibiotics work in different ways. Some stop bacteria from making cell walls (which human cells don't have). Others target the enzymes and ribosomes used in their metabolic reactions, which are different from human enzymes and ribosomes. Since antibiotics are designed to only target bacterial processes, they don't damage human cells.

- Viruses don't have cell walls, or their own enzymes and ribosomes — they use the ones in the host's cells. This means antibiotics can't be produced to destroy viruses — doing so would also harm the body's cells.

Supplement

Bacteria Can Become **Resistant** to **Antibiotics**

1) Mutations (see page 136) can cause the genetic material in bacteria to change. Sometimes this change to bacteria's genetic material can make them resistant to (not killed by) an antibiotic.

2) So, if you have an infection, some of the bacteria might be resistant to antibiotics.

3) This means that when you treat the infection, only the non-resistant strains of bacteria will be killed.

4) The individual resistant bacteria will survive and reproduce, so the population of the resistant strain will increase.

5) This resistant strain could cause a serious infection that can't be treated by antibiotics.

- MRSA (meticillin-resistant *Staphylococcus aureus*) is a type of antibiotic-resistant bacteria. MRSA causes serious wound infections and is resistant to the powerful antibiotic meticillin.

- To slow down the rate of development of resistant strains such as MRSA, it's important for doctors to only provide antibiotics when they are really needed. So you won't get them for a sore throat, only for something more serious.

- It's also important that you finish the whole course of antibiotics and don't just stop once you feel better.

Supplement

Antibiotic resistance is inevitable...

...but that doesn't mean we shouldn't try to do anything about it. We might not be able to stop it from ever happening, but we can limit how quickly it develops. So do your bit, and finish your courses of antibiotics.

Misused Drugs

There's no nice way of saying this — misusing drugs leads to serious negative health and social effects.

Different Types of Drugs can have Different Negative Effects

Alcohol

1) Alcohol has an effect on many chemical processes in the body. It is a powerful depressant drug. This means that it reduces the activity of the nervous system and slows down reaction times.

2) Drinking too much alcohol can lead to impaired judgement and a lack of self-control, which can lead people to do things they wouldn't normally do, such as committing crimes.

3) Alcohol is poisonous and can damage the liver.

> • The liver has an important role in cleaning the blood by breaking down alcohol and other toxins (harmful substances).
>
> • If you drink too much alcohol over a long period of time, the products from its breakdown can cause the death of liver cells. This can lead to cirrhosis (the formation of scar tissue).
>
> • Cirrhosis can stop the liver from doing its normal job, so dangerous substances can start to build up and damage the rest of the body.

4) Alcohol is addictive — some people become dependent on alcohol in their daily lives. It can be difficult for these people to give up alcohol, as they often experience severe withdrawal symptoms (e.g. depression, anxiety, nausea, hand tremors). Once addicted, some people may resort to crimes, such as theft, to get money to buy more alcohol.

Heroin

1) In the UK, heroin is an illegal drug. It can be smoked, snorted or dissolved in water and injected.

2) Heroin has serious negative effects. It is a very powerful depressant, slows down reaction times, results in a lack of self-control, is highly addictive (so can lead to withdrawal symptoms), and it can cause some people to resort to crime to try and get money to buy more of the drug.

3) It's such a powerful depressant that it can slow down breathing rate so much that it leads to death.

4) If people share the same needle to inject heroin, there is a risk of infections such as HIV (p.121) being passed between them.

5) If you're taking the Extended course, read below for how heroin acts at synapses (p.87):

> When heroin reaches the brain, it is converted to morphine by enzymes. The morphine molecules have a similar shape to some neurotransmitter molecules. Because of this, after morphine diffuses into synapses it can bind to the receptors on neurones there. This blocks the receptors so neurotransmitters can't bind and disrupts the normal transmission of nerve impulses. It also leads to an unusual amount of a chemical called dopamine being released. It's this which is responsible for the 'high' that heroin users can feel.

Anabolic Steroids

1) Testosterone is an anabolic steroid. It's a hormone produced naturally by the body (p.92), but it can also be taken as a drug to improve sporting performance.

2) Testosterone can improve sporting performance because it can help to increase the amount of muscle and reduce the amount of fat in the body.

3) Artificial anabolic steroids can be made that copy these effects of testosterone.

4) Many sports have banned the use of anabolic steroids as it's considered to be cheating.

5) Misusing anabolic steroids can lead to negative effects such as infertility (being unable to have children), hair loss and an increased risk of cancer.

Misused Drugs

Tobacco Smoke Can Cause Health Problems

Burning cigarettes produce nicotine, which is what makes smoking addictive. They also produce carbon monoxide and tar — which (along with nicotine) can cause illness and other problems. E.g.:

1) Nicotine in cigarette smoke increases heart rate, which leads to an increase in blood pressure.

2) The carbon monoxide in cigarette smoke reduces the amount of oxygen the blood can carry. To make up for this, heart rate increases which causes blood pressure to increase.

3) High blood pressure can damage the arteries and increase the risk of coronary heart disease (e.g. heart attacks).

4) Tar from cigarette smoke is full of toxic chemicals, some of which are carcinogens. Carcinogens are chemicals that can lead to cancers, such as lung cancer.

5) Smoking can also cause chronic obstructive pulmonary disease (COPD). Symptoms of this include persistent coughing and a shortness of breath. This is what causes it:

- The tar in cigarettes damages the cilia (p.13) in the bronchi and trachea (tubes that allow air to move into the lungs), and encourages more mucus than normal to be produced.

- When these cilia are damaged and too much mucus is produced, the mucus (and the dust and bacteria it has trapped) can't be cleared very well, which causes the persistent coughing.

- Smoke damages the walls inside the alveoli. This reduces the surface area for gas exchange, making it less efficient, and causes shortness of breath.

There's Evidence for a Link Between Smoking and Lung Cancer

1) All diseases have factors that will increase a person's chance of getting that disease. These are called risk factors. For example, it's widely known that smoking is a risk factor for lung cancer.

2) There is a lot of evidence to suggest that the link between smoking and lung cancer is strong.

> Studies have shown that around 7 in 10 lung cancer cases in the UK are directly linked to smoking. (Source: Cancer Research UK)

> Studies have shown that smoking more than 25 cigarettes a day, means that a person is 25 times more likely to get lung cancer than someone who doesn't smoke at all. (Source: NHS)

3) It's also been shown that smoking for a longer period of time strongly increases the risk of developing cancer.

> Someone who smokes one pack of cigarettes a day for 40 years is more likely to develop cancer than someone who smokes two packs a day for 20 years. (Source: Cancer Research UK)

4) We are able to conclude that smoking is a cause of lung cancer. This conclusion can only be made because of studies where other variables (e.g. age and exposure to other things that cause cancer) were controlled. This meant it was clear that smoking, and not any other factor, was the variable increasing people's risk of lung cancer.

5) We also know that tar in cigarette smoke contains carcinogens (see above). This means we can be certain that smoking causes lung cancer, because we understand how it actually causes it.

Supplement

It's important to be careful with drugs and only take ones you should

There are a lot of negative effects you need to learn here, but make sure you take them all in.

Warm-Up & Exam Questions

Even though that was only a few pages, there was still quite a lot to take in.
Try answering these questions to make sure you've remembered it all.

Warm-Up Questions

1) Name a type of antibiotic-resistant bacteria.
2) What is the definition of a drug?
3) What is a potential consequence of heroin users sharing needles?
4) Why can heroin prevent some neurotransmitters from binding to receptors at synapses?

Exam Questions

1 Explain **one** negative effect of each of the following substances found in tobacco smoke:

(a) nicotine,

[2]

(b) tar.

[2]

[Total 4 marks]

2 Misusing alcohol can have several negative effects.

(a) Alcohol is known as a powerful depressant drug. State what this means.

[1]

(b) Alcohol misuse can cause liver damage.
Give **one** other effect of misusing alcohol.

[1]

(c) Liver damage can cause other negative effects in the body. Suggest why.

[2]

[Total 4 marks]

3 Anabolic steroids can be taken to improve sporting performance, but this can have negative effects.

(a) Give **two** negative effects that misusing anabolic steroids can have on the body.

[2]

(b) Explain how anabolic steroids can improve sporting performance.

[2]

[Total 4 marks]

4 A doctor prescribed the correct antibiotics to treat a bacterial infection that a patient had.

(a) Outline why the doctor shouldn't have prescribed antibiotics if the patient had a viral infection.

[1]

(b) After taking all of the antibiotics, the patient still had the infection.
Suggest why the patient still had the bacterial infection.

[3]

[Total 4 marks]

Reproduction

Reproduction is important as it is how all organisms pass on their genes — there are two types to learn...

Asexual Reproduction

Asexual reproduction is the process resulting in the production of genetically identical offspring from one parent.

1) Bacteria reproduce using asexual reproduction, as well as many plants (e.g. strawberry plants) and fungi (e.g. yeast). It also occurs in some animals, such as certain types of lizard and starfish.

2) You need to be able to describe some of the advantages and disadvantages of asexual reproduction:

Advantages

1) Lots of offspring can be produced very quickly. E.g. bacteria, such as *E. coli*, can divide every half an hour to colonise a new area very rapidly.

2) Only one parent is needed so organisms can reproduce whenever conditions are favourable. E.g. aphids reproduce asexually during summer when there is plenty of food.

3) Less energy is needed to reproduce asexually.

4) All offspring are genetically identical to their parents — so, for example, if a crop plant with beneficial characteristics reproduces asexually, you can be certain that its offspring will inherit those same characteristics.

Disadvantages

1) There's no genetic variation between offspring in the population. This means organisms are unlikely to be able to adapt to changes in the environment. If environmental conditions become unfavourable, the whole population may be affected. E.g. Black Sigatoka is a disease that affects banana plants, which reproduce asexually. An outbreak of the disease is likely to affect all plants in a population of the crop.

2) Overpopulation may occur if too many offspring are produced.

Sexual Reproduction

Sexual reproduction is the process involving the fusion of the nuclei of two gametes (fertilisation) to form a zygote and the production of offspring that are genetically different from each other.

Gametes are sex cells.

1) The nuclei of gametes are haploid. When they fuse, they form a zygote with a diploid nucleus.

2) You need to be able to discuss some of the advantages and disadvantages of sexual reproduction:

Advantages

1) It produces genetic variation. If environmental conditions change, it's more likely that some individuals will have the characteristics to survive the change. E.g. if there is an outbreak of disease, it is unlikely that the disease will affect every individual.

2) Diversity can lead to natural selection and evolution (see p.138) as species become better adapted to their new environment.

3) Selective breeding (see p.140) can be used to improve crop production and quality.

Disadvantages

1) It takes more time and energy than asexual reproduction, so organisms produce fewer offspring in their lifetime. Organisms have to find and attract mates. E.g. male bowerbirds build twig structures and then dance to impress females.

2) Two parents are needed, which can be a problem if individuals are isolated. E.g. polar bears often live alone, so males may walk up to 100 miles to find a mate.

Supplement

Sexual Reproduction in Plants

You need to know all about sexual reproduction in plants. Here's how it works...

The **Flower** Contains Both **Male** and **Female Gametes**

You saw on the previous page that sexual reproduction involves fertilisation (fusion of two gamete nuclei). Plants that reproduce sexually have both male and female gametes. Here's where they come from:

The **Stamen**

1) The stamen produces male gametes.
2) It consists of the anther and filament:

The **Carpel**

1) The carpel produces female gametes.
2) It consists of the stigma, style and ovary:

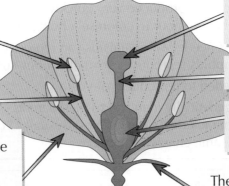

The anther contains pollen grains — these produce the male gametes (sperm).

Filament

In insect-pollinated flowers (see next page) the petals are often brightly coloured to attract insects needed for pollination.

The stigma is the end bit that the pollen grains attach to.

Style

The ovary contains the female gametes (eggs) inside ovules.

The sepals are green and leaf-like. They protect the flower in the bud.

Sexual Reproduction in **Plants** Involves **Pollination**

1) In plants, for fertilisation to occur, a process called pollination has to take place.

 Pollination is the transfer of pollen grains from the anther to the stigma.

2) There are different types of pollination, depending on where the pollen has come from:

 Self-pollination is the transfer of pollen grains from the anther of a flower to the stigma of the same flower or different flower on the same plant.

 Cross-pollination is the transfer of pollen grains from the anther of a flower to the stigma of a flower on a different plant of the same species.

3) There are different implications of self-pollination and cross-pollination:

> Pollinators are any animals that move pollen from the anther to the stigma.

- Self-pollinating plants don't rely on pollinators. This means it is easier for the plant to spread to locations where there aren't pollinators available.
- Cross-pollinating plants rely on pollinators to transfer pollen grains elsewhere. If the pollinator population declines, it becomes harder for a plant to reproduce.
- Cross-pollination produces more variation, meaning cross-pollinating plants are more likely to be able to adapt and survive any changes in the environment.
- Self-pollination produces less variation because the gene pool (the mix of genes in a population) is smaller. This means that self-pollinating plants are less likely to be able to adapt to changes in the environment (see p.138).

 Supplement

Supplement

Plant Pollination

As you saw on the previous page, sexual reproduction in plants involves the transfer of pollen from an anther to a stigma. Plants sometimes need a bit of outside help to get it done.

Some Plants are **Adapted** for **Insect Pollination**

Here's how plants can be adapted for pollination by insects...

1) They have large brightly coloured petals to attract insects to the anthers and stigmas inside.

2) They also have scented flowers and nectaries (glands that secrete nectar) to attract insects.

3) The stigma is sticky so that any pollen picked up by insects on other plants will stick to the stigma.

Insect-pollinated plants make big, sticky pollen grains — the grains stick to insects as they go from plant to plant.

Other Plants are **Adapted** for **Wind Pollination**

Features of plants that are adapted for pollination by wind include...

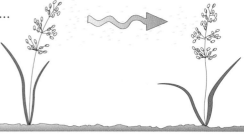

1) Small, dull petals (they don't need to attract insects).

2) No nectaries or strong scents (for the same reason).

3) Long filaments that hang the anthers outside the flower, so that a lot of the pollen gets blown away by the wind.

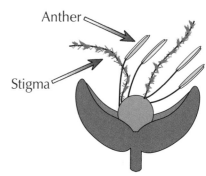

Anther

Stigma

4) A large and feathery stigma to catch pollen as it's carried past by the wind. The stigma often hangs outside the flower too.

Wind-pollinated plants have lots of small, light pollen grains — these grains can easily be carried to other plants by the wind.

Pollination is the transfer of pollen from an anther to a stigma

Flowers like roses (big, bright petals, a strong scent) are pollinated by insects. The feathery looking flowers you sometimes see in long grass, and fluffy willow catkins, are pollinated by the wind. If you're given a picture of a flower in the exam, you should be able to say whether it's most likely to be insect- or wind-pollinated and explain your answer. So get learning this page.

Fertilisation and Germination

On page 105, you saw that sexual reproduction can't occur without fertilisation. Here's more about fertilisation in plants, and what happens after that...

Fertilisation is the Fusion of Gametes

1) Plant fertilisation occurs when the nucleus from a pollen grain (the male gamete) fuses with the nucleus in an ovule (the female gamete).

2) Fertilisation doesn't happen when the pollen grain reaches the stigma — the pollen grain needs to get to the ovule:

- A pollen grain lands on the stigma of a flower, usually with help from insects or the wind (see previous page).

- A pollen tube grows out of the pollen grain and down through the style to the ovary and into the ovule.

- A nucleus from the male gamete moves down the tube to join with a female gamete in the ovule. Fertilisation is when the two nuclei fuse together to make a zygote. This divides by mitosis to form an embryo.

- Each fertilised female gamete forms a seed, which can then grow into a new plant.

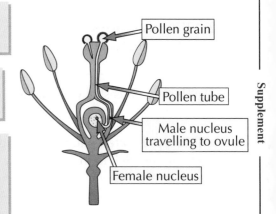

Pollen grain

Pollen tube

Male nucleus travelling to ovule

Female nucleus

Germination is when Seeds Start to Grow

1) Once a seed has formed following fertilisation, it will often lie dormant until the conditions around it are right for germination (growth into a plant).

2) Seeds need the right conditions to start germinating, and germination only starts when all of these conditions are suitable:

- Water — to activate the enzymes that break down the food reserves in the seed.

- Oxygen — for respiration (see page 78), which transfers the energy from food for growth.

- A suitable temperature — for the enzymes inside the seed to work. This depends on what type of seed it is.

The conditions needed for germination are really important

When seeds are exposed to the right conditions, they will start to germinate. This won't happen if the conditions aren't right though. Make sure you've learnt what conditions are needed and why.

Investigating Seed Germination

If you've always wanted to investigate the different conditions needed for germination to take place, then today is your lucky day...

You Can Investigate the Conditions Needed for Germination

You saw on the previous page that seeds need water, oxygen and a suitable temperature for germination to happen. Here's an experiment you can do to investigate these conditions.

1) Take four boiling tubes and put some cotton wool at the bottom of each one.

2) Put 10 seeds on top of the cotton wool in each boiling tube.

3) Set up each boiling tube as follows:

Tube 1   water, oxygen, room temperature (the control).
Tube 2   no water, oxygen, room temperature.
Tube 3   water, oxygen, low temperature.
Tube 4   water, no oxygen, room temperature.

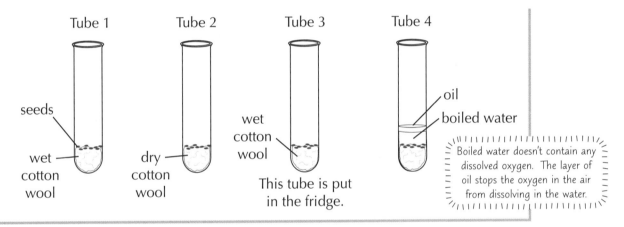

4) Leave the tubes for a few days and then observe what has happened.

5) It's important to control all of the variables during the experiment. You should only be changing one condition at a time so you know that any effect on germination is due to the change in that one condition.

6) So, in Tube 2, the only change from the control (Tube 1) is a lack of water. In Tube 3, only the temperature has changed. In Tube 4, the only change is the lack of oxygen.

Interpreting Your Observations

1) You should only see germination happening in Tube 1.

2) This is because all of the conditions needed for germination are present.

3) The seeds in the other boiling tubes won't germinate — this shows that the seeds need water, oxygen and a suitable temperature to germinate.

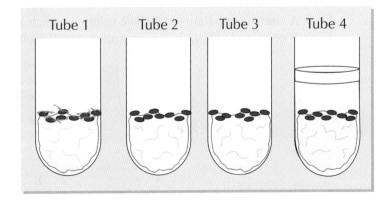

You need the right conditions for germination to happen

It's really important that you label your four boiling tubes — if you don't, you'll end up with no idea about what conditions are set up in each tube, and your results won't mean anything.

Warm-Up & Exam Questions

It's that time again. Don't turn the page just yet — give these questions a go before you move on. They're the only way of finding out if you really know your stuff.

Warm-Up Questions

1) What is sexual reproduction?
2) What is meant by the term 'fertilisation'?
3) What is meant by the term 'self-pollination'?

Exam Questions

1   The diagram below shows cross-sections through two flowers.

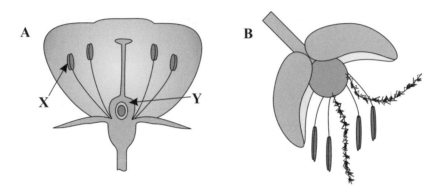

(a) Look at flower **A**. State the name and function of the structures labelled **X** and **Y**.

[4]

(b) Which flower, **A** or **B**, is better adapted for wind pollination? Explain your answer.

[2]

(c) Describe and explain **two** ways in which flowers can be adapted for pollination by insects.

[2]

[Total 8 marks]

2   A student set up a controlled experiment to investigate the conditions needed for germination.

She placed moist cotton wool and soaked alfalfa seeds in two large sealed flasks.
Flask **A** contained sodium pyrogallate solution, which absorbs oxygen from the air.
Flask **B** contained sodium hydroxide solution, which absorbs carbon dioxide from the air.

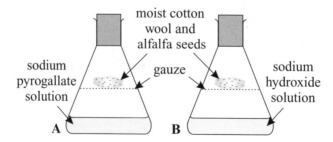

After 24 hours, the student found that the seeds had germinated in flask **B** only.

Explain why germination did not occur in flask **A**.

[Total 2 marks]

Sexual Reproduction in Humans

It's time to learn all about the male and female reproductive systems, and about fertilisation.

The **Male Reproductive System** Makes **Sperm**

Urethra — a tube which carries sperm through the penis during ejaculation. Urine also passes through the urethra to exit the body.

Prostate gland — produces the liquid that's added to sperm to make semen.

Penis — swells when filled with blood, for introducing sperm into the female.

Sperm duct — muscular tube that carries sperm from testis towards the urethra.

Testis — where sperm are made.

Scrotum — hangs behind the penis and contains the testes.

The plural is 'testes'.

The **Female Reproductive System** Makes **Ova (Egg Cells)**

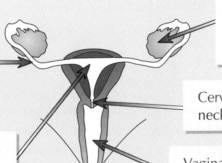

Oviduct — a muscular tube that carries the ovum (egg) from the ovary to the uterus. Fertilisation happens in the oviduct.

Ovary — the organ that produces ova and sex hormones.

Cervix — the neck of the uterus.

Uterus — the organ where an embryo grows.

Vagina — where the sperm are deposited.

Fertilisation is the **Fusion** of the **Nuclei** of **Sperm** and **Egg Cells**

1) As you saw on page 105, sexual reproduction involves the fusion of the nuclei from a male gamete and a female gamete.

2) In humans, the male gametes are sperm and the female gametes are ova (egg cells).

3) During sexual reproduction, the nucleus of an egg cell fuses with the nucleus of a sperm to create a fertilised egg, which then develops into an embryo (see p.113).

REVISION TIP

There's more to learn about sperm and egg cells coming up...

Try drawing out diagrams for both the male and the female reproductive system, with labels for all of the parts. Then make sure you know the function of each part too. Don't worry if your diagram isn't very artistic — it's the knowledge behind it that counts.

Sexual Reproduction in Humans

Fertilisation involves a sperm and an egg cell. The previous page told you where egg cells and sperm are made, but this page is all about how each type of cell is adapted for its function.

Egg Cells and Sperm Are Specialised for Reproduction

Egg Cells

The main functions of an egg cell are to carry the female DNA and to nourish the developing embryo in the early stages. Here are the adaptive features of an egg cell:

1) It contains energy stores in its cytoplasm.
2) It has a jelly coating that changes at fertilisation.

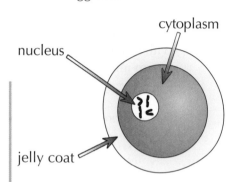

Supplement

- The energy stores provide nutrients for the zygote so that it can divide after fertilisation and form an embryo.
- After fertilisation, the jelly coat changes structure to stop any more sperm getting in. This makes sure the offspring end up with the right amount of DNA.

Sperm

The function of a sperm is to transport the male's DNA to the female's egg. Here are the adaptive features of a sperm:

1) It has a flagellum.
2) It has enzymes in its 'head'.

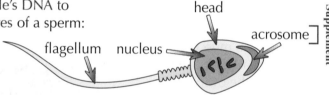

- The flagellum gives the sperm the ability to swim to the egg.
- The enzymes are needed to digest a way through the jelly coat of the egg cell. The enzymes are in a portion of the head called the acrosome.
- Sperm also contain lots of mitochondria. These provide energy for the flagellum to move.

Egg Cells and Sperm are Quite Different

If you couldn't tell from the diagrams, there are some significant differences between female gametes (egg cells) and male gametes (sperm). Here's a handy table with a summary:

	Egg Cell	Sperm
Size	About 0.1 mm in diameter.	About 0.05 mm in length.
Structure	Spherical. Lots of cytoplasm surrounded by jelly coating.	Head and flagellum. Small amount of cytoplasm.
Motility (ability to move)	Do not move independently.	Able to move due to the presence of the flagellum.
Numbers	About 300 000 present at puberty. Released one at a time each month.	Millions produced every day. Millions released at a time.

Pregnancy

Pregnancy occurs if a sperm fertilises an egg cell and the fertilised egg implants into the uterus. You need to know all about how that tiny fertilised egg grows and develops into a little human.

The **Embryo Develops** During **Pregnancy**

1) Once an egg cell has been fertilised, it is called a zygote.
2) Within about four days, the zygote develops into an embryo by dividing several times. This is a ball of cells that implants into the wall of the uterus.
3) Once the embryo has implanted, the placenta develops.
4) The placenta is connected to the embryo by the umbilical cord.
5) The embryo is surrounded by the amniotic sac, which is filled with amniotic fluid.
6) About nine weeks after fertilisation, when it starts to look human, the embryo is called a fetus.

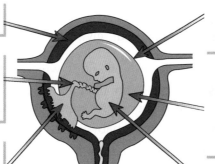

Wall of the uterus

Umbilical cord — carries substances between the fetus and the placenta.

Placenta — where substances are exchanged between the fetus and the mother.

Amniotic sac — contains amniotic fluid.

Amniotic fluid — protects the fetus against knocks and bumps, and supports the fetus as it grows. It also allows the fetus to move.

Developing fetus

Supplement

The **Placenta** and **Umbilical Cord** Transfer **Substances**

1) The placenta allows the blood of the fetus to get very close to the blood of the mother.
2) This allows dissolved nutrients (e.g. glucose and amino acids) and dissolved oxygen to pass into the fetus from the mother. It also allows excretory products (wastes like urea and carbon dioxide) to diffuse into the mother from the fetus.
3) The placenta also provides a barrier to most toxins and pathogens, however some can still pass across the placenta and into the fetus:

> For example, toxins such as nicotine in cigarette smoke and pathogens such as the rubella virus can pass across the placenta from the mother to the fetus, and affect its development.

Supplement

The **Development** of the **Fetus** Changes Over the Pregnancy

1) For the first 12 weeks of the pregnancy, the fetus increases in complexity as different body parts and organs develop.
2) For the rest of the pregnancy, once the fetus is fully developed, the fetus predominantly increases in size.

1 month   9 weeks   3 months   5 months   7 months   9 months

Pregnancy and Birth

The **Mother's Lifestyle** During **Pregnancy** is **Important**

1) Antenatal care is the care for the health of a pregnant woman to ensure her fetus develops properly.

2) It's important to eat a healthy balanced diet during pregnancy. As part of this, a pregnant woman may need to increase the amount of certain vitamins and minerals in her diet. For example, she may need more calcium, which is needed for bone growth, iron, which is needed for the production of blood, and folic acid, which reduces the risk of some types of birth defects. An expectant mother may also need to increase her protein intake to provide the protein the fetus needs for growth.

3) Smoking and alcohol consumption should be avoided during pregnancy, as they can affect the development and growth of the fetus, and increase the risk of miscarriage and stillbirth.

The **Process** of **Giving Birth** is Called **Labour**

1) After roughly nine months of pregnancy, the baby is ready to be born.

2) There are several processes involved in labour (giving birth):

- The amniotic sac bursts to release amniotic fluid, which passes out of the vagina.
- The muscles in the uterus wall start to contract and relax to push the baby out. These contractions get more frequent and stronger with time.
- The cervix dilates (widens) to allow the baby to pass through.
- The baby then passes through the vagina.
- Once the baby has been born, the umbilical cord is tied and cut.
- Finally, the afterbirth is delivered (the placenta detaches from the uterus and comes out of the body).

Breast Milk Provides the **Ideal Nutrients** After Birth

1) After a baby has been born, it can no longer get its nutrients from the mother via the placenta.

2) Instead, the mother produces the ideal food for a newborn baby in her mammary glands.

3) Many mothers choose to breast-feed their babies, rather than bottle-feed using formula milk. There are many advantages to this:

Advantages of Breast-feeding

1) Breast milk contains all of the right nutrients in the right amounts for different stages of development.

2) Antibodies from the mother are passed to the baby through breast milk. These help protect the baby from disease, as a form of passive immunity (see p.72).

3) There is no risk of infection from bottles, or from the water or milk powder used to prepare formula milk.

4) Breast-feeding builds the bond between a mother and her baby.

5) Breast-feeding is free (bottle-feeding is expensive).

6) No preparation of the milk is required, and the milk is at the correct temperature.

Disadvantages of Breast-feeding

1) Breast-feeding can be painful and difficult — difficulties can lead to postnatal depression.

2) Only the mother can feed the baby, unless the milk is pumped and stored. This puts pressure on the mother, and makes it harder for the other parent to bond with the baby.

3) Some toxins and pathogens can be passed to the baby through breast milk, e.g. HIV (see p.121).

Supplement

Supplement

Warm-Up & Exam Questions

Time for some Warm-Up Questions now, to see what you've remembered from the previous few pages. Once you've finished those, move onto the Exam Questions.

Warm-Up Questions

1) Name one example of a toxin or pathogen that can be passed from a mother to her fetus.
2) Describe the development of a fetus during pregnancy, in terms of complexity and size.
3) State two ways that a pregnant woman should take care of her health during pregnancy.

Exam Questions

1 The diagram on the right shows the male reproductive system.

(a) Name the structures labelled **X** and **Y**.

[2]

(b) The structure labelled **Z** is a gland. State its function.

[1]

(c) Add an arrow to the diagram to show where sperm are produced.

[1]

[Total 4 marks]

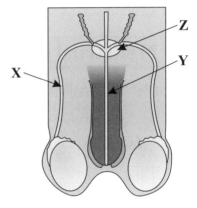

2 The diagram on the right shows the uterus during pregnancy. State the role of the following features shown in the diagram:

(a) the placenta

[1]

(b) the amniotic fluid

[1]

[Total 2 marks]

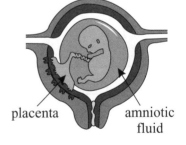

placenta   amniotic fluid

3 Sperm cells are specialised to help them achieve their function. The digram below shows the structure of a sperm cell.

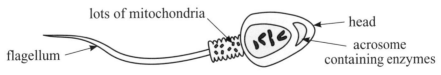

lots of mitochondria   head

flagellum   acrosome containing enzymes

(a) What is the function of a sperm cell?

[1]

(b) Explain how the structure of a sperm cell helps it to carry out its function. Use the diagram to help you.

[3]

[Total 4 marks]

Supplement

Puberty and the Menstrual Cycle

You need to learn the science behind what happens at puberty. Read on, my friend...

Hormones Promote Sexual Characteristics at Puberty

At puberty, your body starts releasing sex hormones — testosterone in men and oestrogen in women.
These trigger off the secondary sexual characteristics:

Testosterone in Men Causes...

1) Extra hair on face and body.
2) Muscles to develop.
3) Penis and testes to enlarge.
4) Sperm production.
5) Deepening of voice.

Oestrogen in Women Causes...

1) Extra hair on underarms and pubic area.
2) Hips to widen.
3) Development of breasts.
4) Egg release and start of periods.

See page 92 for more on hormones.

The Menstrual Cycle Has Four Stages

During the menstrual cycle, the uterus lining changes, and an egg develops and is released from an ovary.

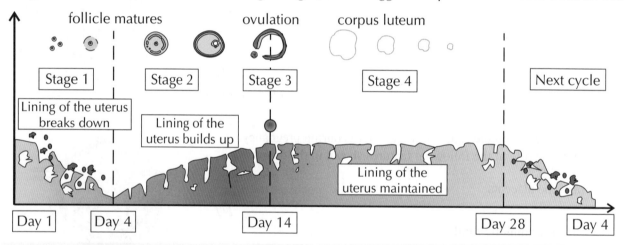

follicle matures   ovulation   corpus luteum

| Stage 1 | Stage 2 | Stage 3 | Stage 4 | Next cycle |

Lining of the uterus breaks down

Lining of the uterus builds up

Lining of the uterus maintained

| Day 1 | Day 4 | Day 14 | Day 28 | Day 4 |

Stage 1: Day 1 — menstruation starts. The uterus lining breaks down for about four days.

Stage 2: The uterus lining builds up (day 4 to 14) into a thick spongy layer full of blood vessels, ready to receive a fertilised egg. A follicle (an egg and its surrounding cells) matures in one of the ovaries.

Stage 3: The egg is released from the follicle at day 14 — this is called ovulation.

Stage 4: The remains of the follicle develop into a structure called a corpus luteum. The wall is then maintained for about 14 days until day 28. If no fertilised egg has implanted in the uterus wall by day 28, the spongy lining starts to break down and the whole cycle starts again.

Sperm can survive in the female reproductive system for up to five days. If sperm are deposited in the vagina in the five days before ovulation, up to the day after ovulation, there is a chance that the egg will be fertilised. On the rest of the days of the month, fertilisation will not take place.

REVISION TIP

The end of the cycle depends on whether the egg's fertilised...

You need to understand how the lining of the uterus changes throughout the menstrual cycle.
Cover up the page and try drawing the graph from memory to see how much you know.

The Menstrual Cycle

If you're taking the Extended course, you need to understand the menstrual cycle in terms of hormones...

The **Menstrual Cycle** is **Controlled** by **Four Hormones**

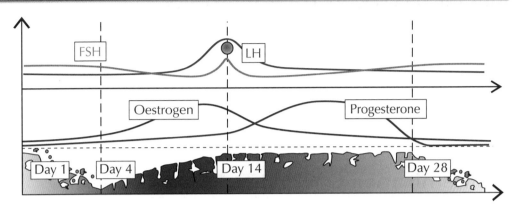

FSH (Follicle-Stimulating Hormone)

1) Causes a follicle to mature in one of the ovaries.
2) Stimulates the ovaries to produce oestrogen.

Oestrogen

1) Produced in the ovaries.
2) Causes the lining of the uterus to grow.
3) Stimulates the release of LH (causing the release of an egg) and inhibits the release of FSH.

LH (Luteinising Hormone)

1) Stimulates the release of the egg from the follicle at day 14 (ovulation).
2) Stimulates the remains of the follicle to develop into a corpus luteum, which secretes progesterone.

Progesterone

1) Produced in the ovaries by the corpus luteum after ovulation.
2) Prepares the uterus to receive a fertilised egg by maintaining the uterus lining during the second half of the cycle. When the level of progesterone falls, the lining breaks down.
3) Inhibits the release of LH and FSH.

The **Four Hormones** Have **Different Roles** During **Pregnancy**

1) During pregnancy, these hormones act in slightly different ways.
2) FSH and LH are inactive during pregnancy. The progesterone and oestrogen levels stay high to maintain the lining of the uterus, and stimulate breast growth and the development of milk ducts.
3) During pregnancy, progesterone is produced in the ovaries and the placenta. Oestrogen is also produced in the placenta.

Fertility Treatments

If a person is infertile, it means they can't reproduce naturally. There are different methods that might help a woman to become pregnant — but there are also social implications to consider.

Hormones can be Used to Treat Infertility

1) Some women are infertile because they don't ovulate or they don't ovulate regularly.

2) These women can be injected with FSH and LH, which stimulate egg maturation and ovulation — see previous page.

3) By knowing when the woman will be ovulating, a couple can have sexual intercourse during this time period to improve the chance of becoming pregnant.

Artificial Insemination Can Lead To Pregnancy

1) Artificial insemination (AI) is the process of directly inserting sperm into a woman's cervix, uterus, or fallopian tubes.

2) AI can be used if a couple are unable to have sexual intercourse, or if the woman's cervical mucus is not suited for getting pregnant.

3) It can also be used for couples in same-sex relationships or single women using donor sperm.

4) Sometimes AI is combined with fertility medicines that contain hormones.

5) The success rate for AI is between 5 and 20% each time.

In Vitro Fertilisation Can Also Help Couples to Have Children

1) *In vitro* fertilisation (IVF) involves collecting eggs from the woman's ovaries and fertilising them in a lab using the man's sperm.

2) The fertilised eggs are then grown into embryos in a laboratory incubator.

3) Once the embryos are tiny balls of cells, one or two of them are transferred to the woman's uterus to improve the chance of pregnancy.

4) The hormones FSH and LH are often given before egg collection to stimulate several eggs to mature (so more than one egg can be collected).

There are Social Implications of Fertility Treatments

1) There are pros and cons of fertility treatments. The biggest advantage is that treatments give infertile couples, single women and couples in same-sex relationships the chance to have a child.

2) However, fertility treatments don't always work — this makes the process incredibly stressful and often upsetting, especially if it ends in multiple failures. It can also be expensive if it is repeated.

3) As well as being emotionally stressful, the process is physically stressful for the woman. Some women have a strong reaction to the hormones — e.g. abdominal pain, vomiting, dehydration.

4) Fertility treatments often lead to multiple births if more than one embryo grows into a baby — these are risky for the mother and babies (there's a higher risk of miscarriage, stillbirth...).

5) The process of IVF often results in unused embryos that are eventually destroyed. Because of this, some people think it is unethical because each embryo is a potential human life.

6) The genetic testing of embryos before implantation also raises ethical issues as some people think it could lead to the selection of preferred characteristics, such as gender or eye colour.

Supplement

Supplement

Birth Control

Pregnancy can happen if sperm reaches the ovulated egg. Birth control tries to stop this happening.

Chemical Birth Control Often Contains Hormones

1) Many chemical methods of birth control contain hormones, which can be used to reduce fertility.

2) Here are four examples:

> - An intrauterine system (IUS) is a T-shaped plastic device similar to an IUD (see below). It releases progesterone into the uterus. It lasts for 3 to 5 years.
>
> - The contraceptive pill can contain oestrogen and progesterone, or just progesterone. The pill has to be taken every day, or every day for 21 days followed by a 7 day break.
>
> - The contraceptive implant is inserted under the skin of the arm. It releases a continuous amount of progesterone. An implant can last for three years.
>
> - The contraceptive injection also contains progesterone. Each dose lasts 2 to 3 months.

3) Here's an example of chemical birth control that doesn't contain hormones:

> An intrauterine device (IUD) is a T-shaped device that is made of copper and plastic. It releases copper into the uterus to prevent sperm surviving. It lasts for 5 to 10 years.

Hormones as Birth Control

Supplement

1) Oestrogen can be used to prevent the release of an egg — so it can be used for birth control.

2) This may seem kind of strange (since naturally oestrogen helps stimulate the release of eggs). But if oestrogen is taken every day to keep the level of it permanently high, it inhibits the production of FSH, and after a while egg development and production stop and stay stopped.

3) Progesterone also reduces fertility, e.g. by stimulating the production of thick cervical mucus, which prevents any sperm getting through and reaching an egg.

Supplement

Pregnancy Can Also Be Prevented Using Barrier Birth Control

1) Barrier birth control puts a barrier between the sperm and the egg so that they don't meet.

2) Here are three examples:

> 1) Condoms are usually made of latex and are worn over the penis during sexual intercourse. This prevents sperm from entering the vagina.
> 2) Femidoms are similar to condoms, but are worn inside the vagina.
> 3) Diaphragms are flexible, dome-shaped devices that fit over the opening of the uterus. They are inserted before sexual intercourse.

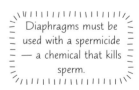
Diaphragms must be used with a spermicide — a chemical that kills sperm.

It's all about stopping the sperm from meeting the egg...

Chemical and barrier methods of birth control are not the only methods you can use. You'll find out about some more methods of birth control on the next page — but make sure you've learnt this page first.

Birth Control

Here are some more methods to prevent pregnancy and some pros and cons of birth control use.

Surgery is a More Drastic Birth Control Method

1) Surgical methods of birth control mean that an individual no longer has to think about birth control, as the procedures are permanent.

2) The procedures for men and women are quite similar:

> • A vasectomy is a procedure that involves cutting or sealing the sperm ducts.
>
> • Female sterilisation involves cutting or sealing the oviducts (tubes which connect the ovaries to the uterus — see page 111).

3) A vasectomy and female sterilisation are both permanent procedures, but there is a very small chance that the sperm ducts or the oviducts can rejoin.

There are Some Natural Birth Control Methods

1) Other methods of birth control are known as 'natural methods'. They're generally not as reliable as chemical, barrier or surgical methods. For example:

> • A woman's body temperature changes very slightly throughout the menstrual cycle. Monitoring body temperature can help a woman predict when she is most fertile so that she can avoid sexual intercourse on those days. It's popular with people who don't want to use other methods of contraception, but it's not very effective.
>
> • The amount of cervical mucus produced also changes during the menstrual cycle, as well as its texture. Monitoring the mucus is another method of predicting when a woman is most fertile, so can be used in a similar way to monitoring body temperature.

2) The only way pregnancy can be avoided for sure is by not having sex at all:

> Abstinence means not having sexual intercourse. This is the only way to be completely sure that sperm and an egg cell don't meet.

There are Social Implications of Contraception

There are pros and cons of the use of contraception:

1) Birth control prevents unwanted pregnancies and gives women more control over when (or if) they start a family.

2) Use of birth control reduces family sizes and limits the increase in the global population.

3) Condoms reduce the spread of STIs (see next page).

4) However, some religious groups are against birth control and discourage its use.

5) Some chemical birth control methods can have side effects.

Supplement (left margin)

Supplement (right margin)

People have a choice to make when picking a contraceptive

You might be asked to evaluate different methods of contraception in your exam. If you are, remember you need to weigh up and write about both the pros and the cons of each method and write a sensible conclusion too. That's how you get your hands on those top marks.

Sexually Transmitted Infections

Some transmissible diseases are transmitted sexually, but there are ways to prevent their spread.

STIs are **Sexually Transmitted Infections**

 KEY TERM A sexually transmitted infection (STI) is an infection that is transmitted via body fluids through sexual contact.

You need to know about one example of an STI:

HIV is the Human Immunodeficiency Virus

1) HIV is spread via infected bodily fluids (e.g. blood, semen, vaginal fluids) during sexual contact and non-sexually (e.g. through sharing needles). HIV can also spread from an infected mother to her baby during pregnancy, childbirth and breastfeeding.

2) HIV infection may eventually lead to AIDS (Acquired Immune Deficiency Syndrome).

3) AIDS is when the infected person's immune system deteriorates and eventually fails — because of this, the person becomes very vulnerable to infections by other pathogens.

Supplement

A person's immune system deteriorates because HIV infects lymphocytes (see p.63). This causes their numbers to decrease, and so reduces a person's ability to produce antibodies (see p.70).

The **Spread** of **STIs** can be **Controlled**

Thankfully, it is possible to control the spread of STIs. Here are some methods:

1) It's important that people are educated and aware of STIs so that their spread can be reduced.
2) The best way to prevent the spread of STIs is abstinence — not having sexual intercourse.
3) Another way to prevent the spread of STIs is to use a condom (see p.119) when having sex.
4) Limiting the number of sexual partners also reduces the spread of infection.
5) Getting tested for infection after unprotected sex or after contact with several sexual partners will also help to control the spread of STIs.
6) Medication can reduce the risk of an infected individual passing some infections (e.g. HIV) on to others during sex or of a mother passing it to her baby during pregnancy.
7) Some vaccines protect against STIs caused by viruses.
8) Drug users should avoid sharing needles.

 REVISION TIP

HIV is an STI but isn't only transmitted sexually...

Draw a table with columns for 'how HIV is spread' and 'how to control spread of STIs', then fill it in with all the things you know. See how much you can write down without looking at this page.

Warm-Up & Exam Questions

There's only one way to do well in the exam — learn the facts and then practise lots of exam questions to see what it'll be like on the big day. We couldn't have made it any easier for you, so jump straight in...

Warm-Up Questions

1) What happens to the lining of the uterus at the start of the menstrual cycle?
2) Where is oestrogen produced during the menstrual cycle?
3) What type of birth control method is a diaphragm?
4) What is the only form of birth control that always prevents pregnancy?

Exam Questions

1 The release of sex hormones begins at puberty.

(a) Name the male sex hormone.

[1]

(b) Give **two** secondary sexual characteristics caused by the male sex hormone.

[2]

(c) Give **one** secondary sexual characteristic that is caused by the female sex hormone, oestrogen.

[1]

[Total 4 marks]

2 HIV is a sexually transmitted infection that eventually leads to AIDS in the people it infects.

(a) State what is meant by the term 'sexually transmitted infection'.

[1]

(b) Drug users are advised not to share needles in order to protect themselves from HIV. Suggest why.

[2]

(c) Describe **one** other way of controlling the spread of HIV.

[1]

(d) Explain why a person with AIDS may become seriously ill due to infection by another pathogen.

[2]

[Total 6 marks]

3 A couple want to have children but the woman has not yet become pregnant. Blood tests have shown that she has a low level of FSH (follicle stimulating hormone). She is treated with a fertility drug.

(a) State why a low level of FSH may be preventing the woman from becoming pregnant.

[1]

(b) In addition to FSH, which other hormone will the fertility drug contain to help the woman become pregnant? Give a reason for your answer.

[2]

[Total 3 marks]

Supplement

Exam Questions

4 The contraceptive pill can contain oestrogen and progesterone.

   (a) Explain how taking oestrogen can prevent pregnancy.

                                                  [2]

   (b) Progesterone can prevent pregnancy by preventing ovulation.
Explain **one** other way in which taking progesterone can prevent pregnancy.

                                                  [2]

One of the problems with the contraceptive pill is that women may forget
to take it on the days they are supposed to.

   (c) Suggest **one** alternative method of chemical birth control that may be more suitable for a woman who is worried about remembering to take the contraceptive pill. Explain your choice.

                                                  [2]

   (d) A couple are considering using barrier birth control to prevent pregnancy.
Describe how barrier birth control prevents pregnancies.

                                                  [1]

   (e) A different couple in their late 30s who have already had three children are looking for a more permanent method of birth control. Suggest **one** birth control method that may be suitable.

                                                  [1]
[Total 8 marks]

5 The menstrual cycle is controlled by several different hormones.

   (a) Describe the effect of progesterone on the release of FSH.

                                                  [1]

   (b) State the day of the menstrual cycle on which the egg is released.

                                                  [1]

Towards the end of the menstrual cycle, the oestrogen level is
low and the progesterone level begins to fall.

   (c) Describe the effect that this will have on the uterus lining.

                                                  [1]

   (d) When a fertilised egg implants in the uterus, the level of progesterone remains high.
State **one** reason why this happens.

                                                  [1]

   (e) State the site of production of progesterone during pregnancy.

                                                  [1]
[Total 5 marks]

6 *In vitro* fertilisation (IVF) is a fertility treatment that can give people the chance to have a child.

   (a) Outline the steps involved in IVF.

                                                  [4]

   (b) Give **two** disadvantages of IVF.

                                                  [2]
[Total 6 marks]

Supplement

124

Revision Summary for Sections 11 & 12

Well, that's Sections 11 and 12 finished. Now it's time to test how much you've taken in...
- Try these questions and tick off each one when you get it right.
- When you've done all the questions for a topic and are completely happy with it, tick off the topic.

Drugs (p.101-103) ☑
1) Give one effect of carbon monoxide from tobacco smoke on the body. ☑
2) Discuss the evidence for the link between smoking and lung cancer. ☑

Reproduction (p.105) ☑
3) What is asexual reproduction? ☑
4) Give two advantages of asexual reproduction compared to sexual reproduction. ☑
5) Give one difference between the nucleus of a gamete and the nucleus of a zygote. ☑
6) Give one advantage of sexual reproduction compared to asexual reproduction. ☑

Sexual Reproduction in Plants (p.106-109) ☑
7) On a plant, what is the function of: a) the petals, b) the sepals? ☑
8) What is pollination? ☑
9) What is cross-pollination? ☑
10) Describe the pollen grains of a wind-pollinated plant. ☑
11) How does pollen get from the stigma to the ovule? ☑
12) What happens during plant fertilisation? ☑
13) Give three conditions that are needed for germination to happen. ☑

Sexual Reproduction in Humans (p.111-114) ☑
14) Give the name and function of three structures in the female reproductive system. ☑
15) State and explain two features of an egg cell that make it adapted for its function. ☑
16) Compare egg cells and sperm in terms of their size and numbers. ☑
17) Describe how a fertilised egg becomes a fetus. ☑
18) Describe the processes involved in labour and birth. ☑
19) Give three advantages of breast-feeding a newborn baby over bottle-feeding with formula milk. ☑

Puberty and the Menstrual Cycle (p.116-117) ☑
20) Name the main female sex hormone. ☑
21) Describe the changes that take place in the ovary during the menstrual cycle. ☑
22) Describe two effects of FSH on the ovaries. ☑
23) Where is progesterone released from during the menstrual cycle? ☑

Fertility Treatments, Birth Control and Sexually Transmitted Infections (p.118-121) ☑
24) Outline the process of artificial insemination. ☑
25) How can monitoring body temperature be used as a form of birth control? ☑
26) Give one positive and one negative social implication of contraception. ☑
27) Give an example of an STI. ☑

Chromosomes and Sex Inheritance

A molecule called DNA carries your genetic code — here's how it is stored and how it determines your sex.

DNA is **Stored** as **Chromosomes** and **Contains Genes**

1) Chromosomes are found in the nucleus of eukaryotic cells.

 A chromosome is a thread-like structure of DNA, which carries genetic information in the form of genes.

 A gene is a length of DNA that codes for a protein.

2) By controlling the production of proteins, genes also control our characteristics.

3) There can be different versions of the same gene, which give different versions of a characteristic — like blue or brown eyes.

 An allele is a version of a gene.

For example, you might have the alleles for blue eyes and your friend might have the alleles for brown eyes.

Two Chromosomes **Determine Sex** in **Humans**

1) In humans, there are two chromosomes responsible for sex determination (whether you turn out male or female). These are the sex chromosomes and can be labelled as either X or Y.

2) Males have an X and a Y chromosome (XY). The Y chromosome causes male characteristics.

3) Females have two X chromosomes (XX). The XX combination allows female characteristics to develop.

4) All eggs have one X chromosome, but a sperm can have either an X chromosome or a Y chromosome. So sex determination in humans depends on whether the sperm that fertilises an egg (see p.111) carries an X or a Y.

5) There's a 50:50 chance that a sperm contains an X or Y chromosome, so there's a 50:50 chance of a child having XX (and being a girl) or XY (and being a boy).

Chromosomes Can Come in **Pairs**

1) Human body cells are diploid — there are two copies of each chromosome, arranged in pairs.

 A diploid nucleus is a nucleus that contains two sets of chromosomes.

2) There are 23 pairs of chromosomes in human diploid cells, so there are 46 chromosomes in total.

3) Gametes (sex cells) are haploid — they have half the number of chromosomes in a normal cell.

 A haploid nucleus is a nucleus containing a single set of unpaired chromosomes.

4) Human gametes each contain 23 chromosomes.

Supplement

Supplement

Protein Synthesis

This page is all about how your body uses the genes in DNA to make the proteins it needs.

Proteins are Made by Reading the Code in DNA

1) DNA strands contain bases which make up genes (see previous page).

2) The order of bases in a gene is the genetic code that determines the order of amino acids in a protein.

3) Each amino acid is coded for by a sequence of three bases in the gene.

4) Amino acids are joined together to make specific proteins, depending on the order of the gene's bases.

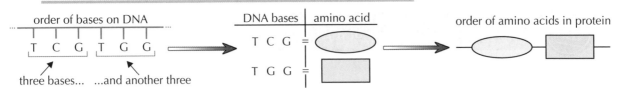

- A cell's function is controlled by DNA, because DNA controls the production of proteins, including enzymes, antibodies (see page 70) and neurotransmitter receptors (p.87).
- All body cells in an organism have the same genes, but cells don't express (make proteins from) all of their genes. Cells only express those genes that lead to the production of the specific proteins they need to carry out their function.

Proteins are Made in the Cytoplasm

1) DNA is found in the cell nucleus. It can't move out of the nucleus because it's really big. The cell needs to get the information from the DNA into the cytoplasm.

2) This is done using a molecule called messenger RNA (mRNA). Like DNA, mRNA is made up of a sequence of bases.

3) mRNA molecules carry a copy of the gene to the cytoplasm.

4) Once in the cytoplasm, the mRNA passes through a ribosome (see page 4).

5) The ribosome assembles amino acids into protein molecules.

6) The sequence of bases in the mRNA determines the specific order of amino acids in the protein.

DNA and mRNA decide the order of amino acids in the protein

It's important that you know why the order of bases in a section of DNA (and the mRNA copy) affects which protein is made. If you're unsure, it's all covered on this page — go back and take another look.

Mitosis and Meiosis

In order to survive and grow, our cells have got to be able to divide. This involves nuclear division (division of the nucleus). There are two types of nuclear division that you need to know about.

Mitosis Makes New Cells for Growth, Development and Repair

1) Body cells divide to produce new cells during mitosis.

 Mitosis is nuclear division that gives rise to two genetically identical cells.

2) Mitosis is used in growth, cell replacement during development, and in the repair of damaged tissues.
3) It is also used in asexual reproduction (see page 105).
4) Before mitosis can happen, the cell's chromosomes are duplicated (copied) exactly — so you end up with twice the normal diploid number of chromosomes (see p.125).
5) During mitosis, the chromosome copies separate and the nucleus divides — one copy of each chromosome ends up in each daughter (new) cell. This means that each daughter cell is diploid and the original chromosome number is maintained.

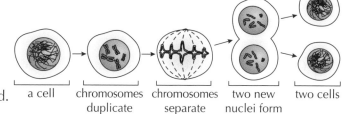

a cell | chromosomes duplicate | chromosomes separate | two new nuclei form | two cells

Mitosis is Important in Stem Cells

1) Stem cells are unspecialised cells.
2) Depending on what instructions they're given, stem cells divide by mitosis to produce identical daughter cells that can then become specialised for specific functions.
3) Stem cells in embryos allow an organism to grow and develop. Stem cells in adults are used to replace damaged cells.

Meiosis is Another Type of Division

1) Gametes are sex cells produced during meiosis.

 Meiosis is nuclear division that gives rise to four genetically different cells.

2) If you're doing the Extended course, you need to know this definition for meiosis instead:

 Meiosis is reduction division in which the chromosome number is halved from diploid to haploid resulting in genetically different cells.

3) In sexual reproduction (p.105), half of an offspring's chromosomes come from its father (paternal) and the other half of its chromosomes come from its mother (maternal). Meiosis gives rise to variation (p.135) by shuffling the paternal and maternal chromosomes to form new chromosome combinations. This produces cells that are genetically different.

 Meiosis is different from mitosis

Don't get meiosis mixed up with mitosis. Try remembering mitosis has "IT" in it and "IT" stands for Identical Twins, because the two cells produced are genetically identical to the original cell. Meiosis doesn't have "IT" and produces four daughter cells which are genetically different.

Warm-Up & Exam Questions

Take a deep breath and go through these Warm-Up and Exam Questions one by one.
Don't panic if you get something wrong — go back to the relevant page and have another look.

Warm-Up Questions

1) What combination of sex chromosomes do human males have?
2) Does mitosis or meiosis produce genetically identical cells?

Exam Questions

1 DNA in plants and animals is found in the form of chromosomes.

(a) What is a chromosome?

[1]

(b) (i) Each body cell in most mammals has a **diploid** nucleus. Explain what this means.

[1]

(ii) State the number of chromosomes in a human **haploid** cell.

[1]

[Total 3 marks]

2 To make a protein, mRNA carries a copy of the gene from the DNA in the nucleus to the cytoplasm.

(a) Name the part of the cell that assembles amino acids into protein molecules.

[1]

(b) State what determines the order of amino acids in a protein.

[1]

(c) Briefly explain how genes affect cell function.

[2]

[Total 4 marks]

3 Mosquitoes have three pairs of chromosomes in their body cells.
The diagram below shows a mosquito cell which is about to divide by meiosis.

(a) The cell in the diagram undergoes meiosis.
State how many chromosomes will be present in each new cell produced.

[1]

(b) Explain how meiosis leads to variation in the mosquito's offspring.

[2]

[Total 3 marks]

Monohybrid Inheritance

Chromosomes contain the same genes in the same places. The genes have different alleles (versions, see p.125), so the characteristics you have depends on which alleles you inherited from your parents.

Here are Some **Definitions** to Learn...

Term	Definition
Inheritance	The transmission of genetic information (DNA) from generation to generation.
Genotype	The genetic make-up of an organism (the alleles present).
Phenotype	The observable features of an organism.
Homozygous	Having two identical alleles of a particular gene.
Heterozygous	Having two different alleles of a particular gene.
Dominant	An allele that is expressed if it is present.
Recessive	An allele that is only expressed when there is no dominant allele of the gene present.

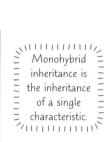

Monohybrid inheritance is the inheritance of a single characteristic.

Genes are **Inherited** From Your **Parents**

1) You have two alleles of every gene in your body — one from each parent.

   The combination of alleles that you inherit is your genotype.

   Your genotype determines what features you have (your phenotype).

   So different combinations of alleles give rise to different phenotypes.

2) Different genotypes arise from different combinations of alleles.

   If an organism has two of the same alleles for a particular gene, then it's homozygous for that trait. Two identical homozygous individuals that breed together will be pure-breeding (they can only pass on one allele, and therefore only one phenotype).

   If an organism has two alleles for a particular gene that are different, then it's heterozygous. A heterozygous organism will not be pure-breeding, as it can pass on two different alleles.

3) Alleles that are dominant (shown with capital letters, e.g. 'C') overrule alleles that are recessive (shown with small letters, e.g. 'c'). If an organism has one dominant and one recessive allele for a gene (e.g. 'Cc'), then the dominant allele will determine the characteristic present.

4) To display a dominant characteristic, an organism can have either two dominant alleles (CC) for a particular gene, or one dominant and one recessive allele (Cc) for that gene.

5) For an organism to display a recessive characteristic, both its alleles must be recessive (cc).

Genetic Diagrams

You can work out the probability of offspring having certain characteristics by using a genetic diagram.

Genetic Diagrams Show the **Possible Alleles** of **Offspring**

Cats with different lengths of hair are bred together. The allele which causes cats to have short hair is dominant ('H'), whilst long hair is due to a recessive allele ('h').

1) A cat with long hair must have the genotype hh. But a cat with short hair could be HH or Hh.

2) Here's what happens if you breed two heterozygous cats:

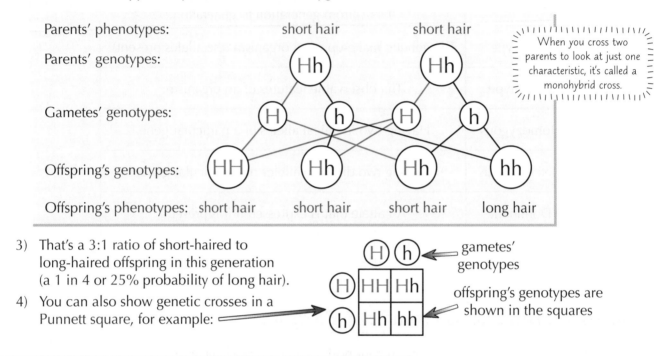

When you cross two parents to look at just one characteristic, it's called a monohybrid cross.

3) That's a 3:1 ratio of short-haired to long-haired offspring in this generation (a 1 in 4 or 25% probability of long hair).

4) You can also show genetic crosses in a Punnett square, for example:

gametes' genotypes

offspring's genotypes are shown in the squares

There Can Be a **1:1 Ratio** in the Offspring

1) A cat with short hair (Hh) was bred with another cat with long hair (hh).

2) The cats had 8 kittens — 4 with short hair and 4 with long hair.

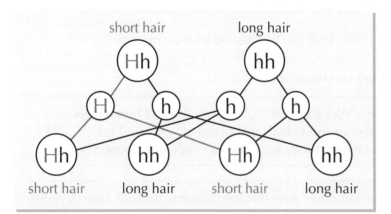

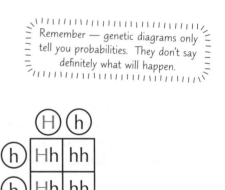

Remember — genetic diagrams only tell you probabilities. They don't say definitely what will happen.

3) This is a 1:1 ratio — it's what you'd expect when a parent with only one dominant allele (heterozygous — Hh) is crossed with a parent with two recessive alleles (homozygous — hh).

Genetic diagrams aren't that scary

EXAM TIP You should know how to produce and interpret both of these types of genetic diagram before exam day. Try drawing a Punnett square from a genetic cross diagram like the ones above, and then try the same but the other way round. Always remember the genotypes and the phenotypes.

Genetic Diagrams

Coming up on this page — another type of genetic diagram you need to know about...

Pedigree Diagrams Can Show How Characteristics Are Inherited

1) Knowing how inheritance works can help you to interpret a pedigree diagram — this is one for a genetic (inherited) disorder called cystic fibrosis.

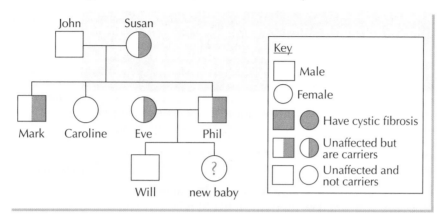

Key
- Male
- Female
- Have cystic fibrosis
- Unaffected but are carriers
- Unaffected and not carriers

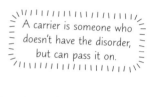
A carrier is someone who doesn't have the disorder, but can pass it on.

2) From the pedigree diagram, you can tell that the allele for cystic fibrosis isn't dominant because plenty of the family carry the allele but don't have the disorder. The allele must be recessive (f).

3) Both of the baby's parents are unaffected but are carriers, meaning they both have the genotype Ff.

4) As both parents are Ff, there is a 25% chance that the new baby will be unaffected and not a carrier (FF), a 50% chance that it will be unaffected but a carrier (Ff), and a 25% chance that the new baby will have the disorder (ff).

This is the same as the 3:1 ratio shown on page 130.

Test Crosses Can Be Used to Identify Unknown Genotypes

1) A test cross can be used to determine the unknown genotype of an organism, by analysing the ratio of phenotypes in the offspring.

2) You can use genetic diagrams when carrying out test crosses.

3) Let's say you're breeding cats again (see p.130). You breed a long-haired cat with a short-haired cat.

A test cross has to involve a homozygous recessive individual — in this case the long-haired cat with the genotype hh.

4) The long-haired cat must have the genotype hh, because long hair is due to a recessive allele.

5) The genotype of the short-haired cat is unknown — it could be homozygous dominant (HH) or heterozygous dominant (Hh). Here's how you can work out which it is:

When the two cats breed, the ratio of the phenotypes in the offspring will be the same as the ratio of the genotypes of the short-haired cat's gametes.

1) If the short-haired parent cat is homozygous (HH), it will produce only one gamete genotype (H). Therefore, when it is bred with the long-haired cat (hh) only one type of offspring phenotype will be produced (Hh — short hair). If all of the offspring produced in a test cross have short hair, the short-haired parent cat must be homozygous (HH).

2) A heterozygous short-haired cat (Hh) bred with the long-haired cat (hh) will produce two gamete genotypes (H and h) in the ratio 1:1, and therefore two offspring phenotypes (Hh — short hair, hh — long hair) in the same ratio. If short-haired and long-haired offspring are produced in a test cross, the short-haired cat must be heterozygous (Hh).

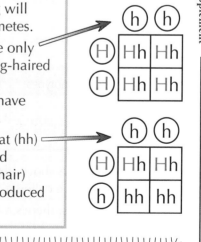

This is the same as the 1:1 ratio shown on page 130.

Supplement

Sex-Linked Genetic Disorders

There are some disorders that you're more likely to end up with if you're a certain sex. This is because these disorders are linked to the sex chromosomes, which are different in males and females (see p.125).

Some **Genetic Characteristics** Are **Sex-Linked**

1) A characteristic is sex-linked if the gene that codes for it is located on a sex chromosome (X or Y).

> **KEY TERM**
>
> A sex-linked characteristic is a characteristic in which the gene responsible is located on a sex chromosome, making it more common in one sex than in the other.

X chromosome

Gene that men have two alleles for.

Y chromosome

Gene that men have only one allele for.

2) The Y chromosome is smaller than the X chromosome and carries fewer genes. So most genes on the sex chromosomes are only carried on the X chromosome.

3) As men only have one X chromosome they often only have one allele for sex-linked genes.

4) Because men only have one allele, the characteristic of this allele is shown even if it is recessive. This makes men more likely than women to show recessive characteristics for genes that are sex-linked.

5) Disorders caused by faulty alleles located on sex chromosomes are called sex-linked genetic disorders.

Colour Blindness is a **Sex-Linked Disorder**

1) Colour blindness is caused by a faulty allele carried on the X chromosome.

2) As it's sex-linked, both the chromosome and the allele are written in the genetic diagram, e.g. X^n, where X represents the X chromosome and n the faulty allele for colour vision. The Y chromosome doesn't have an allele for colour vision so is just represented by Y.

3) Women need two copies of the recessive allele to be colour blind, while men only need one copy. This means colour blindness is much rarer in women than men.

4) A woman with only one copy of the recessive allele is a carrier of colour blindness. This means that she isn't colour blind herself, but she can pass the allele on to her offspring.

5) Here's a genetic diagram showing a carrier female and an unaffected (non-colour blind) male:

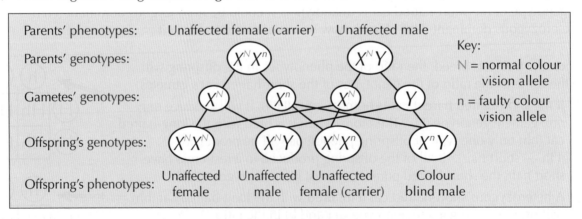

6) In the example above, the ratio of unaffected : colour blind offspring is 3 : 1. Be careful with this one, it could also be called a 2 : 1 : 1 ratio (unaffected : carrier : colour blind), but it means the same thing.

7) In other words, there's a 1 in 4 (25%) chance of a child being colour blind. This rises to 1 in 2 (50%) if you know that the child will be a boy.

Supplement

Inheritance of Blood Groups

This is a bit more complicated than the previous examples, but don't worry, just go through it slowly.

There Are **Multiple Alleles** That Determine **Blood Group**

1) So far you've probably only come across cases where there are two possible alleles for a gene — one that's recessive and one that's dominant.

2) Well, sometimes you'll get more than two (multiple) alleles for a single gene. This makes studying the inheritance of characteristics controlled by these genes a little more complicated.

3) For example, humans have four potential blood types — A, B, AB and O. These are the phenotypes. The gene for blood type in humans has three different alleles — I^A, I^B and I^O.

4) I^A and I^B are co-dominant with each other. That means that when an individual has both of these alleles (genotype $I^A I^B$), then they'll have the blood type AB — one allele isn't dominant over the other one.

5) However, I^O is recessive. So when you get I^O with I^A (genotype $I^A I^O$) you only see the effect of I^A — giving blood type A. In the same way, I^O with I^B (genotype $I^B I^O$) only gives the effect of I^B, making you blood type B.

6) You only get blood type O when you have two of the recessive alleles ($I^O I^O$).

You Can Predict **Blood Groups** Using **Genetic Diagrams**

1) You can draw genetic diagrams for co-dominant alleles in the same way that you would for alleles that are recessive and dominant.

2) The tricky bit is predicting the potential phenotypes in the offspring once you've worked out what the potential genotypes are. You need to remember how the different alleles interact with each other to produce a phenotype.

3) Here's an example showing how you can use genetic diagrams to predict the blood type inherited by the offspring:

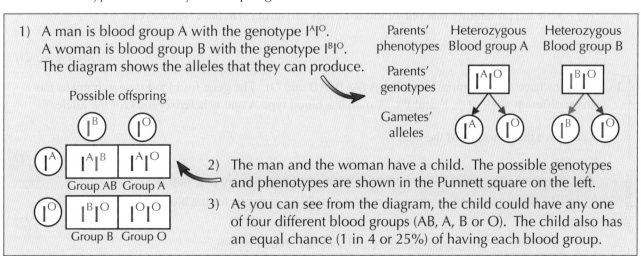

1) A man is blood group A with the genotype $I^A I^O$. A woman is blood group B with the genotype $I^B I^O$. The diagram shows the alleles that they can produce.

Possible offspring

Parents' phenotypes: Heterozygous Blood group A / Heterozygous Blood group B

Parents' genotypes: $I^A I^O$ / $I^B I^O$

Gametes' alleles: I^A I^O / I^B I^O

	I^B	I^O
I^A	$I^A I^B$ Group AB	$I^A I^O$ Group A
I^O	$I^B I^O$ Group B	$I^O I^O$ Group O

2) The man and the woman have a child. The possible genotypes and phenotypes are shown in the Punnett square on the left.

3) As you can see from the diagram, the child could have any one of four different blood groups (AB, A, B or O). The child also has an equal chance (1 in 4 or 25%) of having each blood group.

Co-dominance — both alleles are visible in the phenotype

You need to be able to use genetic diagrams to predict results for co-dominant genotypes. If you're still confused by the diagrams, read over the last few pages again — it will really help for this example.

Supplement

Warm-Up & Exam Questions

You need to test your knowledge with a few Warm-Up Questions, followed by some Exam Questions.

Warm-Up Questions

1) Define inheritance.
2) What is genotype? What is phenotype?
S 3) Where is a gene that codes for a sex-linked characteristic located?

Exam Questions

1 Polydactyly is a genetic disorder transmitted by the dominant allele **D**. The corresponding recessive allele is **d**. The pedigree diagram of a family with a history of polydactyly is shown.

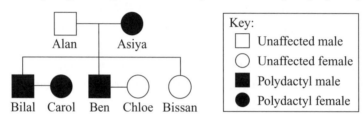

Key:
☐ Unaffected male
○ Unaffected female
■ Polydactyl male
● Polydactyl female

Using the information given above, state what Asiya's genotype must be.
Explain your answer.

[Total 2 marks]

2 Fruit flies usually have red eyes. However, there are a small number of white-eyed fruit flies. Having white eyes is a recessive characteristic. Two fruit flies with red eyes have the heterozygous genotype for this characteristic. They are crossed to produce offspring.

(a) Draw a genetic diagram to show the possible genotypes and phenotypes of the offspring. Use **R** to represent the dominant allele and **r** to represent the recessive allele.

[3]

(b) State the probability that one of the fruit flies' offspring will have white eyes.

[1]

[Total 4 marks]

3 Humans have four potential blood types (A, B, AB and O). The gene for blood type in humans has three different alleles (I^O, I^A and I^B). A man has blood type **A** and is heterozygous for the allele.

(a) Give the genotype of the man.

[1]

(b) The man has a child with a homozygous woman who has blood group **B**.
   (i) Draw a Punnett square to show the possible genotypes for the blood group of the child.

[2]

   (ii) State the probability that the child will have blood type **B**.

[1]

   (iii) State and explain the phenotype of a child who inherits an I^A allele and an I^B allele.

[2]

[Total 6 marks]

Supplement

Variation

You have probably noticed that not all people are identical. There are reasons for this.

Organisms of the **Same Species** Have **Differences**

1) Different species look different — my dog definitely doesn't look like a daisy.

2) But even organisms of the same species usually look at least slightly different — e.g. in a room full of people you'll see different colour hair, individually shaped noses, a variety of heights, etc. This is known as variation.

3) Here's the definition you need to know:

KEY TERM — Variation is the differences between individuals of the same species.

4) Genetic variation is the differences in genotype (the alleles present in an organism — p.129).

5) Phenotypic variation is the differences in phenotype (the characteristics displayed, e.g. hair colour).

6) Genetic variation can cause phenotypic variation.

Supplement

7) An organism's environment (the conditions in which it lives) can also cause phenotypic variation. Most phenotypic variation is determined by a mixture of genetic variation and environmental factors.

Variation can be **Continuous** or **Discontinuous**

Continuous variation is when the individuals in a population have a range of phenotypes which vary between two extremes — there are no distinct categories. E.g. humans can be any height within a range, not just tall or short. Other examples include an organism's mass, and the number of leaves on a tree.

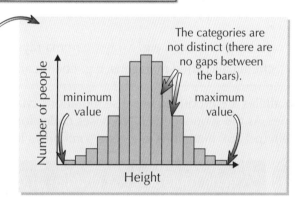

The categories are not distinct (there are no gaps between the bars).

Number of people

minimum value   maximum value

Height

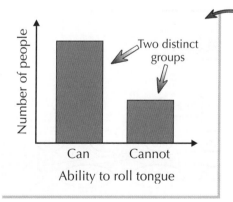

Number of people

Two distinct groups

Can   Cannot

Ability to roll tongue

Discontinuous variation is when there are two or more distinct categories. Each individual falls into only one of these categories, so there is a limited number of phenotypes with no intermediates (nothing in between) — e.g. you either can roll your tongue or you can't.

Discontinuous variation is mostly caused by genes alone. Blood groups in humans are an example of this. Humans can only be blood group A, B, AB or O (see p.133). This is determined by genes and is not affected by environmental factors.

Supplement

Variation is caused by differences in genotype and phenotype

Make sure you properly understand all of the new terms you've come across on this page. It's pretty important stuff, so if you forget what they mean you can always come back to refresh your memory.

Variation

There's more you need to learn about variation I'm afraid — including a practical...

You can **Investigate Variation** in Organisms

An example of a way you can investigate continuous variation is by collecting data on the height of everyone in a group, such as your class. To do this, follow this method:

1) Ask each person to remove their shoes.
2) Use a measuring tape to measure from the top of a person's head to the ground.
3) Record the height of the person using a suitable table (see page 188).
4) Plot your height data against number of people, and compare its shape to the graph on the previous page.

You could investigate discontinuous variation too, e.g. by recording the eye colour of everyone in the group.

Variation Arises Due to **Genetic Mutations**

 KEY TERM — Mutation is genetic change.

1) When mutations occur within a gene they result in a different version of the gene called an allele.
2) By altering genes, mutations can change the genotype and so can also change the phenotype of an organism.
3) Mutations can happen spontaneously, but the rate of mutation is increased by exposing yourself to:

- ionising radiation, e.g. X-rays, gamma rays or ultraviolet rays,
- chemicals called mutagens, e.g. chemicals in tobacco.

4) New alleles are produced because mutations change the sequence of the DNA bases (p.30) in a gene. As the sequence of DNA bases codes for the sequence of amino acids that make up a protein (p.126), mutations to a gene sometimes lead to changes in the protein that it codes for.

 KEY TERM — A gene mutation is a change in the base sequence of DNA.

Sickle-Cell Anaemia is Caused by a **Mutation**

1) Sickle-cell anaemia is a condition where red blood cells become unusually shaped. These cells can get stuck in blood vessels, which stops them delivering oxygen to body cells. Symptoms include tiredness, painful joints and fever.
2) A change in the base sequence of the gene for haemoglobin (p.63) results in abnormal haemoglobin and sickle-shaped red blood cells.
3) Sickle-cell anaemia is caused by inheriting two recessive alleles — Hb^S. The dominant normal allele is Hb^A.
4) If you're a carrier for sickle-cell anaemia (heterozygous Hb^AHb^S) you're less likely to get malaria (you're resistant to it) than if you're unaffected (homozygous for the dominant allele Hb^AHb^A).

carrier Hb^AHb^S — carrier Hb^AHb^S

Hb^A — Hb^S — Hb^A — Hb^S

Hb^AHb^A — Hb^AHb^S — Hb^AHb^S — Hb^SHb^S

unaffected — carrier — carrier — has sickle-cell anaemia

If two people who carry the sickle-cell anaemia allele have children, the probability of each child having the disorder is 1 in 4 — 25% (p.130).

5) So being a carrier is an advantage in places where malaria is common (e.g. parts of Africa). Over time, this advantage has led to an increase in the number of alleles for sickle-cell anaemia (Hb^S) in the population, and therefore an increase in the number of carriers of sickle-cell anaemia.

Supplement

Adaptive Features

It's variation that has allowed life to adapt to so many different environments.

Adaptive Features Allow Organisms to Survive

1) Different organisms are adapted to live in different environmental conditions.

2) The features or characteristics that allow them to do this are called adaptive features.

 KEY TERM — Adaptive features are inherited features that help an organism to survive and reproduce in its environment.

3) Here are some examples of adaptive features:

Arctic animals like the Arctic fox have white fur so they're camouflaged against the snow. This helps them to avoid predators.

Animals that live in cold places (like whales) have a thick layer of blubber (fat) and a small surface area for their size to help them retain heat.

Animals that live in hot places (like camels) have a thin layer of fat to help them lose heat.

4) Adaptive features can also be defined as the inherited functional features of an organism that increase its fitness.

 KEY TERM — Fitness is the probability of an organism surviving and reproducing in the environment in which it is found.

Some Plants are Adapted to Live in Extreme Environments

Xerophytes

- Xerophytes are plants like marram grass (which grows on sand dunes). They're adapted to live in dry climates.

- Marram grass has stomata that are sunk in pits and surrounded by hairs. These slow transpiration (p.55) down because they both trap a layer of humid air close to the leaf's surface.

- Marram grass plants can also roll their leaves to trap humid air.

- Marram grass has a thick, waxy layer on the epidermis to reduce water loss by evaporation.

Look at page 42 again if you need a reminder of a typical leaf structure.

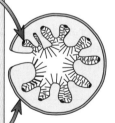

Hydrophytes

- Hydrophytes are plants like water lilies, which are adapted to live in water.

- The leaves contain air spaces, so they can float on the surface of the water and be exposed to the most light.

- Stomata are usually only present on the upper surface of floating leaves. This helps to maximise gas exchange.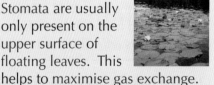

- The stems are flexible to help prevent damage from currents.

Supplement

 EXAM TIP — ## Organisms can adapt to life in a variety of environments

You might be given a picture of an organism in the exam, and asked to suggest what its adaptive features are. Think about things like the type of environment it lives in (e.g. hot or cold, in water or on land) and how it gets its food (e.g. does it need to catch prey or run away from predators).

Natural Selection

Natural selection is all about the organisms with the best characteristics surviving to pass on their alleles.

Natural Selection Means there is a Struggle for Survival

Natural selection results in those organisms that are better adapted to their environment being more likely to survive and reproduce. Here's how it happens:

1) Individuals in a population show genetic variation because of differences in their alleles (see page 135).

2) Some organisms produce many offspring. This means that there aren't enough resources (e.g. food, water, mates, etc.) to support all of the offspring and so there is competition between them.

3) Competition for resources and things like predation and disease affect an organism's chance of surviving and reproducing. There is a 'struggle for survival'.

4) Those individuals with characteristics that make them better adapted to their environment have a better chance of survival and so are more likely to reproduce successfully.

5) This means the alleles that are responsible for beneficial characteristics are more likely to be passed on to the next generation and become more common in the population.

Supplement

Natural Selection Explains how Evolution Occurs

1) Evolution is the change in adaptive features of a population over time as the result of natural selection.

> Imagine that all rabbits used to have short ears and managed ok. Then one day a rabbit was born with big ears who could hear better and so was always the first to hide from predators. Soon the big-eared rabbit had produced a whole family of rabbits with big ears — they all hid from predators before the other rabbits. After more time there were only big-eared rabbits left. The short-eared rabbits couldn't hear the predators coming quick enough.

2) The process of evolution is also known as the process of adaptation.

The process of adaptation is the process, resulting from natural selection, by which populations become more suited to their environment over many generations.

Supplement

Organisms that are better adapted to their environment survive

Natural selection needs variation in a population, competition for resources and a struggle for survival.

Antibiotic Resistance

We can observe the process of evolution by natural selection happening in real-time in bacteria.

Bacteria Provide Evidence for Evolution

1) Like all organisms, bacteria sometimes develop random mutations in their DNA. These can create new alleles, which can change the bacteria's characteristics — e.g. a bacterium could become less affected by a particular antibiotic (a drug designed to kill bacteria or prevent them from reproducing — p.101).

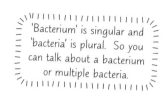
'Bacterium' is singular and 'bacteria' is plural. So you can talk about a bacterium or multiple bacteria.

2) For the bacterium, the ability to resist this antibiotic is a big advantage in the 'struggle for survival'. In a person who's being treated to get rid of the infection, a resistant bacterium is better able to survive than a non-resistant bacterium — and so it lives for longer and reproduces many more times.

3) This leads to the allele for antibiotic resistance being passed on to lots of offspring — it's just natural selection. This is how it spreads and becomes more common in a population of bacteria over time.

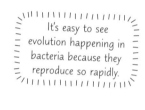
It's easy to see evolution happening in bacteria because they reproduce so rapidly.

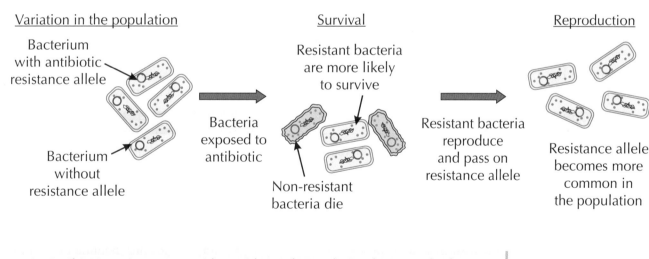

Variation in the population

Bacterium with antibiotic resistance allele

Bacterium without resistance allele

Bacteria exposed to antibiotic

Survival

Resistant bacteria are more likely to survive

Non-resistant bacteria die

Resistant bacteria reproduce and pass on resistance allele

Reproduction

Resistance allele becomes more common in the population

4) Antibiotic resistance provides evidence for evolution by natural selection because it makes the bacteria better adapted to an environment in which antibiotics are present. And as a result, antibiotic resistance becomes more common in the population over time.

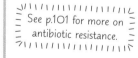
See p.101 for more on antibiotic resistance.

Don't become resistant to revision...

A good way of testing whether you really know something is to try and teach it to someone else. Cover up this page and explain to a friend how strains of antibiotic resistant bacteria evolve through natural selection. You'll soon find out whether you need to do some more revision.

Supplement

Supplement

Selective Breeding

'Selective breeding' sounds like it has the potential to be a tricky topic, but it's actually quite simple. You take the best plants or animals and breed them together to get the best possible offspring. That's it.

Selective Breeding is Very Simple

Selective breeding is when humans artificially select the plants or animals that are going to breed so that the frequency of the alleles for desired characteristics increases in a population. Organisms are selectively bred to develop features that are useful or attractive, for example:

- Animals that produce more meat or milk.
- Crops with disease resistance.
- Dogs that are well-behaved and gentle.
- Decorative plants with big or unusual flowers.

This is the basic process involved in selective breeding:

1) Select the plants or animals which have desirable features.
2) Cross them with each other to produce the next generation.
3) Select the offspring showing the desirable features, and cross them together.
4) Continue this process over several generations, and the desirable feature becomes more and more common. Eventually, all the offspring will have the feature.

Selective breeding is also known as 'artificial selection'.

In agriculture (farming), selective breeding can be used to improve crop plants and farm animals. E.g. to increase the amount of meat produced, a farmer could breed together the cows and bulls with the best characteristics for producing meat, e.g. large size. By repeating this over generations the farmer would get cows that produce lots of meat.

Natural and Artificial Selection are Different

You might be able to think of some obvious differences between natural and artificial selection from what you've already read. But here are some differences that you need to know:

Artificial Selection

- The individuals that reproduce have characteristics that humans think are desirable.
- It's a faster process than natural selection.
- It only happens to the organisms humans choose.
- Artificial selection involves breeding from closely related organisms, which causes inbreeding — this is where variation in a population is reduced and individuals may be more likely to have genetic disorders.
- If a new disease appears, or the environment changes, the chances of survival are lower for the offspring of artificially selected organisms because there's not much variation in the population.

Natural Selection

- The individuals that survive and reproduce have characteristics that suit their environment.
- It's a long and slow process.
- It happens to all wild organisms.
- Individuals are 'healthier' because they are less likely to be inbred.
- The offspring's chances of survival are increased because there's more variation in the population.

Selective breeding is just breeding the best to get the best...

Different breeds of dog came from selective breeding. For example, somebody thought 'I really like this small, yappy wolf — I'll breed it with this other one'. After thousands of generations, we got poodles.

Warm-Up & Exam Questions

That's the end of this section — have a go at these questions to see how much you know.

Warm-Up Questions

1) What is the difference between phenotypic variation and genetic variation?
2) State how new alleles arise in a population.
3) Define the term fitness.
4) Why might it be an advantage to be heterozygous for sickle-cell anaemia?

Exam Questions

1 The penguin shown on the right lives in Antarctica, where the temperature is very cold. It moves between the land and the sea.

Give **one** adaptive feature of the penguin and briefly suggest how it allows it to survive and reproduce in its environment.

[Total 2 marks]

2 The characteristics of two varieties of wheat plants are shown in the table below.

Variety	Grain yield	Resistance to bad weather
Tall stems	High	Low
Dwarf stems	Low	High

Selective breeding is used to create a wheat plant with a high grain yield and high resistance to bad weather. Choose words from the list to complete the sentences about this process. Each word may be used once, more than once or not at all.

increases   tall   lowest   stronger   highest   dwarf   weaker   decreases

A tall stem plant and a .... stem plant could be bred together. The offspring with the

.... grain yield and .... resistance to bad weather could then be bred together.

Repeating this over several generations means the frequency of the desirable features ....

[Total 4 marks]

3 Explain **two** ways in which hydrophytes are adapted to their environment.

[Total 4 marks]

4 The image on the right shows a type of stingray.
The stingray's appearance mimics a flat rock.
It spends most of its time on a rocky sea bed.

Explain how the stingray might have evolved to look like this.

[Total 6 marks]

Supplement

Revision Summary for Sections 13 & 14

So you've finished Sections 13 and 14 — time to do some questions to test your knowledge.
- Try these questions and tick off each one when you get it right.
- When you've done all the questions for a topic and are completely happy with it, tick off the topic.

Chromosomes and Sex Inheritance (p.125) ☑

1) What is a gene? ☑
2) What is an allele? ☑
3) A couple have a child.
   What's the probability that the child will have the XX combination of sex chromosomes? ☑
4) How many pairs of chromosomes are there in a human diploid cell? ☑

Protein Synthesis, Mitosis and Meiosis (p.126-127) ☑

5) Which process takes place in ribosomes?
6) a) Name the type of cell division used in asexual reproduction.
   b) Apart from asexual reproduction, what else is this type of cell division used for? ☑
7) What happens to the chromosomes in a cell before mitosis takes place? ☑
8) State the type of cell division used to make gametes in humans. ☑

Inheritance and Genetic Diagrams (p.129-133) ☑

9) What does it mean if an organism is: a) homozygous for a gene? b) heterozygous for a gene? ☑
10) True or False? "A heterozygous individual will be pure-breeding." ☑
11) Explain how a test cross can be used to identify an unknown genotype. ☑
12) Why are men more likely to show recessive characteristics that are sex-linked? ☑
13) What are co-dominant alleles? ☑
14) What blood group does an individual have if they have the genotype $I^B I^O$? ☑

Variation (p.135-136) ☑

15) What is variation? ☑
16) True or False? Phenotypic variation is caused by environmental factors only. ☑
17) What type of variation results in a range of phenotypes between two extremes? ☑
18) How can the rate of mutation be increased? ☑
19) What are the symptoms of sickle-cell anaemia? ☑
20) Why are there often more people who are heterozygous for sickle-cell anaemia
    in areas where malaria is present than where malaria isn't present? ☑

Adaptive Features, Natural Selection, Evolution and Selective Breeding (p.137-140) ☑

21) How are the adaptive features of an organism linked to its fitness? ☑
22) Describe the process of natural selection. ☑
23) What is the process of adaptation? ☑
24) Describe how bacteria can become resistant to antibiotics. ☑
25) What is selective breeding? ☑
26) How might farmers use selective breeding? ☑
27) State two differences between natural and artificial selection. ☑

Food Chains and Food Webs

Food chains and food webs are a way of representing feeding relationships between organisms.

Food Chains Show the Transfer of Energy Between Organisms

1) Food chains always start with a producer, e.g. a plant. Producers make (produce) their own organic nutrients (food), usually using energy from the Sun during photosynthesis.

2) Energy is then transferred through the ecosystem when organisms are eaten (ingested).

3) Consumers are organisms that get energy by feeding on other organisms. Producers are eaten by primary consumers. Primary consumers are then eaten by secondary consumers and secondary consumers are eaten by tertiary consumers.

4) All these organisms eventually die and get ingested by decomposers, e.g. bacteria. Decomposers get energy by breaking down (decomposing) dead material and waste.

Here's an example of a food chain:

The arrows show the direction of energy flow.

Producers   Primary consumers   Secondary consumer

5000 dandelions... feed... 100 rabbits... which feed... 1 fox.

5) In the food chain above, the rabbits are herbivores — this means they get their energy by eating plants. Carnivores, e.g. foxes, are animals that get their energy by eating other animals.

6) You may be asked to construct a simple food chain in your exam or to interpret a food chain or food web (see below).

A Food Web is a Network of Interconnected Food Chains

1) There are many different species within an environment — which means lots of different possible food chains that are all interconnected. You can draw a food web to show this. For example:

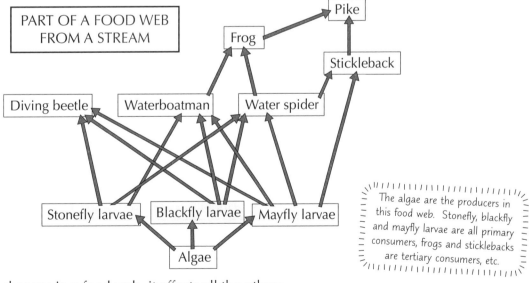

PART OF A FOOD WEB FROM A STREAM

Pike
Frog
Stickleback
Diving beetle
Waterboatman
Water spider
Stonefly larvae
Blackfly larvae
Mayfly larvae
Algae

The algae are the producers in this food web. Stonefly, blackfly and mayfly larvae are all primary consumers, frogs and sticklebacks are tertiary consumers, etc.

2) If one species changes in a food web, it affects all the others.
In the food web above, if lots of water spiders died, then:

- There would be less food for the frogs, so their numbers might decrease.
- The number of mayfly larvae might increase since the water spiders wouldn't be eating them.
- The diving beetles wouldn't be competing with the water spiders for food, so their numbers might increase.

Pyramids of Numbers and Biomass

Food chains can be represented visually with either a pyramid of numbers or a pyramid of biomass.

You Need to Understand **Pyramids of Numbers**

Here's a pyramid of numbers for the dandelions, rabbits and fox food chain on the previous page.

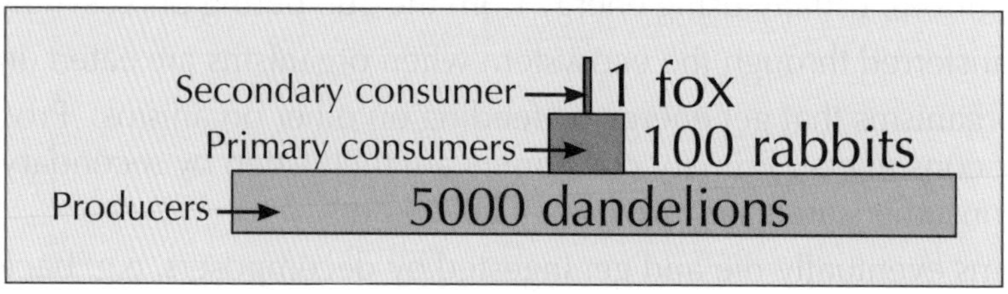

1) Each bar on a pyramid of numbers shows the number of organisms at that stage of the food chain.
2) So the 'dandelions' bar on this pyramid would need to be longer than the 'rabbits' bar, which in turn should be longer than the 'fox' bar.
3) Dandelions go at the bottom because they're at the bottom of the food chain.
4) This is a typical pyramid of numbers, where every time you go up a level, the number of organisms goes down. This is because it takes a lot of food from the level below to keep one animal alive.

Pyramids of **Biomass** Show the **Relative Masses** of **Trophic Levels**

Supplement

KEY TERM

A trophic level is the position of an organism in a food chain, food web, pyramid of numbers or pyramid of biomass.

Biomass is the mass of living material — it's a store of energy.

In the food chain above, there could be 500 fleas feeding on the fox, which would mean the number of organisms increases when you move up to the next trophic level. This doesn't represent the food chain very well though, because the amount of energy transferred between trophic levels always decreases as you move up to the next trophic level (see p.146). So a better way to look at the food chain is often to think about biomass instead of number of organisms.

1) Each bar on a pyramid of biomass shows the relative mass of living material at a trophic level — basically how much all the organisms at each level would "weigh" if you put them all together.
2) So the one fox above would have a big biomass and the hundreds of fleas would have a very small biomass. Biomass pyramids are practically always pyramid-shaped:

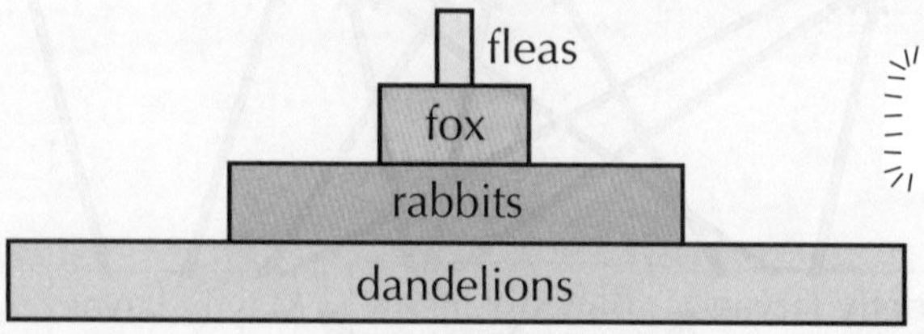

Biomass and energy are lost at each trophic level.

3) The big bar along the bottom of the pyramid shows trophic level 1. It always represents the producer (e.g. plants or algae).
4) The next bar will be the primary consumer (trophic level 2), then the secondary consumer (trophic level 3) and so on up the food chain.

Pyramids of biomass are nearly always pyramid-shaped

There are actually a couple of exceptions where pyramids of biomass aren't quite pyramid-shaped, e.g. when the producer has a very short life but reproduces a lot, like with plankton at certain times of year.

More on Pyramids

A bit more on interpreting pyramids of biomass next, plus how you can draw pyramids of numbers or biomass accurately for yourself, if given the right information.

Pyramids of Biomass Give You Information About Food Chains

It's easy to look at pyramids of biomass and explain what they show about the food chain — just remember, the biomass at each stage should be drawn to scale. For example:

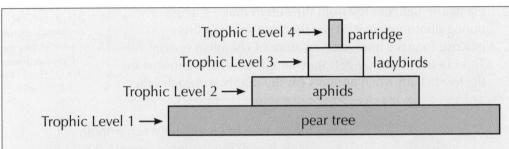

1) Even if you know nothing about the natural world, you're probably aware that a tree is quite a bit bigger than an aphid.

2) So what's going on here is that lots (probably thousands) of aphids are feeding on one great big tree.

3) Quite a lot of ladybirds are then eating the aphids, and a few partridges are eating the ladybirds.

4) Biomass decreases every time you go up a trophic level — but a pyramid of numbers for this food chain would show the number of organisms increasing between trophic levels 1 and 2, and then decreasing again up to trophic level 4.

Make Sure You Can Draw Pyramids of Numbers or Biomass

1) If you're given actual numbers, you can use them to draw bars of the correct scale.

If you're studying the Core course, you only need to be able to draw pyramids of numbers.

2) Don't forget that the order of organisms in the pyramid must follow the order of the food chain (starting with the producer).

3) Each bar must also be labelled.

EXAM TIP

Use a sharp pencil and a ruler to draw pyramids

If you need to draw a pyramid of numbers or biomass to scale in the exam, you may be given a grid or graph paper to draw it on. You'll need to work out a sensible scale to use — think about how easy your diagram will be to draw and interpret (something like '5 small squares on the grid = 1 kg' might work) and make sure that your pyramid takes up at least half of the space available.

Supplement

Energy Flow

Some organisms get their energy from the Sun and some get it from other organisms.

Energy is Transferred Along a Food Chain

1) The Sun is the source of energy for nearly all life on Earth.

2) Plants use light energy from the Sun to make glucose during photosynthesis. They then use some of this glucose to make biomass — a store of chemical energy. This chemical energy gets transferred to other organisms in the food chain when animals eat the plants and each other.

Animals also use some of their food to produce biomass.

3) The transfer of energy between trophic levels is very inefficient — around 90% of the energy is lost in various ways.

Material and energy are both lost at each stage of the food chain.

4) Some parts of food, e.g. roots or bones, aren't eaten by organisms so the energy isn't taken in. Some parts of food are indigestible (e.g. fibre) so pass through organisms and come out as waste, e.g. faeces.

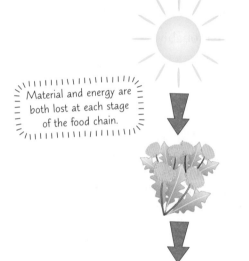

ENERGY LOST AS HEAT

MATERIALS LOST IN ANIMALS' WASTE

5) A lot of the energy that does get taken in is used for staying alive, i.e. in respiration (see page 78), which powers all life processes.

6) Most of this energy is eventually lost to the atmosphere as heat.

7) Only around 10% of the total energy available becomes biomass, i.e. it's stored or used for growth.

8) This is the energy that's transferred from one trophic level to the next.

9) This explains why you hardly ever get food chains with more than about five trophic levels. So much energy is lost at each stage that there's not enough left to support more organisms after four or five stages. You also tend to get fewer organisms at each trophic level (although this isn't always the case).

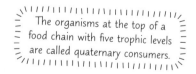
The organisms at the top of a food chain with five trophic levels are called quaternary consumers.

Food chains rely on the Sun for energy

Most of the energy from the producers doesn't make it up to the top of the food chain. If you're doing the Extended course, you need to make sure you know the different reasons why energy is lost.

Supplement

Humans and Food Webs

Looking at food chains and food webs can help us to understand how human activities affect habitats.

Humans Impact Food Webs Through Over-Harvesting

1) Over-harvesting is when people take so much of an organism that its population is unable to reproduce quickly enough to keep up, and the population size falls. Eventually, this can lead to extinction.

2) When one species is over-harvested, the other species connected to it in the food web are all affected.

> Overfishing is a type of over-harvesting. For example, there used to be a lot of cod in the Grand Banks area of the Atlantic Ocean, but their numbers had dropped significantly by the 1990s due to overfishing. Cod are consumers in several different food chains, so the disappearance of so many led to a huge increase in the populations of species that the cod used to feed on, such as shrimp and crab.

Introducing Foreign Species to a Habitat Affects Food Webs

1) A foreign species is one that doesn't naturally occur in an area. They can be introduced intentionally (e.g. for food or hunting) or unintentionally (e.g. accidentally on a ship).

2) Introducing a foreign species to a food web may affect the populations already in the habitat. E.g.:

| Cane toads were introduced to Australia in the 1930s, to eat beetles that were damaging crops. | ⟹ | Water monitors (a type of lizard in Australia) ate the cane toads. They were poisoned by chemicals in the toads and died. | ⟹ | The water monitor population fell, which led to an increase in the crimson finch population, as fewer of them were eaten by water monitors. |

Plants are a More Efficient Source of Human Food than Animals

1) Because energy is lost at each trophic level in a food chain (see previous page), it is more efficient for humans to eat plants than to eat animals.

2) For example, if you were to eat meat from a pig that had been fed on vegetables, you would be higher up the food chain than if you were eating the vegetables themselves. This means that less of the energy originally in the vegetable plants would reach you, because there would be an extra trophic level between you and the plants (in which energy is lost):

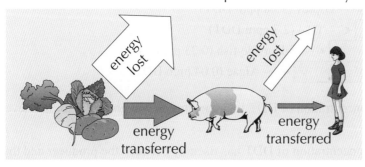

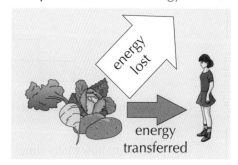

3) So, farming crops to directly feed humans is a lot more efficient than farming crops to feed livestock (farm animals) that are then used to feed humans.

The whole food web can be affected when a species is added or lost

As well as being at the top of many food chains, humans have disturbed natural food webs in a number of ways — e.g. through farming, fishing, and introducing species to areas where they didn't previously exist.

Warm-Up & Exam Questions

Right, now you've got to grips with how energy is transferred through a food chain, have a go at these practice questions. If there's anything you're struggling with, go back and read that bit again.

Warm-Up Questions

1) What is the word for an organism that makes its own organic nutrients?
2) What is meant by the term herbivore? What is a carnivore?
3) What is a trophic level?
4) Why do you hardly ever get food chains with more than five trophic levels?

Exam Questions

1 The diagram shows part of a food web from Nebraska, USA. The flowerhead weevil is not native to this area. It was introduced by farmers to eat the musk thistle, which is a weed.

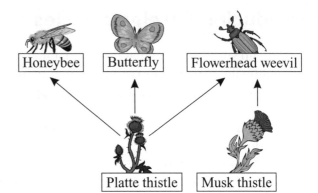

(a) Explain how the introduction of the flowerhead weevil could affect the amount of wild honey produced in the area.

[2]

(b) When the organisms in the food web above die, they are broken down by microorganisms. What name is given to the organisms that break down dead material?

[1]

[Total 3 marks]

2 In the 1950s a chemical called DDT was used to control insect pests. DDT was later discovered to be toxic to other animals and was detected at very high levels in the tissues of organisms across food chains. The pyramid of biomass below shows the concentration of DDT in the tissues of organisms at each trophic level in parts per million (ppm).

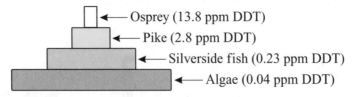

Osprey (13.8 ppm DDT)
Pike (2.8 ppm DDT)
Silverside fish (0.23 ppm DDT)
Algae (0.04 ppm DDT)

(a) Describe what happens to the concentration of DDT in organisms as you go up the trophic levels.

[1]

(b) Calculate how many times the concentration of DDT has risen by between the producer and the tertiary consumer. Show your working.

[2]

(c) Suggest why a pyramid of biomass is a suitable diagram for displaying the problem with DDT.

[1]

[Total 4 marks]

The Carbon Cycle

All the nutrients in our environment are constantly being recycled — it's all about balance.

Materials are Constantly Recycled in an Ecosystem

1) Living things are made of materials they take from the world around them. E.g. plants turn elements like carbon, oxygen, hydrogen and nitrogen from the soil and the air into the complex compounds (carbohydrates, proteins and fats) that make up living organisms. These get passed up the food chain.

2) These materials are returned to the environment in waste products, or when the organisms die.

3) Dead or waste organic material is broken down (decomposed) — usually by microorganisms.

4) Decomposition puts the stuff that plants need to grow (e.g. mineral ions) back into the soil.

The Constant Cycling of Carbon is called the Carbon Cycle

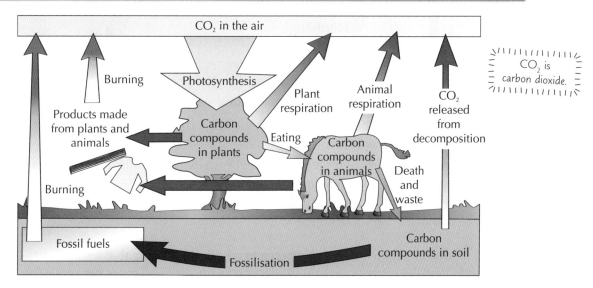

That can look a bit complicated at first, but it's actually pretty simple:

1) CO_2 is removed from the atmosphere by green plants and algae during photosynthesis. The carbon is used to make glucose, which can be turned into carbohydrates, fats and proteins that make up the bodies of the plants and algae.

2) When the plants and algae respire, some carbon is returned to the atmosphere as CO_2.

3) When the plants and algae are eaten by animals, some carbon becomes part of the fats and proteins in their bodies. The carbon then moves through the food chain.

4) When the animals respire, some carbon is returned to the atmosphere as CO_2.

5) When plants, algae and animals die, decomposers feed on their remains. Decomposers can be types of animal (detritus feeders) or microorganisms. When these organisms respire, CO_2 is returned to the atmosphere.

6) Animals also produce waste that is broken down by decomposers.

7) Not all dead organic material decomposes — some dead organisms have been compressed over millions of years, forming fossil fuels (coal, oil and natural gas).

8) The combustion (burning) of wood and fossil fuels also releases CO_2 back into the air.

9) So the carbon (and energy) is constantly being cycled — from the air, through food chains (via plants, algae and animals, and decomposers) and eventually back out into the air again.

The Nitrogen Cycle

Nitrogen, just like carbon, is constantly being recycled. So the nitrogen in your proteins might once have been in the air. And before that it might have been in a plant. Or even in some horse wee. Nice.

Nitrogen is Recycled in the Nitrogen Cycle

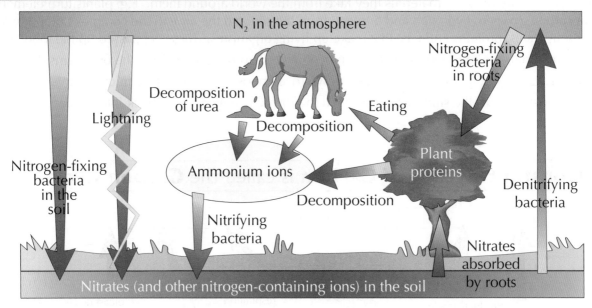

1) The atmosphere contains about 78% nitrogen gas, N_2. This is very unreactive and so it can't be used directly by plants or animals.

2) Nitrogen is needed for making proteins for growth, so living organisms have to get it somehow.

3) Nitrogen in the air has to be turned into mineral ions, such as nitrate ions (NO_3^-), in the soil before plants can use it. This happens through a process called nitrogen fixation — there are two main ways it occurs:

 a) LIGHTNING — there's so much energy in a bolt of lightning that it's enough to make nitrogen react with oxygen in the air to give nitrates.

 b) NITROGEN-FIXING BACTERIA in soil and the roots of some plants (see below).

Compounds containing nitrate ions are called nitrates.

4) Plants absorb these ions from the soil and use the nitrogen in them to produce amino acids, which join together to make proteins.

5) Nitrogen is then passed along food chains in the form of proteins, as animals eat plants (and each other). When the proteins are digested, they are converted back into amino acids (see p.49).

6) In animals, excess amino acids are broken down in the liver in a process called deamination. Ammonia (a nitrogen compound, NH_3) is a waste product from this process, which gets converted to urea and excreted. The urea is then decomposed and nitrogen ions are eventually returned to the soil.

7) There are four different types of microorganisms involved in the nitrogen cycle:

 a) DECOMPOSERS — break down proteins (in rotting plants and animals) and urea (in animal waste) and turn them into ammonia. This forms ammonium ions (NH_4^+) in the soil.

 b) NITRIFYING BACTERIA — turn ammonium ions in decaying matter into nitrite ions (NO_2^-) and then nitrates. This process is called nitrification.

 c) NITROGEN-FIXING BACTERIA — turn atmospheric N_2 into nitrogen compounds that plants can use (e.g. ammonia).

 d) DENITRIFYING BACTERIA — turn nitrates back into N_2 gas (denitrification). This is of no benefit to living organisms.

When ammonia is dissolved in water, ammonium ions are formed.

Most of these bacteria live in the soil. Some nitrogen-fixing bacteria live in nodules (swellings) on plant roots.

Supplement

The Water Cycle

The amount of water on Earth is pretty much constant — but where it is changes.
Water moves between rivers, lakes, oceans and the atmosphere in what's known as the water cycle.

The **Water Cycle** Means Water is **Endlessly Recycled**

The water here on planet Earth is constantly recycled.
There are four key steps you should understand:

As warm water vapour rises
it cools down and forms clouds.

1) Energy from the Sun makes water evaporate from the land and sea, turning it into water vapour. Water also evaporates from plants — this is known as transpiration (see p.55).

2) The warm water vapour is carried upwards (as warm air rises). When it gets higher up it cools and condenses to form clouds.

3) Water falls from the clouds as precipitation (usually rain, but sometimes snow or hail) onto land, where it provides fresh water for plants and animals.

4) It then drains into the sea, before the whole process starts again.

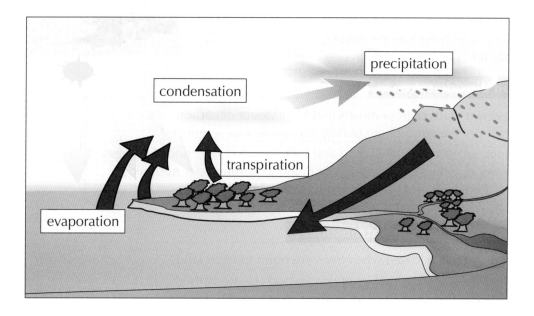

Evaporation, transpiration, condensation, precipitation

The water cycle is really easy — there are four main stages and they're all pretty straightforward.
So there's absolutely no excuse not to learn it inside out. The most important thing to remember
is that it's a cycle — try copying out the diagram and seeing if you can remember all the labels.

Fossil Fuels and Deforestation

Human activities are increasing the amount of carbon dioxide in the atmosphere. This page covers two of the main ways this is happening — the combustion of fossil fuels and the cutting down of forests.

Burning Fossil Fuels Releases Carbon Dioxide

1) Fossil fuels are fuels that have formed over millions of years from the remains of dead organisms (see p.149). Coal, oil and natural gas are all types of fossil fuel.

2) When fossil fuels are burnt, they release lots of carbon dioxide. During the last century, humans have been releasing increasing levels of carbon dioxide through the burning of fossil fuels, e.g.:

> 1) Fossil fuels are burnt in power stations — they are the major source of electricity for most of the world.
>
> 2) We also rely on them for transport — most cars, lorries, ships and planes run on fossil fuels.

3) Carbon dioxide is a greenhouse gas. Greenhouse gases trap energy in the atmosphere, helping to keep the Earth warm. But increasing levels of greenhouse gases are causing the global temperature to rise. This is global warming. (See p.172 for more on the greenhouse effect.)

Deforestation Means Chopping Down Trees

1) Deforestation is the cutting down of forests.

2) This causes big problems when it's done on a large-scale, such as cutting down rainforests in tropical areas.

3) It's done for various reasons, e.g. to clear land for growing crops for food or biofuels.

4) Deforestation affects the carbon dioxide concentration of the atmosphere in two ways:

Less carbon dioxide taken in

1) Cutting down loads of trees means that the amount of carbon dioxide removed from the atmosphere during photosynthesis is reduced.

2) Trees 'lock up' some of the carbon that they absorb during photosynthesis in their wood, which can remove it from the atmosphere for hundreds of years. Removing trees means that less is locked up.

More carbon dioxide in the atmosphere

1) Carbon dioxide is released when trees are burnt to clear land.

2) Microorganisms feeding on bits of dead wood release carbon dioxide as a waste product of respiration.

3) Carbon in wood doesn't contribute to atmospheric pollution until the wood is burnt or decomposed.

Not a very cheerful page, I know...

There's a general agreement among scientists that human activities are increasing the carbon dioxide concentration in the atmosphere, and that this is contributing to climate change (p.172).

Warm-Up & Exam Questions

You can't just stare at these pages and expect it all to go in. Have a go at these questions to see how well you really know the three cycles, and how humans are affecting the atmospheric CO_2 concentration.

Warm-Up Questions

1) Describe the role of lightning in the nitrogen cycle.
2) Describe the effect of decomposers on proteins in dead plant and animal matter.
3) Describe how water vapour forms clouds.
4) Give one way that deforestation contributes to an increase in the level of atmospheric carbon dioxide.

Exam Questions

1 Carbon is constantly being recycled. The diagram below shows some of the processes occurring in the carbon cycle.

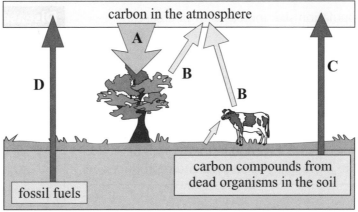

(a) (i) Name the process, labelled **A**, that removes carbon from the atmosphere.

[1]

(ii) Name the gas in which carbon is removed from the atmosphere by process **A**.

[1]

(b) Name the process, labelled **B**, by which all living organisms return carbon to the atmosphere.

[1]

(c) Explain how carbon is released from dead organisms in the soil (process **C**).

[2]

(d) (i) Explain why fossil fuels contain carbon.

[1]

(ii) Describe how the carbon from fossil fuels is released back into the atmosphere (process **D**).

[1]

[Total 7 marks]

2 Several different types of bacteria are involved in the nitrogen cycle. Which bacteria convert nitrogen in the atmosphere into nitrogen compounds that plants can use?

☐ **A** nitrifying   ☐ **B** denitrifying   ☐ **C** nitrogen-fixing   ☐ **D** decomposers

[Total 1 mark]

Population Sizes

Over time, the sizes of populations might increase, decrease, or remain stable —
there are various reasons why.

Here are Some **Terms** You Need to **Know**

Term	Definition
Population	A group of organisms of one species living in the same area at the same time.
Community	All the populations of different species living in an ecosystem.
Ecosystem	A unit containing the community of organisms and its environment, interacting together.

(Supplement)

Ecosystems can be a range of sizes, e.g. a decomposing log or a whole lake.

Population Growth Rate is Affected by Several Factors

The rate at which population size increases or decreases
depends on various factors, including:

Food supply

1) If more food is available, a population is likely to grow.
2) E.g. during a year when plants produce an usually high number of berries, the population of blackbirds might increase because there'll be enough food for all of them, so they're more likely to survive and reproduce.

Disease

1) The presence of pathogens (disease-causing organisms — see p.69) in the environment affects a population's growth rate.
2) E.g. if a new pathogen is introduced then a population may decrease in size due to illness.

Predation

1) Consumers that hunt and kill other animals are called predators. Their prey are what they eat.
2) If the population of prey increases, then so will the population of predators. For example, if the number of gazelles (prey) increases then the number of lions (predators) will also increase because there are more gazelles available to be eaten by the lions.
3) As the predator population increases, the number of prey will decrease. E.g. more lions will eat more gazelles, causing the gazelle population to decrease.
4) It takes time for one population to respond to changes in the other population, so predator-prey cycles are always out of phase with each other.
5) Population sizes often start to increase slowly. The rate of increase then gets faster as the number of organisms reproducing increases.

Population

A peak in prey numbers is followed by a peak in predator numbers.

Prey

Predator

Time

6) If the predator population was removed, the population size of the prey would increase until the number of prey reached the maximum the environment could support. The prey population would then level off or start to decrease.

A population's size is influenced by the rest of the ecosystem

When organisms share the same habitat, different species are often dependent on each other. When the
size of one population changes, the growth rates of other populations in the area are likely to be affected.

The Human Population

The number of people living on planet Earth has been growing for a long time, but in the last 250 years, the rate of growth has really sped up. This has some major implications for society and the environment.

The **Human Population** is **Growing**

1) Over the last 250 years, the size of the human population has increased rapidly, and it is continuing to rise.

2) In 1800, there were around 1 billion humans on Earth. Now, there are over 7.5 billion.

3) This is mostly due to modern medicine and farming methods, which have reduced the number of people dying from disease and hunger.

4) The 20th century had the fastest rate of population increase, especially in the 1960s. Population growth has slowed down slightly, but shows no signs of stabilising.

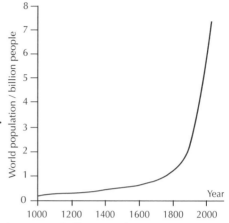

5) It has been predicted that the human population will reach almost 10 billion in the next 50 years.

Human Population Growth has a Big **Impact** on the **Environment**

- As the population increases, more resources need to be taken from the environment for people to survive, e.g. for food, fuel and building materials.

- Many raw materials are being used up quicker than they're being replaced. So if we carry on like we are, one day we're going to run out.

- Taking resources often involves major damage to the environment. E.g. chopping down forests for wood, drilling in the Arctic for oil.

- As humans make more things, we produce more waste. Unless this waste is properly handled, it will cause more harmful pollution.

- Pollution affects water, land and air (p.170-172), and kills plants and animals.

An increasing number of people means more land is needed for building, farming, etc. so more of the planet's natural environment is being destroyed to make space.

The Population Increase also has **Social Implications**

1) Rapid population growth has some serious implications for human health, for example:

- Overcrowding is becoming more common — when many people are living in the same small space, diseases are much more likely to spread.

- More pollution means more health problems, e.g. air pollution can cause heart disease, lung cancer and respiratory infections.

- It is going to get increasingly difficult to produce enough food and transport it to the people who need it, so there will be more health problems caused by lack of nutrition.

2) Another social implication of population growth is an increase in conflict — as natural resources (e.g. oil) get used up, countries are more likely to fight over them, and there may be more tension within countries as it gets harder to ensure everyone has fair access to water, etc.

The human population was small for thousands of years

Humans existed for around 200 000 years before the population size reached one billion. It only took 200 more years to get to 7 billion. In the context of the whole of human history, that's hardly any time at all.

Population Growth

Populations don't just grow at the same rate over time — their growth tends to follow a standard pattern.

Learn the **Phases** of the **Sigmoid Population Growth Curve**

1) If a population were to have an unlimited supply of the resources it needs (e.g. water, nutrients) then it would grow exponentially (more and more rapidly).

2) However, populations usually exist in an environment with limited resources, where population growth tends to take the shape of a sigmoid curve ('sigmoid' means 's'-shaped).

3) There are four phases to the curve:

Lag phase
- At the beginning, there are just a few individuals, so the rate of reproduction is low.
- The population size is increasing slowly.

Exponential (log) phase
- There is an increasing number of individuals reproducing, so the population size increases more and more quickly.
- There are plenty of resources available for the number of individuals. The population is able to rapidly reproduce, as the environment has enough resources to support more individuals.

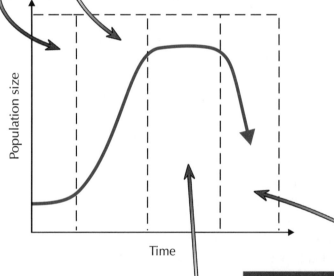

Stationary phase
- Eventually, the population size levels off and stays fairly stable (birth and death rates are in equilibrium).
- Limiting factors are factors that prevent the population size from increasing during this stage. E.g. the environment might only have enough shelter, food or water to support a certain number of individuals. Once this limit is reached, the population size stabilises.
- The population has reached the carrying capacity (the maximum population size that the environment can support).

Death phase
- Some populations have a phase where the rate at which individuals are dying is faster than the reproductive rate, and the population size drops.
- This might happen because the population has used up so many of the resources that the environment can no longer support it.

The population growth curve levels off due to limiting factors

Don't get put off if you get a population graph in the exam and it doesn't match this exactly. The stationary phase is usually actually quite a wobbly line, as the population rises slightly above and below a certain level — just look for part of the graph where there's no overall growth or decline.

Warm-Up & Exam Questions

You know what happens now — test yourself with these questions to see if you've learnt what was covered over the last few pages. If you struggle with anything, go back to that page and have another read.

Warm-Up Questions

1) What is a population?
2) What is an ecosystem?
3) Describe how the human population size has changed in the last 250 years.
4) What is happening in the lag phase of a sigmoid population growth curve?

Exam Questions

1 Walruses are a predator of clams. Which **one** of the following statements describes how the population sizes of walruses and clams are likely to be related to one another?

   ☐ **A** If the walrus population increases, the clam population will then increase.

   ☐ **B** If the walrus population decreases, the clam population will then decrease.

   ☐ **C** If the clam population increases, the walrus population will then increase.

   ☐ **D** If the clam population decreases, the walrus population will then increase.

   [Total 1 mark]

2 Give **two** social implications of rapid human population growth.

   [Total 2 marks]

3 The graph below shows how the size of a population of microorganisms changed over time.

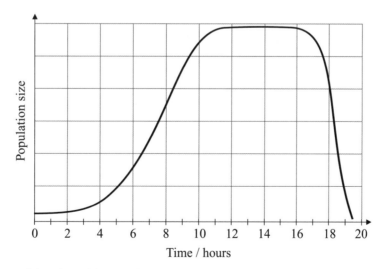

   (a) Which phase of the sigmoid growth curve was the population in at 7 hours?

   [1]

   (b) Suggest why the rate of population change at 12 hours was different to at 7 hours.

   [2]

   [Total 3 marks]

Supplement

Genetic Engineering

Genetic engineering is a relatively new area of science (well, it began in the 1970s). We've already put the technology to good use and it has many more exciting possibilities too...

Genetic Engineering is Used to Transfer Genes

KEY TERM — Genetic engineering is the changing of an organism's genetic material by removing, changing or inserting individual genes.

Genetic engineering allows us to transfer a gene responsible for a desirable characteristic from one organism into another organism, so that it also has the desirable characteristic.

Bacteria can be Engineered to Produce Human Insulin

Bacteria can be genetically engineered to produce human proteins. For example, insulin can be made by inserting the human insulin gene into bacteria. Here's how:

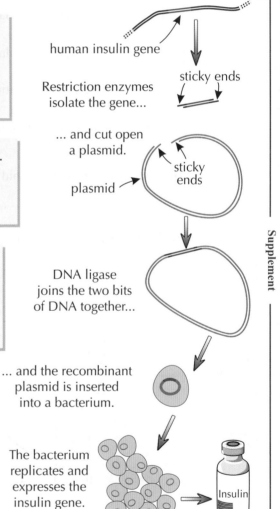

human insulin gene

Restriction enzymes isolate the gene...

sticky ends

... and cut open a plasmid.

plasmid →   sticky ends

DNA ligase joins the two bits of DNA together...

... and the recombinant plasmid is inserted into a bacterium.

The bacterium replicates and expresses the insulin gene.

Insulin

1) The DNA making up the human insulin gene is isolated using a restriction enzyme. Restriction enzymes recognise specific sequences of DNA and cut the DNA at these points. The cut leaves one of the DNA strands with unpaired bases — these are called 'sticky ends'.

2) A plasmid (a loop of DNA) is removed from a bacterium. The plasmid is cut open using the same restriction enzyme that was used to isolate the human insulin gene — leaving complementary (matching) sticky ends.

3) The human insulin gene is inserted into the bacterial plasmid DNA by mixing them together with DNA ligase (an enzyme). This joins the sticky ends together to produce a recombinant plasmid (a plasmid made of two different bits of DNA stuck together).

4) The recombinant plasmid is inserted into a bacterium.

5) The modified bacterium replicates, leading to millions of bacteria that express the human insulin gene and so produce insulin. The insulin can be harvested and purified to treat people with diabetes.

Supplement

It looks hard, but it's just like a fancy cut and paste...

Bacteria aren't the only organisms that can be genetically engineered for human benefit (there are more examples coming up on the next page) but the process can be a bit more complicated in larger organisms.

Genetic Engineering

You need to know about some more examples of genetic engineering.

Bacteria are Really Useful for Genetic Engineering

Bacteria are useful for genetic engineering and biotechnology (see pages 160-162) for several reasons:

1) They reproduce very quickly in the right conditions.

2) They are able to produce complex molecules (such as insulin, see previous page).

Supplement
3) There aren't really any ethical concerns over the engineering and growth of bacteria. (Some people don't agree with the modification of animals and plants.)

4) The genetic code in bacteria is the same as that in other organisms, so bacteria are able to make proteins even though the genes that code for them come from other organisms.

5) Bacteria have plasmids — small rings of DNA that are easy to modify and transfer between cells.

Crops can be Genetically Engineered Too

1) Crops can be made herbicide-resistant by inserting herbicide resistance genes. This means farmers can spray areas where crops are grown to kill weeds, without affecting the crop itself.

> One type of soya has been genetically engineered to be resistant to a herbicide called glyphosate.

2) Crops can be made insect-resistant by inserting insect resistance genes. This improves crop yield, because less of the crop is eaten by insects.

> One type of maize has been genetically engineered to be resistant to the larvae of certain moths, which normally eat the crop.

Insect resistance also means farmers don't have to spray as many pesticides (see page 167) — so wildlife that doesn't eat the crop isn't harmed.

3) Crops can be genetically engineered by inserting genes to provide additional vitamins.

> 'Golden Rice' has been made to produce a chemical that's converted in the body to vitamin A.

Supplement

Genetically Engineering Crops has Advantages and Disadvantages

Crops such as soya, maize and rice can all be genetically modified to produce crops that have different characteristics. There are advantages and disadvantages to this:

- Herbicide- and insect-resistant crops have improved yields. Crops can also be engineered to grow in poor conditions, which also improves yield.
- Crops with additional nutritional value could be valuable in places where there isn't enough food to eat or where the diet is not sufficiently varied.

- There is a concern that transplanted genes may be passed on to other organisms, e.g. weeds may become herbicide-resistant.
- Changing an organism's genes could also create unforeseen problems that get passed on to the organisms' offspring.
- Some people are worried that genetically engineered crops might affect food chains and human health.
- Crops could become more expensive.

Supplement

Genetic engineering has huge potential benefits...

Scientists have used genetic engineering to produce organisms that benefit humans in all sorts of ways — but, as with any new technology, we need to be aware of the risks that it carries too.

Biotechnology

Biotechnology is where living things and biological processes are manipulated to produce a useful product. Using yeast to make bread is an example of biotechnology, so put your apron on and read on.

We Use **Yeast** for **Making Bread**

1) Yeast is a fungus that respires both aerobically and anaerobically (see p.78-79) to produce CO_2.
2) It's used in baking, where it's mixed into dough to create bubbles of CO_2 that make the dough rise.

1) A bread dough is made by mixing yeast (e.g. *S. cerevisiae*) with flour, water and a bit of sugar.

2) The dough is then left in a warm place to rise — this happens with the help of the yeast.

3) Enzymes break down the carbohydrates in the flour into sugars.

4) The yeast then uses these sugars in aerobic respiration, producing carbon dioxide.

5) When the oxygen runs out, the yeast switches to anaerobic respiration. This is also known as fermentation, and it produces carbon dioxide and alcohol (ethanol).

6) The carbon dioxide produced is trapped in bubbles in the dough.

7) These pockets of gas expand, and the dough begins to rise.

8) The dough is then baked in an oven, where the yeast continues to ferment until the temperature of the dough rises enough to kill the yeast. Any alcohol produced during anaerobic respiration is boiled away.

9) As the yeast dies, the bread stops rising, but pockets are left in the bread where the carbon dioxide was trapped.

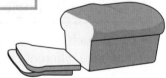

We Also Use **Yeast** to Make **Biofuels**

1) Biofuels are fuels made from living material (biomass). Bioethanol is one of the most common biofuels.
2) The biomass is processed (e.g. using enzymes) to break down large carbohydrates into sugars.
3) Yeast then breaks down these sugars to produce ethanol during anaerobic respiration.
4) This is carried out on a large scale in vessels called fermenters (see p.162). The ethanol produced can be collected, purified and used as a biofuel.

Respiration in yeast produces carbon dioxide, making bread rise

You might not have thought there was much of an overlap between baking and biology, but you thought wrong. Understanding how yeast works has allowed humans to make bread for thousands of years.

Uses of Biotechnology

As you saw on p.31, enzymes are important molecules in living organisms. Here are some more of their uses.

Pectinase is Used in Fruit Juice Production

1) Pectin is a carbohydrate found in plant cell walls.
2) Pectinase is an enzyme that breaks down pectin. It is produced by bacteria and fungi to speed up fruit and vegetable decomposition.
3) Fruit juice manufacturers use pectinase to break down fruit so that juice can be extracted more easily.
4) You can investigate the effect of pectinase on fruit juice production:

- Chop two pears into equal-sized cubes and place 100 g of each in two separate beakers.
- Add 5 cm³ of pectinase solution to one of the beakers, and 5 cm³ of water to the other beaker.
- Place the beakers in a water bath at 45 °C for 30 minutes.
- Remove the beakers from the water bath and measure the volume of the liquid in each beaker.

5) The beaker with the pectinase will have a greater volume of liquid. This is because the pectinase breaks down the cell walls, releasing more juice from the fruit.

Biological Washing Powders Contain Enzymes

1) Biological washing powders contain enzymes to break down and remove stains from clothes.
2) A few different enzymes are used. For example, lipases digest fat stains, amylases digest carbohydrate-based stains and proteases digest protein-based stains.

There's more about these enzymes on page 49.

3) Because they contain enzymes, biological washing powders are more effective at low temperatures (e.g. 30 °C) than other types of washing powders.
4) You can investigate the effectiveness of biological versus non-biological washing powders at 30 °C:

- Prepare stained samples of fabric with, for example, ketchup, juice or gravy.
- Prepare dilute solutions of biological and non-biological washing powders in separate beakers.
- Add a fabric sample to each beaker and place them in a water bath at 30 °C for an hour.
- Remove and rinse the fabric samples, and leave them to dry. Assess the stain removal.

5) The fabric sample that was in the solution of biological washing powder is likely to look cleaner than the sample in the solution of non-biological washing powder. You could carry out the same experiment at different temperatures to investigate the effect of temperature on enzyme activity.

Lactase is Used in the Production of Lactose-Free Milk

1) Lactose is a sugar that is found in milk. Some people are lactose intolerant — they cannot digest lactose because they don't produce the enzyme lactase.
2) Lactase breaks lactose down into glucose and galactose. It can be used to make lactose-free milk.
3) You can investigate the use of lactase in producing lactose-free milk:

- Take two beakers and add 10 cm³ of milk to each. To one, add 1 cm³ of lactase solution.
- Let both beakers stand for a minute before testing both samples using glucose test strips — these strips change colour in the presence of glucose.

4) The beaker that contains lactase will have a positive result for glucose, as the lactose in the milk has been broken down into glucose (and galactose). The beaker without lactase will have a negative result for glucose, because the lactose has not been broken down.

Supplement

More Uses of Biotechnology

In industry, if you want to grow lots of microorganisms, it's best to use a big vessel called a fermenter. Here's a page all about penicillin and how it is made on a huge scale.

A **Fungus** Called *Penicillium* Produces **Penicillin**

1) Penicillin is one of the most common antibiotics (see p.101) used in medicine.
2) It is produced by fungi from the *Penicillium* genus.
3) The fungus is grown on a huge scale in industrial fermenters and the penicillin produced is collected and processed to be used in medicine.

The **Conditions** in **Fermenters** are Carefully **Controlled**

1) The fermenters used to grow *Penicillium* are full of a liquid 'culture medium' in which the fungus can grow and reproduce.
2) The conditions inside the fermenters are kept at the optimum (best) levels for growth — this means the yield of penicillin (the product) is as big as possible. Here's how:

Nutrients needed by the *Penicillium* for growth are provided in the liquid culture medium.

Vessels are sterilised between uses with superheated steam that kills unwanted microbes. This increases the penicillin yield because the *Penicillium* aren't competing with other organisms. It also means that the penicillin produced doesn't get contaminated.

The pH is monitored and kept at the optimum level by adding acid or alkali. This allows *Penicillium's* enzymes to work more efficiently (see p.32). This keeps the rate of reaction and therefore the yield of penicillin as high as possible.

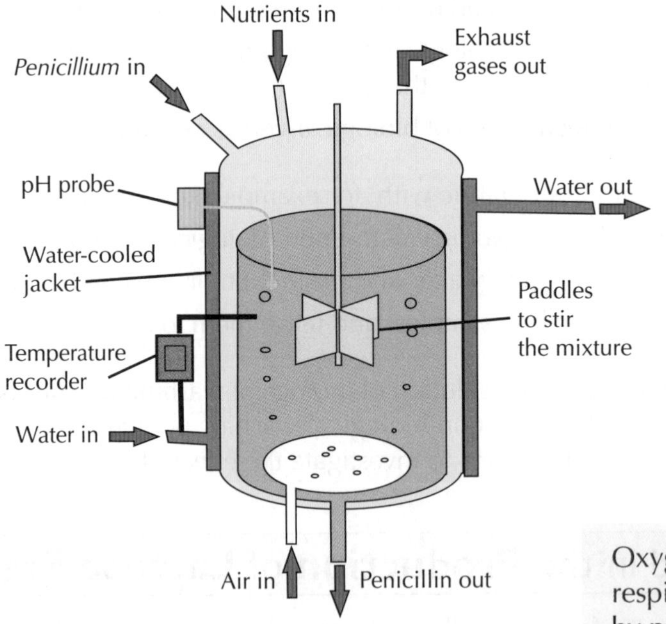

The fungi are kept in contact with fresh medium by paddles that circulate (or agitate) the medium around the vessel. This increases the penicillin yield because the fungi can always access the nutrients needed for growth.

Diagram labels:
Nutrients in
Penicillium in
Exhaust gases out
pH probe
Water out
Water-cooled jacket
Paddles to stir the mixture
Temperature recorder
Water in
Air in
Penicillin out

Oxygen is needed for respiration, so it's added by pumping in sterile air. This increases the penicillin yield because the fungi can always respire to provide the energy for growth.

The temperature is also monitored and kept at an optimum level for enzyme action. Heat is released as the fungus respires, causing the temperature inside the fermenter to increase. A water-cooled jacket makes sure it doesn't get so hot that the enzymes denature.

Optimum conditions for *Penicillium* = high yield of penicillin

Penicillium will happily grow in a fermenter even when it's cold outside. That is why fermenters are so great — you can control all the conditions so they're perfect. The more *Penicillium* that grow, the more penicillin you can make, so it's important to keep them happy.

Warm-Up & Exam Questions

Now's your chance to practise some incredibly life-like Exam Questions, but do the Warm-Up first — you don't want to end up straining something.

Warm-Up Questions

1) Name a type of organism that has been genetically engineered to produce a human protein.
2) How are plasmids involved in genetic engineering?
3) Apart from restriction enzymes, name another type of enzyme needed for the process of genetic engineering.
4) State two enzymes that might be found in biological washing powders.
5) State two conditions that are controlled in fermenters.

Exam Questions

1   Genetic engineering is being investigated for use in a wide variety of applications.

  (a)   What is genetic engineering?

[1]

  (b)   Give **one** example of how genetic engineering has been used to treat human diseases.

[1]

The process of genetic engineering has several steps.

  (c)   The useful gene is first isolated from an organism's DNA.
       Explain how this is done.

[2]

  (d)   The gene is then inserted into the target organism's DNA. Explain how this is
       achieved in bacteria, so that the bacteria replicate with the desired characteristics.

[4]

[Total 8 marks]

2   Genetic engineering can be used to produce genetically modified maize plants.

  (a)   (i)   State **one** characteristic which a maize crop might be genetically engineered to have.

[1]

       (ii) Suggest **one** way in which genetically engineering maize plants to have this
            characteristic could help to feed people in areas with a growing population.

[1]

  (b)   Give **two** reasons why some people may have concerns about the use of
       genetically engineered crops in agriculture.

[2]

[Total 4 marks]

Exam Questions

3   Biotechnology is the use of living organisms and processes to produce useful products.

(a)   Describe **two** benefits of using bacteria in biotechnology.

[2]

Lactose-free milk is produced using the enzyme lactase, which breaks lactose down. Lactase can be produced industrially by a fungus called *Aspergillus niger*.

(b)   When producing lactose-free milk using lactase from *A. niger*, it is important that the temperature is carefully controlled. Explain why.

[2]

[Total 4 marks]

4   The diagram below shows a fermenter that could be used to produce penicillin.

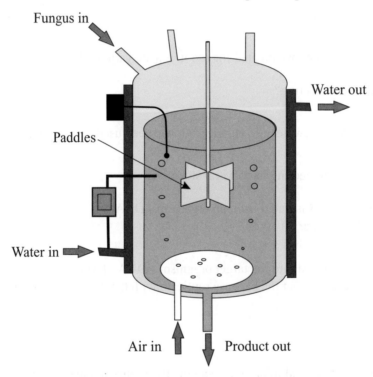

(a)   What is the name of the fungus used to produce penicillin on an industrial scale?

[1]

(b)   Explain the purpose of the air supply in the fermenter.

[2]

(c)   Suggest and explain why paddles are used in the fermenter.

[2]

(d)   Give **one** substance not labelled in the diagram that would also need to be added to the fermenter in order to produce penicillin.

[1]

[Total 6 marks]

Revision Summary for Sections 15 & 16

Sections 15 & 16 are now complete. Now would be a great time to figure out what you do and don't know.
- Try these questions and tick off each one when you get it right.
- When you've done all the questions for a topic and are completely happy with it, tick off the topic.

Food Chains and Webs, Pyramids of Number and Pyramids of Biomass (p.143-145) ☑

1) What is a food chain? ☑
2) How is energy transferred between organisms in a food chain? ☑
3) What is a food web? ☑
4) What does a pyramid of numbers show? ☑
5) Why might it be better to draw a pyramid of biomass to represent a food chain instead of a pyramid of numbers? ☑

Energy Flow, Humans and Food Chains (p.146-147) ☑

6) Give one way in which energy is lost from a food chain. ☑
7) How can over-harvesting affect food chains? ☑
8) Why are plants a more efficient source of human food than animals? ☑

Nutrient Cycles, Fossil Fuels and Deforestation (p.149-152) ☑

9) Name three processes that return carbon to the atmosphere. ☑
10) What role do nitrifying bacteria play in the nitrogen cycle? ☑
11) Name three types of ion in the nitrogen cycle. ☑
12) Describe two ways in which water form the land returns to the atmosphere during the water cycle. ☑
13) What are fossil fuels? ☑
14) True or false? Carbon in wood doesn't contribute to atmospheric pollution until the wood is burnt or decomposed. ☑

Ecosystems and Populations (p.154-156) ☑

15) What name is given to all the organisms of different species living in an ecosystem? ☑
16) Give three factors that affect the growth of a population. ☑
17) What's happening in the exponential (log) phase of a sigmoid population growth curve? ☑

Genetic Engineering (p.158-159) ☑

18) What is meant by 'sticky ends'? ☑
19) Describe the function of DNA ligase. ☑
20) What is a recombinant plasmid? ☑

Biotechnology (p.160-162) ☑

21) Describe how yeast is used to make bread rise. ☑
22) Describe how yeast is used to produce biofuels. ☑
23) Describe an investigation that shows why pectinase is used in fruit juice production. ☑

Food Production

Maintaining our food supply is important — there are more than 7 billion people on our planet to feed.

Modern Technology has Increased Food Production

Farms and gardens supply a lot of the food that we eat. Modern technology has increased the amount of food that can be produced. For example:

Agricultural Machinery

1) Agricultural machinery includes tractors and combine harvesters.
2) This machinery can be used instead of manual labour (people) and working animals.
3) Using machinery is quicker and more efficient than manual labour and means that crops can be grown and harvested over larger areas of land.

Chemical Fertilisers

1) Plants need certain mineral ions (see page 42).
2) If they don't get enough mineral ions, their growth can be affected.
3) Sometimes these ions are missing from the soil because they've been used up by a previous crop planted in the same soil.
4) Farmers use chemical fertilisers to replace these missing ions or to provide more of them. This helps to improve crop yields by boosting plant growth.

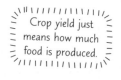
Crop yield just means how much food is produced.

Insecticides

1) Insects that eat or damage crops can be killed using insecticides.
2) These are chemicals that are sprayed onto crops by farmers.
3) They kill the insects without killing the actual crop.
4) This means that fewer plants are damaged or destroyed by insects, which increases crop quality and yield.

Herbicides

1) Herbicides are chemicals that can be sprayed around crops to kill weeds.
2) This means that crop plants face less competition from weeds for nutrients, water and light.
3) This increases the quality and yield of crop plants.

Selective Breeding

1) Humans use selective breeding (p.140) to improve crops and livestock.
2) This includes cattle (cows), fish and poultry that are larger and produce more meat, and crop plants that grow faster and are disease resistant.

Food Production

Some ways of producing food have negative impacts on the environment.

Monocultures can have Negative Impacts on an Ecosystem

A monoculture is where a single crop species is grown at one time on a piece of land.
Large-scale monocultures of crop plants can have many negative impacts on an ecosystem, such as:

- If there's a pest or disease that affects the species, it could kill all of the crop being grown.
- Farmers use a lot of pesticides (chemicals that kill pests) to stop this from happening. Excess pesticides can be washed into water and pollute the freshwater environment. They can also kill beneficial insects, and build up in food chains (bioaccumulation, see p.170).
- Monocultures can also reduce biodiversity because they contain fewer plant species than a natural ecosystem, so they don't provide habitats (see next page) for as many organisms.

Intensive Livestock Production has Negative Impacts Too

Intensive livestock production involves limiting the movement of animals (e.g. pigs and chickens) and keeping them in a temperature-controlled environment. This means the animals use less energy moving around and controlling their own body temperature, so more energy is available for growth and more meat can be produced. This has negative impacts on an ecosystem, including:

- Waste from the livestock can build up, meaning that diseases can spread easily between animals. The waste can run into water sources and pollute them (see p.170-171).
- The chemicals used to treat diseases, like antibiotics, can also pollute the environment.
- Producing feed for animals raised in this way is inefficient. It is more efficient to farm crops that are used to feed humans directly (see page 147).
- Some people have ethical objections to this farming method, as they think that making animals live in unnatural and uncomfortable conditions is cruel.

Intensive livestock production is sometimes called 'factory farming'.

Supplement

Producing Enough Food has Implications

As the human global population increases, food production must also increase to feed the population. Providing sufficient food for the increasing population has many implications:

1) Environmental — e.g. deforestation (p.152) to clear space for crops or livestock is happening at an increasing rate. Methane gas from livestock contributes to global warming (p.172).

2) Social — e.g. the more land that is needed for growing food, the less land there is available for people to live on. Also, if food is scarce, it may become too expensive for some people to afford.

3) Economic — e.g. the high input costs of farming (such as the price of seeds and livestock) can make it too expensive for people in some countries to start or maintain food production, meaning not enough food is produced.

Famine is due to a Widespread Shortage of Food

Famine is when there isn't enough food to feed a population. It can result from:

- An unequal distribution of food — some parts of the world have too much food and other parts don't have enough.
- Climate change can cause extreme weather events like droughts and flooding, which can destroy crops and farmland.
- The human population is increasing which makes it harder to feed everyone.
- People living in poverty often don't have the money or resources to buy or produce food.

Famine can also be caused by a combination of these factors.

Habitat Destruction

Human activities destroy many different kinds of habitats and have many undesirable effects.

Habitats are Destroyed for Different Reasons

1) A habitat is a place where an organism lives.

2) Human activities can have a negative impact on habitats by affecting food webs and chains. E.g. if a predator is removed, its prey may increase in numbers and destroy the habitat by consuming more vegetation (trees or plants).

3) Habitat destruction can also negatively affect food webs. E.g. if habitat destruction causes the numbers of a prey species to decrease, predator numbers may decrease too.

4) Many human activities destroy habitats. For example:

- As the human population increases, more habitats are being destroyed to increase the area of land available for food crop growth, livestock production and housing.

- Habitats are often destroyed during the extraction of natural resources. For example, the extraction of fossil fuels often requires road and pipeline construction which breaks up and destroys habitats. Extracting wood involves cutting down trees (see below).

- Cities and factories create waste that is often dumped in rivers and ends up in the sea. This causes marine pollution that can harm marine environments.

Deforestation is an Example of Habitat Destruction

1) Deforestation is the clearing of forests.

2) This has many undesirable effects, especially when it's done on a large-scale. These include extinction, loss of soil, flooding and increasing the carbon dioxide in the atmosphere.

3) These effects have a big impact on the environment:

Effect	Explanation
Extinction	Forest habitats can contain a wide variety of different plant and animal species. When these habitats are destroyed, there is a danger of many species becoming extinct (see p.178).
Loss of soil	When trees are removed, there are no roots to stabilise the soil during heavy rain. Soil is easily washed away and nutrients are lost. This makes it harder for new trees to grow later.
Flooding	Trees slow down rain as it falls to the ground because the rain hits leaves first. The water can then gradually be absorbed by the soil then the roots. Without trees, flooding is more likely.
Increase of carbon dioxide in the atmosphere	Photosynthesis removes CO_2 from the atmosphere and stores it as carbon in trees. CO_2 is then released when trees are burnt to clear land (see p.152).

Supplement

Supplement

Human activities can have a negative impact on habitats

The huge increases in human population mean that more land is required to provide food and shelter for everyone. However, clearing land has negative impacts on many organisms. It can even lead to extinction.

Warm-Up & Exam Questions

Time to see how much you've learnt over the previous few pages. Have a go at these questions.

Warm-Up Questions

1) State three kinds of modern technology that have helped to increase food production.
2) Give one economic implication of producing enough food to feed a growing population.
3) What is famine?
4) Give three factors that can lead to famine.

Exam Questions

1 Some methods of food production have negative impacts on ecosystems.

(a) Describe **two** ways that monocultures can negatively impact ecosystems.

[2]

(b) Describe **two** ways that intensive livestock production can negatively impact ecosystems.

[2]

[Total 4 marks]

2 The photo below shows a type of habitat destruction taking place.

(a) Give **two** reasons why the habitat in the photo above might be being destroyed.

[2]

(b) Extinction can be an undesirable effect of the above type of habitat destruction.
State **two** other undesirable effects of the above type of habitat destruction.

[2]

(c) Explain how the two effects you gave in **(b)** impact the environment.

[2]

[Total 6 marks]

3 Describe **one** social implication of producing enough food to feed an increasing population.

[Total 1 mark]

Land and Water Pollution

Here's another environmental problem for you to learn about — pollution of land and water.

There are **Several Sources** of **Land** and **Water Pollution**

Human activities can pollute the land, as well as water bodies such as rivers, lakes and the sea. Sources of pollution include:

Insecticides and Herbicides

- Insecticides sprayed onto crops can kill beneficial insects and affect birds that rely on insects for food.

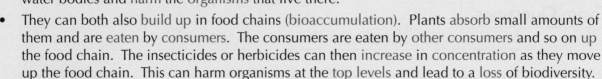
There's more on insecticides and herbicides on page 166.

- Insecticides and herbicides can be washed into water bodies and harm the organisms that live there.
- They can both also build up in food chains (bioaccumulation). Plants absorb small amounts of them and are eaten by consumers. The consumers are eaten by other consumers and so on up the food chain. The insecticides or herbicides can then increase in concentration as they move up the food chain. This can harm organisms at the top levels and lead to a loss of biodiversity.

Nuclear Fall-out

Nuclear fall-out is when radioactive material that comes from using nuclear weapons or from nuclear accidents at nuclear plants is thrown into the air. The fall-out can pollute the land and spread to sources of groundwater, where it can remain for many years and cause serious health problems.

There are **Other Sources** of **Water Pollution**

It's not just insecticides, herbicides and nuclear fall-out that can affect rivers, lakes and the sea. Other sources of water pollution include:

Chemical Waste

Toxic waste chemicals from manufacturing or industrial processes can be washed into water bodies. They can build up in food chains (bioaccumulation), destroy aquatic life and be hazardous to human health.

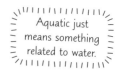
Aquatic just means something related to water.

Discarded Rubbish

Rubbish, like plastics (see p.174), can build up in waterways, spoiling the scenery and causing blockages. Toxic chemicals can leak out of rubbish that is disposed of in water bodies.

Untreated Sewage and Fertilisers

- Untreated sewage can contaminate the environment. If it gets into drinking water, it can cause problems for humans, e.g. diarrhoea.
- If fertilisers get into water bodies, they can release nutrient ions which can cause the rapid growth of producers called algae. This can reduce the oxygen level in the water and eventually lead to the death of other aquatic organisms. The presence of untreated sewage in the water can have a similar effect.

Pollution has negative impacts on both land and water

Pollution often remains in the environment for a long time and can have devastating effects on organisms and their habitats. Make sure you have learnt about all the different sources of pollution of land and water.

Water Pollution

There's more you need to learn about water pollution I'm afraid — including the effects of female contraceptive hormones and fertilisers...

Hormones in Water Courses Can Have Negative Impacts

1) Female contraceptive hormones are used to prevent pregnancy (see p.119). If they end up in water courses they can have negative impacts on organisms.

A water course is a channel that water flows through.

2) For example, oestrogen in the urine of women on the contraceptive pill sometimes remains in sewage after it has been treated, so oestrogen can end up in our rivers.

3) This can lead to the feminisation (development of female characteristics in males) of aquatic organisms that are sensitive to these hormones. E.g. some male fish can develop eggs in their testes.

4) The oestrogen can also end up in tap water and be consumed by men. Over time, it's thought that this may lead to a reduced sperm count (producing fewer sperm than normal), which affects fertility (being able to have children).

Fertilisers Can Run into Water and Cause Eutrophication

You might think fertiliser would be a good thing for the environment because it makes plants grow faster. Unfortunately it causes big problems when it ends up in lakes and rivers — here's how...

- Nitrates and other ions are put onto fields as mineral fertilisers.
- If too much fertiliser is applied and it rains afterwards, nitrates are easily leached (washed through the soil) into rivers and lakes.
- The result is eutrophication, which can cause serious damage to river and lake ecosystems:

1) Fertilisers enter the water, adding extra nutrients (nitrates and other ions).

2) The extra nutrients cause producers like algae to grow faster and block out the light.

3) Plants can't photosynthesise due to lack of light and start to die.

4) With more food available, microorganisms that feed on dead plants (decomposers) increase in number. They respire aerobically (see p.78) so the amount of dissolved oxygen in the water is reduced as decomposition increases.

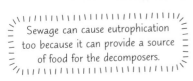

Sewage can cause eutrophication too because it can provide a source of food for the decomposers.

5) Organisms that need the oxygen dissolved in water (e.g. fish) die.

Supplement

Lots of tricky words on this page...

...like 'feminisation', 'nitrates' and 'eutrophication'. If you're writing an answer on this stuff in the exam, using technical words like these will really impress the examiners.

Air Pollution

Human activities can cause air pollution by increasing the quantities of certain gases in the atmosphere.

Carbon Dioxide and Methane can Pollute the Air

1) Humans release carbon dioxide into the atmosphere all the time as part of our everyday lives — in car exhausts, industrial processes, as we burn fossil fuels etc. People around the world are also cutting down large areas of forest (deforestation) for timber and to clear land for farming — and this activity affects the level of carbon dioxide in the atmosphere (see page 152).

2) Methane gas is produced naturally from various sources, e.g. rotting plants in marshland. However, two 'man-made' sources of methane are on the increase: growing rice and raising cattle.

Nuclear fall-out (p.170) also pollutes the air.

Increasing concentrations of these gases are enhancing (increasing) the greenhouse effect — the natural process that helps to keep the Earth warm. This enhanced greenhouse effect is causing the Earth to heat up, which is causing climate change.

Here's How the Greenhouse Effect Works...

1) The temperature of the Earth is a balance between the energy it gets from the Sun and the energy it radiates back out into space.

2) Gases in the atmosphere absorb most of the heat that would normally be radiated out into space, and re-radiate it in all directions (including back towards the Earth). This is the greenhouse effect.

3) If this didn't happen, then at night there'd be nothing to keep any energy in, and it would be very cold.

4) There are several different gases in the atmosphere that help keep the energy in. They are called "greenhouse gases" and include carbon dioxide and methane.

Energy from the Sun

Heat radiation trapped by gases

CO_2 and Methane

Enhancing the Greenhouse Effect is Causing Climate Change

1) Humans are increasing the amount of carbon dioxide and methane in the atmosphere (see above). This has enhanced the greenhouse effect. As a result of all this, the Earth is heating up — this is global warming. Global warming is a type of climate change and causes other types of climate change, e.g. changing rainfall patterns.

2) Climate change could lead to things like extreme weather, rising sea levels and flooding due to the polar ice caps melting. This could cause habitat loss, and could affect food webs and crop growth.

We need the greenhouse effect, but it's starting to go too far

The greenhouse effect is linked to climate change. We don't know yet what the long-term effects will be.

Supplement

Supplement

Acid Rain

Sulfur dioxide is another gas that can cause air pollution. It can cause acid rain which has many harmful effects on organisms and ecosystems. Read on for more on how it's caused and the effects it has.

Acid Rain is Caused by Sulfur Dioxide

1) Burning fossil fuels releases harmful gases like carbon dioxide (a greenhouse gas, see previous page) and sulfur dioxide (SO_2).

2) When SO_2 mixes with rain clouds it forms dilute sulfuric acid.

3) This then falls as acid rain.

4) Internal combustion engines in cars and power stations are the main causes of acid rain.

Acid rain is also caused by nitrogen oxides that are produced by burning fossil fuels.

Acid Rain Kills Fish and Trees

1) Acid rain can cause a lake to become more acidic. This has a severe effect on the lake's ecosystem. Many organisms are sensitive to changes in pH and can't survive in more acidic conditions. Many plants and animals die.

2) Acid rain can kill trees. The acid damages leaves and releases toxic substances from the soil, making it hard for the trees to take up nutrients.

Sulfur Dioxide Pollution can be Reduced

1) The impact of acid rain can be reduced by reducing sulfur dioxide pollution.

2) Coal-burning power stations can do this using the following measures:

> • Burning coal that contains less sulfur.
> • 'Washing' the coal to remove some of the sulfur before it is burnt.
> • Installing 'scrubbers' in chimneys to remove sulfur dioxide before it is released.

3) Producing power without using fossil fuels (e.g. using solar energy or wind turbines) would also reduce acid rain.

The negative impacts of acid rain can be reduced

Acid rain can cause big problems in ecosystems, but its impacts can be reduced by taking measures to reduce sulfur dioxide pollution. Make sure you can name a few ways that this can be done.

Non-Biodegradable Plastics

It's easy to throw away old plastic bottles and plastic packaging without giving it much thought — but doing this can have negative impacts on both aquatic and terrestrial (land) ecosystems.

Non-Biodegradable Plastics Cannot be Broken Down

1) Decomposing microorganisms have not evolved to break down the chemicals found in plastics.
2) So non-biodegradable plastics cannot be broken down through biological decomposition.
3) This means that they will remain in the environment for a very long time.
4) Common causes of plastic pollution are plastic bags and plastic bottles.
5) They often build up in landfills (sites where waste is disposed of by burying it), litter public spaces and can wash into aquatic ecosystems.

Non-Biodegradable Plastics Affect Aquatic Ecosystems

Food Chain Contamination

Eating plastic items after mistaking them for food can cause intestinal blockages in organisms or poisoning from chemicals that slowly leak from the plastics. It also means that plastic enters the food chain — e.g. consumers eat plastic by eating organisms with plastic inside them.

Entrapment of Organisms

Large quantities of plastic, along with other kinds of rubbish, can build up in the ocean. Rotating ocean currents can form the build up into an 'island'. Organisms can get entangled, trapped or strangled by plastic islands or even just by individual plastic items.

Non-Biodegradable Plastics Affect Terrestrial Ecosystems

Food Chain Contamination

Over time, plastics can give out poisonous toxins and chemicals that cause land pollution. Once they enter the food chain they can kill many organisms.

Air Pollution

If not carefully controlled, toxic gases can be released into the atmosphere when plastics are disposed of by burning. Carbon dioxide is also produced, which contributes to global warming (see p.172).

Landfill

Landfills take up valuable space that could be used to feed and house our increasing global population (see p.155). Plastic in landfills takes a long time to decompose and landfills look unsightly. The buried waste also releases toxins into the surrounding soil making it unsuitable for crops or grazing animals.

Non-biodegradable plastics remain in the environment

Non-biodegradable plastics can create serious problems in the environment. Cover up this page and write a list of effects that plastics can have in aquatic and terrestrial ecosystems. It's a good way of testing what you've learnt — you may be asked to discuss these effects in the exam.

Supplement

Warm-Up & Exam Questions

Pollution isn't the most exciting topic, but it's important for you to learn about.
Have a go at these questions to see what you can remember from the last few pages.

Warm-Up Questions

1) State one source of land pollution.
2) State two gases that cause air pollution.

Exam Questions

1 Which gas can lead to acid rain?

☐ **A** carbon dioxide ☐ **B** methane ☐ **C** sulfur dioxide ☐ **D** oxygen

[Total 1 mark]

2 Non-biodegradable plastics can have negative effects on ecosystems.

(a) Give **two** ways that non-biodegradable plastics can affect aquatic ecosystems.

[2]

(b) Give **two** ways that non-biodegradable plastics can affect terrestrial ecosystems.

[2]
[Total 4 marks]

3 Certain gases in the atmosphere can cause air pollution.

(a) State **two** ways that sulfur dioxide pollution can be reduced.

[2]

(b) Explain the relationship between greenhouses gases and climate change.

[3]
[Total 5 marks]

4 Human activities can pollute rivers, lakes and the sea.

(a) Give **one** way in which waste produced by humans pollutes water.

[1]

(b) Give **two** negative impacts of female contraceptive hormones getting into water courses.

[2]

(c) An investigation was carried out into the number of decomposer microorganisms along a stream. A sewage pipe was located mid-way along the study site. The results are shown to the right.

Describe and explain the change in number of decomposer microorganisms downstream from the pipe.

[4]

[Total 7 marks]

Section 17 — Human Influences on Ecosystems

Sustainable Resources

Some resources will run out, but others are sustainable if we maintain them.

Resources can be Renewable or Non-Renewable

1) Non-renewable resources include energy resources such as fossil fuels (coal, oil and gas).

2) Fossil fuels are typically burnt to release energy or used to make products (such as making plastics from oils).

3) They take a very long time to reform so we can't replace them. If no new resources are found, some fossil fuel stocks may run out within a hundred years. This means that it's important to conserve them.

4) Some resources are renewable, which means they are sustainable.

 A sustainable resource is one which is produced as rapidly as it is removed from the environment so that it does not run out.

Fish Stocks and Forests are Sustainable Resources

Fish Stocks

- Fish stocks are particular populations of fish in the sea.
- Fish stocks are getting smaller because we're fishing so much.
- We can maintain (conserve) fish stocks by keeping them at a level where fish continue to breed.

Forests

- Deforestation removes trees in an area (see p.152).
- We can plant trees to replace the ones that are removed (reforestation).
- This means that the number of trees can be maintained, so we can continue to use them to make, e.g. paper.

Fish stocks and forests can be sustained using these methods:

1) Restocking — this involves breeding fish that can then be released into the ocean when they're big enough to survive, to increase fish stocks. For forests, this involves replanting areas of woodland that have been cut down to increase the number of trees.

2) Education — knowing about the importance of conserving fish stocks means that people shopping for fish can make better choices. If people understand the value of the biodiversity in forests, they will want to protect them from deforestation.

3) Legal quotas — there are limits on the number and size of fish that can be caught in certain areas, as well as the time of year they can be caught in. This prevents certain species from being overfished. Quotas can also be applied to the number of trees that can be cut down in forests.

It is Important that Development is Sustainable

1) The human population is increasing. We need to find ways to develop (e.g. make sure everyone has enough food, water and places to live) without using up all our natural resources.

 Sustainable development is development providing for the needs of an increasing human population without harming the environment.

2) Development often involves conflicting demands. For example, developing new places for people to live can destroy habitat for wildlife. Growing more food for people to eat can reduce soil quality and affect future harvests. Sustainable development requires managing these conflicting demands.

3) This means that there must also be development planning and co-operation at local, national and international levels to balance the current and future needs of the human population.

Recycling

Recycling is an important part of conservation. If we recycle materials, we reduce the amount of waste we produce and it means we don't have to take as much from natural environments.

Lots of Materials can be Recycled

1) Society produces large amounts of waste. This waste can be reduced by reusing products or recycling them (turning them into new products).

2) Reusing and recycling conserves the products we already have and reduces the need for extracting raw materials from the environment, which protects natural habitats and saves energy.

3) Here are some examples of waste being reused or recycled:

- Waste paper can be turned into new paper products. This means that fewer trees need to be cut down.

- Glass waste can be separated into different colours, cleaned, then melted and reshaped into new glass products. Glass bottles are often washed and reused.

- Waste plastic can be reprocessed into useful products. Plastic takes a very long time to break down, so recycling reduces the amount of plastic sent to landfills (p.174), or burnt. It also means that fewer fossil fuels need to be extracted to make plastics.

- Metals can be melted down and moulded into new metal objects, which often uses less energy than extracting metals.

Sewage is Treated to Produce Drinking Water

Water can be recycled by processing sewage. Some of the processes involved in treating waste water at sewage treatment plants include:

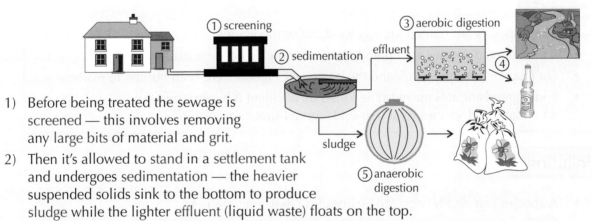

1) Before being treated the sewage is screened — this involves removing any large bits of material and grit.

2) Then it's allowed to stand in a settlement tank and undergoes sedimentation — the heavier suspended solids sink to the bottom to produce sludge while the lighter effluent (liquid waste) floats on the top.

3) The effluent in the settlement tank is removed and treated by biological aerobic digestion. This is when air is pumped through the water to encourage aerobic bacteria to break down any organic matter — including other microbes in the water.

4) For waste water containing toxic substances, additional stages of treatment may involve using chemicals or UV radiation. E.g. chlorine is added to water to kill microorganisms. This makes the water safe to consume as drinking water or to return to the environment.

5) The sludge from the bottom of the settlement tank is also removed and transferred into large tanks. Here it gets broken down by bacteria in a process called anaerobic digestion. The digested waste can be used as a fertiliser.

Recycling helps us to conserve natural resources

Recycling the water from sewage back into drinking supplies is a good way of conserving water. Some people don't like the idea of drinking water that used to be sewage, but once treated it can't make you ill.

Endangered Organisms

When the population size of a species drops, the species can become endangered.

Several Factors Cause Organisms to Become Endangered

1) Extinction is when no individuals of a species remain.
2) An endangered species is a species that is considered to be at a high risk of extinction.
3) The reasons for organisms becoming endangered or extinct include:

Climate Change

- Global warming is a type of climate change (p.172) that is causing the Earth to heat up.
- All organisms have an ideal temperature range. If organisms can't adapt to changing temperatures or other environmental conditions quickly enough, they risk becoming extinct.
- For example, whales need specific ocean temperatures for, e.g. feeding and reproduction. Rising sea temperatures mean the whales might not be able to survive.

Habitat Destruction

- As a species' habitat is destroyed, fewer of the organisms can be supported.
- As their numbers start to decrease, the species can become endangered.
- For example, great apes live in forests in Southeast Asia. They risk extinction because large areas of forest are being deforested.

> Competition from humans for resources can decrease the population size of an endangered species.

Hunting

- Many species are hunted for, e.g. food, fur or medicines.
- If endangered species are hunted, they can quickly become extinct.
- For example, the great auk and the passenger pigeon were both hunted to extinction.
- Endangered animals may also be killed by accident if hunters mistake an endangered species for a non-endangered species.

Pollution

- A species can also be affected by pollution in its environment.
- For example, the oceans are heavily polluted with plastics (p.174). Sea turtles can mistake plastic bags for jellyfish and eat them. This often causes their death.

Introduced Species

> An invasive species is a species that threatens local biodiversity.

- Introduced species often thrive in their new environment and become invasive.
- Native species often can't defend themselves against, or compete with, the invaders.
- For example, a species of lake newt went extinct in China because it couldn't compete with introduced fish and frog species in its environment.

4) Endangered species have a reduced population size and lower genetic variation (see p.135).
5) Variation is not restored if the population size simply increases again — mutations also need to happen over many generations. This means that even if a population recovers its size, it can still face extinction if it has low variation and can't adapt to changing environmental conditions.

Supplement

Conserving Endangered Species

We can try to conserve endangered species before they become extinct.

There are **Several** Ways to **Conserve Endangered Species**

There are several different ways to try and stop the population sizes of endangered species decreasing. These include:

Monitoring and Protecting Species and Habitats

1) Monitoring species' numbers helps scientists to identify the species that are most under threat.

2) Protected areas can be set up to protect these organisms and habitats that are under threat, e.g. from hunting.

3) Protected areas include places like national parks and nature reserves, where development of the land is restricted — this includes building houses and using the land for farming.

Education

Teaching people about the natural world helps them to understand the importance of conservation and what they can do to help.

Seed Banks

1) The seeds of endangered plant species can be kept in a seed bank.

2) This is a place with the conditions necessary to keep the seeds alive for a long time.

3) This protects and saves plant genetic diversity.

Captive Breeding Programmes

1) Captive breeding programmes are where animals are bred in captivity (e.g. zoos). Many have been set up to help prevent endangered species from becoming extinct.

2) This is because it's easier for animals to increase their numbers in captivity — there is less infant mortality (death) so more offspring survive to reproduce.

3) Some of these individuals may then be released into the wild to boost or re-establish a population. This can help make sure the species survives if it dies out in the wild.

Pandas are an endangered species. Many efforts have been made to breed pandas in captivity.

There are **Different Reasons** for **Conservation Programmes**

1) Conserving one species may stop others from becoming extinct. If one species becomes extinct it will affect all the organisms that feed on and are eaten by that species, so the whole food web (see p.143) is affected.

2) Conserving species means that ecosystem functions like nutrient cycling (p.149-151) can be maintained.

3) By protecting vulnerable environments, organisms can continue to live in their natural habitat. For example, controlling water levels will help to conserve wetlands and trimming trees will help to conserve woodlands.

4) Humans rely on many resources from the environment, such as animals for food, plants for drugs, wood for fuel and genes from organisms. Conservation programmes mean that resource provision from the environment can continue.

It is important to do what we can to conserve endangered species

Zoos provide a safe space where animals are protected from harmful human activities, such as hunting and habitat destruction. They often have captive breeding programmes so the numbers of an endangered species can be increased before they are reintroduced back into their natural habitats.

Warm-Up & Exam Questions

That's the end of this section. Have a go at these questions to see how much you know.
If there's anything you've forgotten, have a look back over the previous few pages to remind yourself.

Warm-Up Questions

1) Define the term 'sustainable resource'.
2) Name three products that can be recycled.
3) List three stages of treatment that sewage undergoes at a sewage treatment plant.

Exam Questions

1 The Siberian tiger is an endangered species. Explain how captive breeding
   programmes could help to increase the number of Siberian tigers in the wild.

[Total 2 marks]

2 Give **three** reasons why organisms become endangered or extinct.

[Total 3 marks]

3 Which **one** of the following statements describes what can happen
   if the population size of a species drops?

   ☐ **A**   The species will lose genetic variation, but it will regain variation quickly
            if its population size recovers.

   ☐ **B**   The species will lose genetic variation, and it may still face extinction even
            if its population size recovers.

   ☐ **C**   The species will lose genetic variation, but it won't risk extinction if its
            population size recovers.

   ☐ **D**   The population will gain genetic variation, so it won't risk extinction if its
            population size recovers.

[Total 1 mark]

4 A fish stock is a particular population of fish in the sea.

   (a) Suggest **one** reason why it might be important to conserve fish stocks.

[1]

   (b) Give **three** ways that fish stocks can be conserved.

[3]

[Total 4 marks]

Revision Summary for Section 17

So you've finished Section 17 and you're nearly at the end of the book.
Here are some questions to see what you've learnt in this section.
- Try these questions and tick off each one when you get it right.
- When you've done all the questions for a topic and are completely happy with it, tick off the topic.

Food Production and Habitat Destruction (p.166-168) ☐

1) How does using agricultural machinery help to increase food production?
2) How do herbicides increase food production?
3) How does selective breeding increase food production?
4) What is a monoculture?
5) What is intensive livestock production?
6) Give one environmental implication of producing enough food to feed a growing population.
7) Give one reason for habitat destruction.
8) What is deforestation?

Pollution, Acid Rain and Non-Biodegradable Plastics (p.170-174) ☐

9) Describe one way in which insecticides can pollute the land.
10) State the effect of nuclear fall-out entering water ecosystems.
11) What is the name of the process that occurs when fertilisers run into bodies of water and cause rapid growth of producers?
12) Explain the effects of this process on aquatic organisms.
13) Explain what is meant by the enhanced greenhouse effect.
14) Describe the effects of acid rain on the environment.
15) What are non-biodegradable plastics?
16) True or false? Non-biodegradable plastics only affect aquatic ecosystems.

Sustainable Resources, Recycling and Conservation (p.176-179) ☐

17) What is a non-renewable resource?
18) Why do we need to conserve non-renewable resources?
19) What is sustainable development?
20) Sustainable development requires managing conflicting demands.
    Name one other thing that sustainable development requires.
21) True or false? Sewage can be treated to produce drinking water.
22) Explain why climate change can cause a species to become extinct.
23) Explain why introduced species can cause native species to become extinct.
24) Describe how education can be used to help conserve endangered species.
25) Describe how monitoring and protecting species and habitats can conserve endangered species.
26) Describe how seed banks can conserve endangered species.

Designing Investigations

Before you start carrying out an investigation, it's important to spend some time designing it.

Evidence Can Support or Disprove a Hypothesis

1) Scientists observe things and come up with hypotheses to test them.
   A hypothesis is just a possible explanation for what they've observed. For example:

   > Observation: People with big feet have spots. Hypothesis: Having big feet causes spots.

2) To determine whether or not a hypothesis is right, you need to do an investigation to gather evidence. To do this, you need to use your hypothesis to make a prediction — something you think will happen that you can test. E.g. people who have bigger feet will have more spots.

3) Investigations are used to see if there are patterns or relationships between two variables, e.g. to see if there's a pattern or relationship between the variables 'number of spots' and 'size of feet'.

Results Need to be Reliable and Valid

1) RELIABLE results come from experiments that give the same data each time the experiment is repeated (by you) and each time the experiment is reproduced (copied) by other scientists.

2) VALID results are both reliable and come from experiments that were designed to be a fair test.

Make an Investigation a Fair Test By Controlling the Variables

1) In a lab experiment you usually change one variable and measure how it affects another variable.

2) To make it a fair test, everything else that could affect the results should stay the same — otherwise you can't tell if the thing you're changing is causing the results or not.

3) The variable you CHANGE is called the INDEPENDENT variable.

4) The variable you MEASURE when you change the independent variable is the DEPENDENT variable.

5) The variables that you KEEP THE SAME are called CONTROL variables.

   > You could find how temperature affects reaction rate. The independent variable is temperature. The dependent variable is rate. Control variables include concentration of reactants, pH, etc.

6) Because you can't always control all the variables, you often need to use a control experiment. This is an experiment that's kept under the same conditions as the rest of the investigation, but doesn't have anything done to it. This is so that you can see what happens when you don't change anything at all.

Results Also Need to be Accurate

1) Accurate results are those that are close to the true answer.

2) The accuracy of your results usually depends on your method. To make sure your results are as accurate as possible, you need to make sure you're measuring the right thing and that you don't miss anything or include anything that you shouldn't include.

   > E.g. if you wanted to measure the amount of gas released from an enzyme-controlled reaction you could estimate how much gas is produced by counting the number of bubbles that are released. But the bubbles could be different sizes, and if they're produced really quickly you might miss some when counting. It would be more accurate to collect the gas (e.g. in a gas syringe) and measure its volume.

Designing Investigations

You Need to Look out for **Errors** and **Anomalous Results**

1) The results of your experiment will always vary a bit because of random errors —
   unpredictable differences caused by things like human errors in measuring.
   E.g. the errors you make when reading from a measuring cylinder are random.
   You have to estimate or round the distance when it's between two marks (see page 186) —
   so sometimes your figure will be a bit above the real one, and sometimes it will be a bit below.

2) You can reduce the effect of random errors by taking repeat readings and finding the
   mean (a type of average — see page 188). This will make your results more reliable.

3) If a measurement is wrong by the same amount every time, it's called
   a systematic error. For example, if you measured from the very end
   of your ruler instead of from the 0 cm mark every time, all your
   measurements would be a bit small. Repeating the experiment in the
   exact same way and calculating a mean won't correct a systematic error.

   If there's no systematic error, then doing repeats and calculating a mean could make your results more accurate.

4) Just to make things more complicated, if a systematic error is caused by using equipment that
   isn't zeroed properly, it's called a zero error. For example, if a mass balance always reads
   1 gram before you put anything on it, all your measurements will be 1 gram too heavy.

5) You can make up for some systematic errors if you know about them, e.g. if a mass balance
   always reads 1 gram before you put anything on it, you can subtract 1 gram from all your results.

Sometimes you get a result that doesn't fit in with the rest at all. This is an anomalous result.
You should investigate it and try to work out what happened. If you can work out what
happened (e.g. you measured something wrong) you can ignore it when processing your results.

Make Sure You're **Working Safely** in the **Lab**

1) Before you start any experiment, make sure you know about any safety precautions
   to do with your method or the chemicals you're using. You need to follow any
   instructions that your teacher gives you carefully. The chemicals you're using may
   be hazardous — for example, they might be flammable (catch fire easily),
   or they might irritate or burn your skin if it comes into contact with them.

2) Make sure that you're wearing sensible clothing when you're in the lab (e.g. open
   shoes won't protect your feet from spillages). When you're doing an experiment,
   you should wear a lab coat to protect your skin and clothing. Depending on the
   experiment, you may need to also wear safety goggles and gloves.

3) You also need to be aware of general safety in the lab, e.g. keep anything
   flammable away from lit Bunsen burners, don't directly touch any hot equipment,
   handle glassware (including microscope slides) carefully to avoid breakages, etc.

Designing an investigation is an involved process...

Collecting data is what investigations are all about. Designing a good investigation is really
important to make sure that any data collected is reliable, valid, accurate and done in a safe way.

Planning Experiments

In the exam, you could be asked to plan or describe how you'd carry out an experiment. It might be one you've already come across or you might be asked to come up with an experiment of your own.

You Need to Be Able to Plan a **Good Experiment**

Here are some general tips on what to include when planning an experiment:

1) Say what you're measuring (i.e. the dependent variable).

2) Say what you're changing (i.e. the independent variable) and describe how you're going to change it.

3) Describe the method and the apparatus you'd use (i.e. to measure the variables).

4) Describe what variables you're keeping constant — and how you're going to do it.

5) Say that you need to repeat the experiment at least three times, to make the results more reliable.

6) Say whether you're using a control or not.

Here's an idea of a type of question you might be asked in the exam and what you might write as an answer...

Exam-style Question:

1   Describe an investigation to find out what effect temperature has on the rate of photosynthesis in Canadian pondweed.   *[6]*

Example Answer:

Set up a test tube containing a measured amount of Canadian pondweed, water and sodium hydrogencarbonate. Connect the test tube up to a capillary tube containing water and a syringe, then place it in a water bath in front of a source of white light.

Leave the pondweed to photosynthesise for a set amount of time. As it photosynthesises, the oxygen released will collect in the capillary tube. At the end of the experiment, use the syringe to draw the gas bubble in the tube up alongside a ruler and measure the length of the gas bubble. This is proportional to the volume of O_2 produced.

Repeat the experiment with the water bath set to different temperatures (e.g. 10 °C, 20 °C, 30 °C and 40 °C).

The pondweed should be left to photosynthesise for the same amount of time at each temperature (monitored using a stopwatch). The test tubes should also be set up the same distance away from the light source (measured using a ruler) and the same mass of pondweed should be used in each test tube (measured using a balance).

A control should also be set up at each temperature. This should be a test tube containing water and boiled pondweed (so that it can't photosynthesise).

Repeat the experiment three times at each temperature. Use the results to find a mean rate of photosynthesis at each temperature. This will make the results more reliable.

You Can Make **Reasoned Predictions** Based on Your **Knowledge**

1) You can use your hypothesis (p.182) and the stuff you know to make sensible predictions about what the results of an experiment might be.

2) For example, you can use your knowledge of the effects of temperature on the rate of photosynthesis to predict the results of the experiment above. You might predict that as the temperature increases, the rate of photosynthesis increases up to a point.

3) The results of your experiment would then tell you if your prediction was correct. This will help you to determine if your hypothesis is likely to be correct, or whether it needs to change.

Taking Measurements

There are lots of pieces of equipment you can use to take measurements. You need to know how to use each one correctly and when you need to use them. Luckily, that's what these next two pages are all about.

The **Right Apparatus** Depends on **What** You're **Measuring**

1. **Length**

1) Length can be measured in different units (e.g. mm, cm, m). Smaller units have a higher degree of accuracy. You'll need to decide on the appropriate level of accuracy for your experiment. For example, the length of a leaf would be better measured in mm, but the length of a field would be better measured in m.

2) It is also important to choose the right equipment — a ruler would probably be best for measuring short lengths, but a metre rule or tape measure would be better for larger distances.

2. **Mass**

1) To weigh a solid, put the container you are weighing your substance into on a balance.

2) Set the balance to exactly zero and then weigh out the correct amount of your substance.

3. **Temperature**

1) You can use a thermometer to measure the temperature of a solution.

2) Make sure that the bulb of the thermometer is completely submerged in the solution and that you wait for the temperature to stabilise before you take your initial reading.

3) Read off the scale on the thermometer at eye level to make sure it's correct.

thermometer bulb

4. **Volume** of a **Liquid**

There's more than one way to measure the volume of a liquid. Whichever method you use, always read the volume from the bottom of the meniscus (the curved upper surface of the liquid) when it's at eye level.

Read volume from here — the bottom of the meniscus.

Using a pipette

- Pipettes are used to suck up and transfer volumes of liquid between containers.
- Dropping pipettes are used to transfer drops of liquid.
- Graduated pipettes are used to transfer accurate volumes.
- A pipette filler is attached to the end of a graduated pipette, to control the amount of liquid being drawn up.

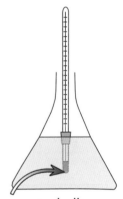

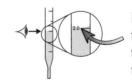

Syringes can also be used to measure small volumes of liquids.

Using a measuring cylinder

Measuring cylinders come in many different sizes (ranging from about 10 cm³ to several dm³). Make sure you choose one that's the right size for the measurement you want to make (see next page for more).

Taking Measurements

5. Volume of a Gas

1) To accurately measure the volume of gas, you should use a gas syringe.

2) Alternatively, you can use an upturned measuring cylinder filled with water. The gas will push the water out so you can read the volume of gas off the scale.

3) Other methods to measure the amount of gas include:
   - counting the bubbles produced,
   - measuring the length of a gas bubble drawn along a tube (see page 38).

   These methods are less accurate, but will give you relative amounts of gas to compare results.

4) When you're measuring a gas, you need to make sure that the equipment is set up so that none of the gas can escape, otherwise your results won't be accurate.

6. pH

The method you should use to measure pH depends on what your experiment is.

1) Indicators are dyes that change colour depending on whether they're in an acid or an alkali. You use them by adding a couple of drops of the indicator to the solution you're interested in. Universal indicator is a mixture of indicators that changes colour gradually as pH changes. It's useful for estimating the pH of a solution based on its colour.

2) Indicator paper is useful if you don't want to colour the entire solution that you're testing. It changes colour depending on the pH of the solution it touches. You can also hold a piece of damp indicator paper in a gas sample to test its pH.

Blue litmus paper turns red in acidic conditions and red litmus paper turns blue in alkaline conditions.

3) pH meters have a digital display that gives an accurate value for the pH of a solution.

Your Equipment has to be Right for the Job

1) The measuring equipment you use has to be sensitive enough to measure the changes you're looking for. For example, if you need to measure changes of 1 cm³ you need to use a measuring cylinder that can measure in 1 cm³ steps — it'd be no good trying with one that only measures 10 cm³ steps.

2) The smallest change a measuring instrument can detect is called its resolution. E.g. some mass balances have a resolution of 1 g, some have a resolution of 0.1 g, and some are even more sensitive.

3) The more sensitive your equipment is, the more precise your measurements will be. E.g. a measurement of 10.1 g is more precise than a measurement of 10 g. You should make sure you record your measurements with the same precision (number of digits) as your measuring instrument.

4) Unfortunately, your readings may not always perfectly match the scale on the instrument. When this happens, you need to interpolate (estimate) where your reading lies between two marks on the scale.

5) Also, equipment needs to be calibrated by measuring a known value. If there's a difference between the measured and known value, you can use this to correct the inaccuracy of the equipment.

Read off the scale carefully when taking readings

Whether you're reading off a thermometer, a pipette or a measuring cylinder, make sure you take all readings at eye level. And, if it's volume you're measuring, read from the bottom of the meniscus.

Observing and Drawing Biological Specimens

You need to be able to observe, record and measure biological specimens, e.g. cells in a microscope image.

This is How to **View** a **Specimen** Using a **Light Microscope:**

1) Take a thin slice of your specimen, e.g. a layer of onion cells.

2) Next, take a clean slide and use a pipette to put one drop of water in the middle of it — this will hold the specimen in place. Use tweezers to place your specimen on the slide.

3) Add a drop of stain if your specimen is transparent or colourless — this makes the specimen easier to see.

4) Place a cover slip over the specimen. Press it down gently so that no air bubbles are trapped under it. Then clip the slide onto the stage.

5) Select the lowest-powered objective lens. Use the coarse adjustment knob to move the stage up so that the slide is just underneath the objective lens. Then, looking down the eyepiece, move the stage downwards until the specimen is nearly in focus.

6) Then adjust the focus with the fine adjustment knob, until you get a clear image.

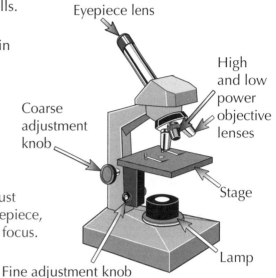

Eyepiece lens

High and low power objective lenses

Coarse adjustment knob

Stage

Fine adjustment knob

Lamp

You Might Need to Produce a **Scientific Drawing** of a **Specimen**

1) You should do your drawing using a pencil with a sharp point.

2) Make sure your drawing takes up at least half of the space available and that it is drawn with clear, unbroken lines.

3) Your drawing should not include any colouring or shading.

4) If you are drawing cells, the structures inside them should be drawn in proportion.

5) Remember to include a title of what you were observing and write down the magnification that it was observed under.

6) You should also label the important features of your drawing (e.g. nucleus, chloroplasts), using straight lines drawn with a ruler. Make sure that none of these lines cross each other because this can make them hard to read.

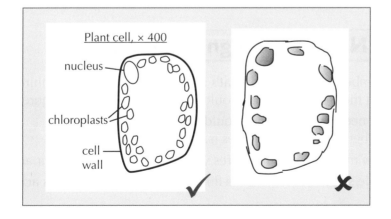

Plant cell, × 400

nucleus

chloroplasts

cell wall

If you know the power of the microscope lenses used to view an image, you can work out the magnification of the image using the formula:
total magnification = eyepiece lens magnification × objective lens magnification.
Otherwise, you can use the magnification formula on page 16.

PRACTICAL TIP

Take your time when you're doing scientific drawings

When you look at a real specimen under a microscope, it might not look exactly like the diagrams you see in books. But don't be put off — just draw what you can see.

Processing Data

Once you've had fun collecting all your data, a few calculations might be needed to work out what your data actually shows. Some simple calculations include the mean, range, median and mode.

Data Needs to be Organised

1) Tables are useful for organising data. E.g. to record the volumes of gas collected in two test tubes, you might draw a table like the one on the right.

Test tube	Volume / cm³		
	Repeat 1	Repeat 2	Repeat 3
A	28	37	32
B	47	51	16

2) When you draw a table, use a ruler to make sure your rows and columns are straight.

3) Make sure each result column has a heading that includes a physical quantity, e.g. volume, and units.

4) You should draw a table for your results before you begin an experiment. It allows you to record your results in a neat and organised way.

5) Recording your results in a table can also help you spot any results that might be anomalous (p.183) more easily, so you can try to figure out what's gone wrong or correct them early in your investigation.

You Might Have to Process Your Data

1) When you've done repeats of an experiment you should always calculate the mean (average). To do this add together all the data values and divide by the total number of values in the sample.

2) You might also need to calculate the range (how spread out the data is). To do this find the largest number and subtract the smallest number from it.

Ignore anomalous results when calculating these.

Example: The results of an experiment to find the volume of gas produced in an enzyme-controlled reaction are shown below. Calculate the mean volume and the range.

Volume / cm³				
Repeat 1	Repeat 2	Repeat 3	Mean	Range
28	37	32	(28 + 37 + 32) ÷ 3 = 32	37 − 28 = 9

3) You might also need to calculate the median or mode (two more types of average). To calculate the median, put all your data in numerical order — the median is the middle value. The number that appears most often in a data set is the mode.

If you have an even number of values, the median is halfway between the middle two values.

Example: If you have the data set: 1 2 1 1 3 4 2
The median is: 1 1 1 <u>2</u> 2 3 4. The mode is 1 because 1 appears most often.

Round to the Lowest Number of Significant Figures

The first significant figure of a number is the first digit that's not zero. The second and third significant figures come straight after (even if they're zeros). You should be aware of significant figures in calculations.

1) In any calculation where you need to round, you should round the answer to the lowest number of significant figures (s.f.) given.

2) Remember to write down how many significant figures you've rounded to after your answer.

3) If your calculation has multiple steps, only round the final answer, or it won't be as accurate.

EXAMPLE: **A plant produces 10.2 cm³ of oxygen in 6.5 minutes whilst photosynthesising. Calculate the rate of photosynthesis.**

rate = 10.2 cm³ ÷ 6.5 min = 1.5692... = 1.6 cm³/min (2 s.f.)

3 s.f.   2 s.f.   Final answer should be rounded to 2 s.f.

More on Processing Data

Another way to process data is to calculate percentage change.

Percentage Change Allows you to Compare Results

1) When investigating the change in a variable, you may want to compare results that didn't have the same initial value.

> For example, you may want to compare the change in mass of potato cylinders left in different concentrations of sugar solution that had different initial masses (see page 22).

2) One way to do this is to calculate the percentage change. You work it out like this:

$$\text{percentage (\%) change} = \frac{\text{final value} - \text{original value}}{\text{original value}} \times 100$$

3) Below is an example that shows how percentage change can be calculated:

 **EXAMPLE:** A student is investigating the effect of the concentration of sugar solution on potato cells. She records the mass of potato cylinders before and after placing them in sugar solutions of different concentrations. The table below shows some of her results. Which potato cylinder had the largest percentage change?

Potato cylinder	Concentration / M	Mass at start / g	Mass at end / g
1	0.0	7.5	8.7
2	1.0	8.0	6.8

1) Put each set of results into the equation:

$$\frac{\%}{\text{change}} = \frac{\text{final value} - \text{original value}}{\text{original value}} \times 100$$

1. $\dfrac{8.7 - 7.5}{7.5} \times 100 = 16\%$

The mass at the start is the original value and the mass at the end is the final value.

2) Compare the results.

2. $\dfrac{6.8 - 8.0}{8.0} \times 100 = -15\%$

16% is greater than 15%, so the potato cylinder in the 0.0 M sugar solution had the largest percentage change.

Here, the mass has decreased so the percentage change is negative.

 EXAM TIP

Don't forget your calculator...

It's not only important that you're able to collect and record the data, but that you can then do something with it once you've got it. In the exam you could be given some data and be expected to process it in some way. Even if it looks easy enough to do in your head, it's always worth checking on a calculator just to be sure. You don't want to lose marks by making a silly error.

Presenting Data

Once you've processed your data, e.g. by calculating the mean, you can present your results in a nice chart or graph. This will help you to spot any patterns in your data.

Bar Charts can be Used to Show Categoric Data

1) Bar charts are used to display categoric data — data that comes in distinct categories, e.g. flower colour, blood group, that is not numerical.

2) There are some golden rules you need to follow for drawing bar charts:

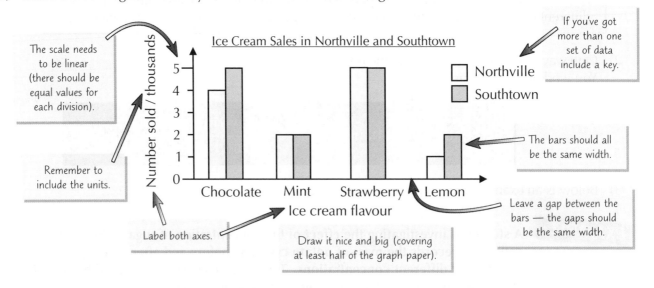

The scale needs to be linear (there should be equal values for each division).

Remember to include the units.

If you've got more than one set of data include a key.

The bars should all be the same width.

Label both axes.

Draw it nice and big (covering at least half of the graph paper).

Leave a gap between the bars — the gaps should be the same width.

With Histograms it's the Area NOT the Height that Matters

1) Histograms are a way to show frequency data (data on the number of times something occurs) when the independent variable is continuous. Continuous data is numerical data that can have any value in a range, e.g. length, volume, temperature.

2) Histograms may look like bar charts, but it's the area of the bars that represents the frequency rather than the height. The height of each bar is called the frequency density.

3) The continuous data is divided into groups called classes. For example, if the data relates to the height of students in a class, you might have the classes: $0 \text{ cm} \leq x < 140 \text{ cm}$, $140 \text{ cm} \leq x < 150 \text{ cm}$, $150 \text{ cm} \leq x < 160 \text{ cm}$, etc. The classes can be different widths. The width of each bar on a histogram is the class width.

$0 \text{ cm} \leq x < 140 \text{ cm}$ means the data in the class is more than or equal to 0 cm and less than 140 cm.

4) Here's what a histogram might look like:

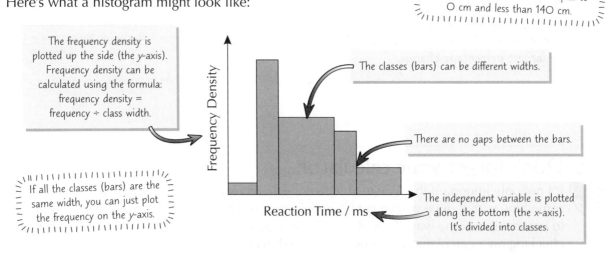

The frequency density is plotted up the side (the y-axis). Frequency density can be calculated using the formula:
frequency density = frequency ÷ class width.

If all the classes (bars) are the same width, you can just plot the frequency on the y-axis.

The classes (bars) can be different widths.

There are no gaps between the bars.

The independent variable is plotted along the bottom (the x-axis). It's divided into classes.

Presenting Data

Graphs can be Used to Plot Continuous Data

1) If both variables are continuous you should use a graph to display the data.

2) Here are the rules for plotting points on a graph:

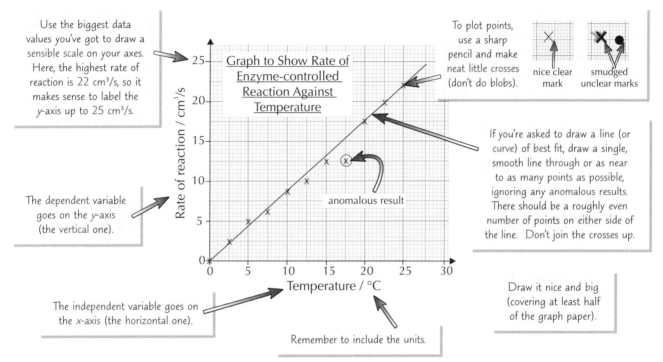

Use the biggest data values you've got to draw a sensible scale on your axes. Here, the highest rate of reaction is 22 cm³/s, so it makes sense to label the y-axis up to 25 cm³/s.

The dependent variable goes on the y-axis (the vertical one).

To plot points, use a sharp pencil and make neat little crosses (don't do blobs).

nice clear mark   smudged unclear marks

If you're asked to draw a line (or curve) of best fit, draw a single, smooth line through or as near to as many points as possible, ignoring any anomalous results. There should be a roughly even number of points on either side of the line. Don't join the crosses up.

anomalous result

The independent variable goes on the x-axis (the horizontal one).

Remember to include the units.

Draw it nice and big (covering at least half of the graph paper).

3) If you have a graph of the amount of product formed (or reactant used up) against time, then the gradient (slope) of the graph will be equal to the rate of the reaction — the steeper the slope, the faster the rate.

4) The gradient of a straight line is given by the equation:

$$\text{gradient} = \text{change in y} \div \text{change in x}$$

Pie Charts Show Proportions

1) Pie charts are a good way to compare different categories in data.

2) The amount of the whole chart a section takes up tells you the proportion (e.g. a percentage) of results in that category — the whole chart represents the entire data set.

3) When drawing pie charts there are a few rules you need to follow:

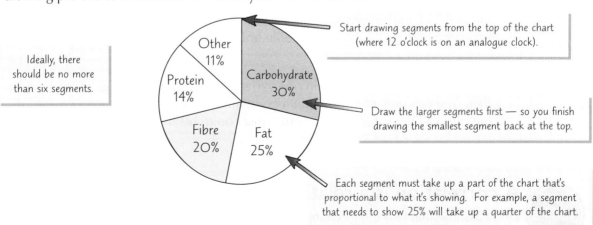

Ideally, there should be no more than six segments.

Start drawing segments from the top of the chart (where 12 o'clock is on an analogue clock).

Draw the larger segments first — so you finish drawing the smallest segment back at the top.

Each segment must take up a part of the chart that's proportional to what it's showing. For example, a segment that needs to show 25% will take up a quarter of the chart.

4) When analysing pie charts, it's important to remember that they show proportions, not the actual number in each category.

Interpreting Data

Graphs aren't just fun to plot, they're also really useful for showing trends in your data.

You Need to be Able to **Interpret** Graphs

1) A graph is used to show the relationship between two variables — you need to be able to look at a graph and describe this relationship.

> Example: The graph on the previous page shows that as temperature increases, so does rate of reaction.

A relationship is directly proportional if one variable increases at the same rate as the other variable. E.g. if one variable doubles, the other also doubles. This is only true if the line is straight and goes through the origin (O,O).

2) You also need to be able to read information off a graph. In the example on the previous page, to find what the rate of reaction was at 11 °C, you'd draw a vertical line up to the graph line from the x-axis at 11 °C and a horizontal line across to the y-axis. This would tell you that the rate of reaction at 11 °C was around 9.7 cm³/s.

Graphs Show the **Correlation** Between Two Variables

1) You can get three types of correlation (relationship) between variables:

2) Just because there's correlation, it doesn't mean the change in one variable is causing the change in the other — there might be other factors involved.

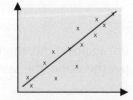

POSITIVE correlation:
as one variable increases
the other increases.

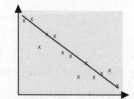

INVERSE (negative) correlation:
as one variable increases
the other decreases.

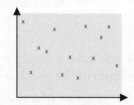

NO correlation:
no relationship between
the two variables.

3) There are three possible reasons for a correlation:

- CHANCE: It might seem strange, but two things can show a correlation purely due to chance.

- LINKED BY A 3RD VARIABLE: A lot of the time it may look as if a change in one variable is causing a change in the other, but it isn't — a third variable links the two things.

- CAUSE: Sometimes a change in one variable does cause a change in the other. You can only conclude that a correlation is due to cause when you've controlled all the variables that could, just could, be affecting the result.

A correlation is a relationship between two variables

Don't assume that two things changing together means that one is causing the other to change — it could be due to chance or to a third variable. Stop and think about what your results are really showing before drawing any sort of conclusion.

Conclusions and Evaluations

Hurrah! The end of another investigation. Well, now you have to worry about conclusions and evaluations.

You Can **Only Conclude** What the Data Shows and **NO MORE**

1) Drawing conclusions might seem pretty straightforward — you just look at your data and say what pattern or relationship you see between the dependent and independent variables.

The table on the right shows the heights of pea plant seedlings grown for three weeks with different fertilisers.

CONCLUSION: Fertiliser B makes pea plant seedlings grow taller over a three week period than fertiliser A.

Fertiliser	Mean growth / mm
A	13.5
B	19.5
No fertiliser	5.5

2) But you've got to be really careful that your conclusion matches the data you've got and doesn't go any further.

You can't conclude that fertiliser B makes any other type of plant grow taller than fertiliser A — the results could be totally different.

3) You also need to be able to use your results to justify your conclusion (i.e. back up your conclusion with some specific data).

Over the three week period, fertiliser B made the pea plants grow 6 mm more on average than fertiliser A.

4) When writing a conclusion you need to refer back to the original hypothesis and say whether the data supports it or not. If data backs up a prediction, it increases confidence in the hypothesis (although it doesn't prove the hypothesis is correct). If the data doesn't support the prediction, it can decrease confidence in it.

The hypothesis for this experiment might have been that adding fertiliser would increase the growth of plants because it would provide plants with nutrients. The prediction may have been that fertiliser B contained more nutrients and so would increase growth more than fertiliser A. If so, the data increases confidence in the hypothesis.

You Need to **Evaluate** Your **Data**

1) Before you make any conclusions based on your data, you need to perform an evaluation. An evaluation is a critical analysis of the whole investigation, including the data you obtained.

2) You should comment on the method — was it valid? Did you control all the other variables to make it a fair test?

3) Comment on the quality of the results — were the results reliable and accurate? Were there sources of random or systematic error?

4) Were there any anomalous results? If there were none then say so. If there were any, try to explain them — were they caused by errors in measurement? Were there any other variables that could have affected the results?

5) All this analysis will allow you to say how confident you are that your conclusion is right.

6) Then you can suggest any changes to the method that would improve the quality of the results, so that you could have more confidence in your conclusion. For example, you might suggest changing the way you controlled a variable, carrying out further repeats or increasing the number of measurements you took. Taking more measurements at narrower intervals could give you a more accurate result.

When suggesting improvements to the investigation, always make sure that you say why you think this would make the results better.

7) You could also make more predictions based on your conclusion, then further experiments could be carried out to test them.

Always look for ways to improve your investigations

There are 40 marks available in the practical assessment part of your exam (Paper 5 or 6). So you need to be able to describe experiments, process data, draw conclusions, etc. all in an appropriate way. Make sure you're happy with everything in this section. Best of luck.

Practice Papers

Once you've been through all the questions in this book, you should feel pretty confident about the exams. As final preparation, here is a set of practice exam papers to really get you ready for the real thing.

CGP Practice Exam Paper
Cambridge International
GCSE Biology

Cambridge International GCSE Biology

Paper 1 Multiple Choice (Core)

In addition to this paper you should have:
- A soft pencil.
- A calculator.
- An eraser.

Centre name					
Centre number					
Candidate number					

Time allowed:
- 45 minutes

Candidate name
Candidate signature

Instructions to candidates
- Write your name and other details in the spaces provided above.
- Use pencil to record your answers.
- For each question, clearly shade the oval next to your chosen answer. For example: ⬤
  If you wish to change your answer, use an eraser to remove your original answer.
- Do all rough work on the paper.

Information for candidates
- There are 40 marks available for this paper.
- Each question is worth one mark.

1 Where is DNA found in plant and animal cells?

    A cytoplasm

    B cell membrane

    C nucleus

    D vacuoles

2 A bean plant produces carbohydrate during photosynthesis.
Which structure allows the cells of a bean plant to photosynthesise?

    A cell wall

    B chloroplast

    C cytoplasm

    D vacuole

3 The diagram shows a root hair cell viewed under a microscope at × 100 magnification.

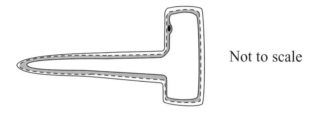

Not to scale

The real length of the root hair cell is 0.08 mm.
What is the length of the root hair cell in the microscope image?

    A 0.0008 mm

    B 0.8 mm

    C 8 mm

    D 8 cm

4 The diagram shows a cell and the surrounding tissue fluid.
Oxygen moves between the cell and the tissue fluid by diffusion.

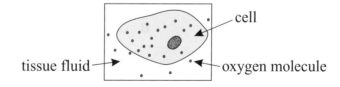

Which row describes how most of the oxygen molecules in the diagram will move?

	Direction of movement	Description of movement
A	cell → tissue fluid	against concentration gradient
B	cell → tissue fluid	down concentration gradient
C	tissue fluid → cell	against concentration gradient
D	tissue fluid → cell	down concentration gradient

196

5 In which of these examples is osmosis occurring?

    A A plant is absorbing water from the soil. ◯

    B Sugar is being taken up into the blood from the gut. ◯

    C Water is evaporating from a leaf. ◯

    D Oxygen is entering the blood from the lungs. ◯

6 Which statement about active transport is correct?

    A It is the way in which oxygen enters the blood from the lungs. ◯

    B It can only occur down a concentration gradient. ◯

    C It needs energy from respiration. ◯

    D Particles move from a region of higher concentration to a region of lower concentration. ◯

7 The biuret test is used on a sample of an unknown substance in solution. The solution turns purple. What is the unknown substance in the solution?

    A carbohydrate ◯

    B fat ◯

    C protein ◯

    D water ◯

8 A student investigates how temperature affects the rate at which starch is broken down by the enzyme amylase. Which graph correctly shows how the rate of the reaction is affected by temperature?

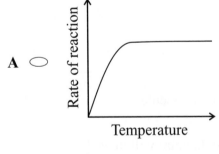

A ◯

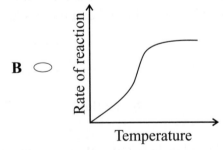

B ◯

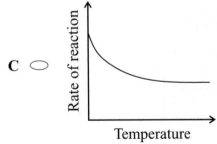

C ◯

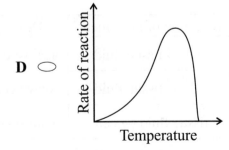

D ◯

9   Which of these is **not** part of the overall equation for photosynthesis?

   A   carbon dioxide

   B   nitrates

   C   light

   D   chlorophyll

10   The apparatus below is used to investigate the effect of different factors on the rate of photosynthesis.

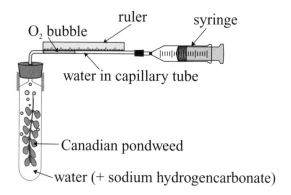

The apparatus is left in the following places for one hour.
In which place will the longest oxygen bubble be produced?

   A   a dark fridge

   B   a dark room

   C   a fridge with the light switched on

   D   a room with the light switched on

11   Which row shows a correct source of the nutrients needed for the body to carry out each function?

	Function			
	Making bones and teeth	Calcium absorption	Making haemoglobin	Maintaining the immune system
A	milk	citrus fruits	red meat	eggs
B	milk	eggs	red meat	citrus fruits
C	red meat	eggs	milk	citrus fruits
D	red meat	citrus fruits	milk	eggs

12 What is 'assimilation'?

A The movement of digested food molecules into the cells of the body
where they are used, becoming part of the cells.

B The taking of substances into the body through the mouth.

C The passing out of food that has not been digested or absorbed, through the anus.

D The movement of small food molecules and ions through the intestine wall into the blood.

13 What molecule is digested by amylase and where in the alimentary canal is amylase produced?

	molecule digested	where produced
A	starch	salivary glands
B	protein	salivary glands
C	starch	stomach
D	protein	stomach

14 The diagram shows a section through a leaf.

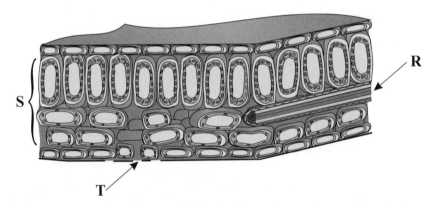

Which statement correctly describes how water is lost from the leaf via transpiration?

A Water evaporates from **R**, then diffuses through **T**.

B Water diffuses through **R**, then evaporates at **T**.

C Water evaporates from cells in **S**, then diffuses through **T**.

D Water evaporates from cells in **S**, then diffuses through **R**.

15 The diagram shows the equipment used to investigate transpiration rate.

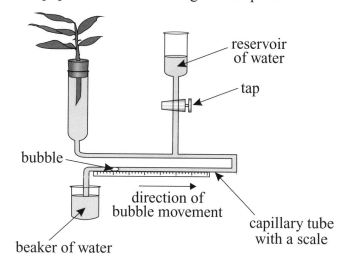

The experiment is carried out once as a control, and the distance moved by the bubble in 30 minutes is recorded. The experiment is then repeated in different environmental conditions. In which conditions will the bubble travel furthest?

A warm, humid air

B warm, dry air

C cool, humid air

D cool, dry air

16 The bar chart below shows the average pulse rate for four different levels of physical activity in a study. The four activities are shown on the right.

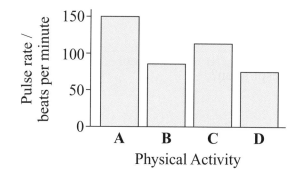

1. Sitting
2. Walking
3. Jogging
4. Running

Which physical activity on the graph is likely to be jogging?

A

B

C

D

17 Blood is carried around the body in blood vessels.
    Three types of blood vessel are shown below.

P   Q   R

Which statement is correct?

A Vessels **Q** and **R** have one-way valves. ◯

B Vessel **P** carries blood really close to every cell in the body. ◯

C Vessel **R** has permeable walls. ◯

D Vessel **Q** carries blood from the heart to the rest of the body. ◯

18 Which diagram shows a mechanical defence of the body against pathogens?

A ◯   **B** ◯   **C** ◯   **D** ◯

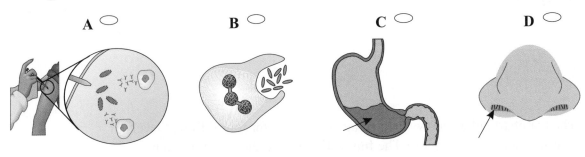

19 What reacts with glucose in aerobic respiration?

A water ◯

B carbon dioxide ◯

C lactic acid ◯

D oxygen ◯

20 Which of these is **not** a possible product of anaerobic respiration?

A water ◯

B carbon dioxide ◯

C lactic acid ◯

D alcohol ◯

21 What substance is filtered out of the blood in the kidneys for removal in the urine?

   A proteins

   B carbon dioxide

   C oxygen

   D urea

22 Which row is correct for a reflex action?

	speed of action	decision
A ⬯	slow	under conscious control
B ⬯	slow	automatic
C ⬯	rapid	under conscious control
D ⬯	rapid	automatic

23 The diagram shows a section through the human eye.

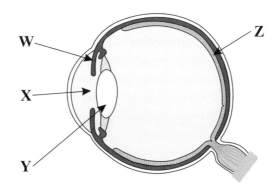

Which statement about the diagram is **false**?

   A **W** controls how much light enters **X**.

   B **Y** focuses light onto **Z**.

   C The diameter of **X** increases in bright light.

   D **Z** contains light receptors.

24 The optic nerve carries impulses.
Where do the impulses go once they have left the retina?

   A cornea

   B brain

   C blind spot

   D lens

25 Parts of the endocrine system are shown below.

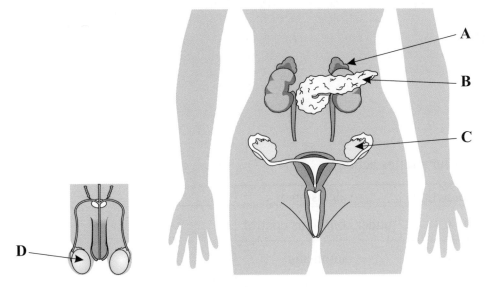

A hormone causes increased breathing and pulse rate in 'fight or flight' situations.
Which labelled gland is this hormone secreted from?

A ◯

B ◯

C ◯

D ◯

26 Which disease could be treated using antibiotics?

A HIV ◯

B cholera ◯

C coronary heart disease ◯

D scurvy ◯

27 Part of a flower is shown below.

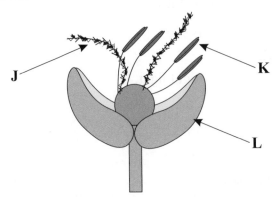

Which statement about the diagram is correct?

A Structure **K** catches pollen from other plants. ◯

B Structure **L** is likely to be brightly coloured. ◯

C Structure **J** produces big, sticky pollen grains. ◯

D Structure **K** releases many small, light pollen grains. ◯

28 The female reproductive system is shown below.

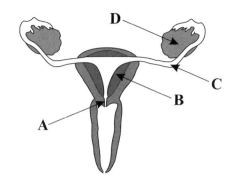

In which labelled structure does fertilisation take place?

A ○

B ○

C ○

D ○

29 The male reproductive system is shown below.

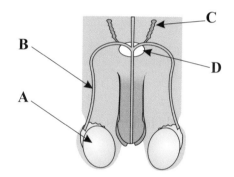

In which labelled structure is sperm produced?

A ○

B ○

C ○

D ○

30 Which row is correct for each method of birth control?

		Natural	Chemical	Barrier	Surgical
A	○	IUD	abstinence	diaphragm	vasectomy
B	○	monitoring body temperature	femidom	contraceptive implant	female sterilisation
C	○	monitoring cervical mucus	IUS	condom	vasectomy
D	○	abstinence	contraceptive pill	female sterilisation	diaphragm

31 Biological sex in humans is determined by sex chromosomes.
Which statement is **true**?

    A The presence of a Y chromosome results in male features.

    B The presence of two X chromosomes results in male features.

    C The presence of an X and a Y chromosome results in female features.

    D The presence of two Y chromosomes results in female features.

32 Which row is correct?

	produces genetically identical cells	used in asexual reproduction	produces gametes
A	mitosis	mitosis	meiosis
B	mitosis	meiosis	mitosis
C	meiosis	meiosis	mitosis
D	meiosis	mitosis	meiosis

33 What term is used to describe the observable features of an organism?

    A genotype

    B homozygous

    C phenotype

    D heterozygous

34 Fruit flies can either have normal wings or small, deformed wings. The gene for normal wings is dominant (N). In an experiment, a scientist wanted to produce a population of fruit flies made up of 75% flies with normal wings and 25% flies with small, deformed wings.

Which cross would have the best chance of producing this population?

    A NN × Nn

    B NN × nn

    C nn × Nn

    D Nn × Nn

35 Which row is correct for variation in height?

	an example of continuous variation	an example of discontinuous variation	an example of phenotypic variation
A ◯	✓	✗	✗
B ◯	✓	✗	✓
C ◯	✗	✓	✗
D ◯	✗	✓	✓

36 Which description would **not** be used when describing selective breeding?

   A Competition for resources and struggle for survival. ◯

   B Selection by humans of individuals with desirable features. ◯

   C Selection of offspring showing desirable features. ◯

   D Crossing individuals with desirable features to produce a new generation. ◯

37 The statements below describe how different organisms obtain energy or nutrients.

    1.   By eating plants.

    2.   By eating other animals.

    3.   By breaking down dead material and waste.

    4.   From the soil.

How do carnivores get their energy?

   A 1, 2, 3 and 4 ◯

   B 1, 2 and 3 only ◯

   C 1 only ◯

   D 2 only ◯

38 The diagram shows some of the feeding relationships in a rocky shore environment.

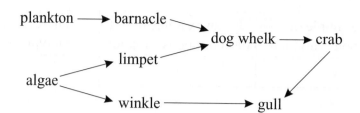

Which of the following organisms is **not** a secondary or a tertiary consumer?

A crab

B limpet

C gull

D dog whelk

39 The diagram shows part of the water cycle.

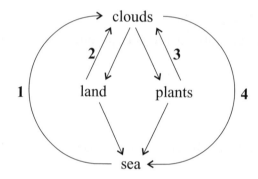

In which labelled stage(s) is transpiration occurring?

	1	2	3	4
A ○	✓	✓	✓	✗
B ○	✗	✓	✓	✗
C ○	✗	✗	✓	✗
D ○	✓	✗	✓	✓

40 Which of these is an example of genetic engineering?

A The production of ethanol for biofuels using yeast.

B The production of a bacterium that can produce human insulin.

C The production of fruit juice using the enzyme pectinase.

D The use of enzymes in biological washing powders.

END OF QUESTIONS

Cambridge International GCSE Biology

Paper 2 Multiple Choice (Extended)

In addition to this paper you should have:
- A soft pencil.
- A calculator.
- An eraser.

Centre name				
Centre number				
Candidate number				

Time allowed:
- 45 minutes

Candidate name
Candidate signature

Instructions to candidates
- Write your name and other details in the spaces provided above.
- Use pencil to record your answers.
- For each question, clearly shade the oval next to your chosen answer. For example: ⬤
  If you wish to change your answer, use an eraser to remove your original answer.
- Do all rough work on the paper.

Information for candidates
- There are 40 marks available for this paper.
- Each question is worth one mark.

Turn over ▶

1   Which of the following organisms is a myriapod?

   A ○   B ○   C ○   D ○

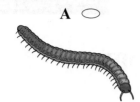 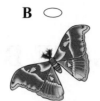  

2   Which row correctly shows two features of fungi?

	Feature 1	Feature 2
A ○	Can store carbohydrate	Has cell walls containing cellulose
B ○	Reproduce using spores	Has cell walls containing chitin
C ○	Can photosynthesise	Reproduce using spores
D ○	Has cell walls containing chitin	Can photosynthesise

3   The diagram shows a cell.

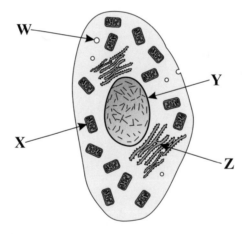

Which of these statements is **false**?

A This cell has a high rate of metabolism.

B This cell can photosynthesise.

C Prokaryotes do not have structures **X**, **Y** or **Z**.

D Structure **W** transports substances in and out of the cell.

○
○
○
○

4 The diagram shows a blood cell viewed under a microscope.
The real width of the blood cell is 12 μm.

24 mm

What is the magnification of the cell?

A × 500

B × 1000

C × 2000

D × 4000

5 The diagram shows the set-up for an investigation into the rate of diffusion.
The faster the rate of diffusion, the quicker the agar cubes turn colourless.

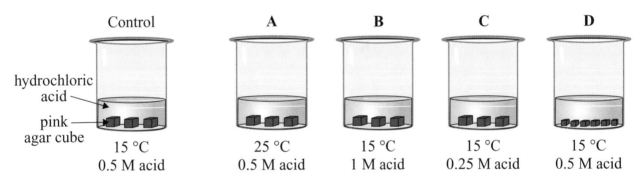

Control	A	B	C	D
15 °C	25 °C	15 °C	15 °C	15 °C
0.5 M acid	0.5 M acid	1 M acid	0.25 M acid	0.5 M acid

hydrochloric acid
pink agar cube

In which beaker will the rate of diffusion **not** be faster than in the control?

A

B

C

D

6 A plant tissue is placed in a solution with a higher water potential than itself.

Which statement correctly describes the effect on the plant tissue?

A The cells will become turgid.

B There will be no turgor pressure in the cells.

C The cells will become flaccid.

D Plasmolysis of the cells will occur.

7 In which scenario does active transport **not** occur?

    A Ion uptake by root hair cells in the soil.

    B Glucose uptake by epithelial cells of the villi.

    C Water uptake by root hair cells in the soil.

    D Glucose uptake by epithelial cells of the kidney tubules.

8 Which of the following can be used to test for vitamin C in a food sample?

    A Benedict's solution

    B DCPIP solution

    C ethanol

    D biuret solution

9 The diagram shows an example of enzyme action.

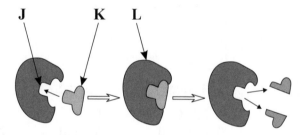

Which row correctly labels the diagram?

	J	K	L
A ◯	active site	substrate	product
B ◯	substrate	active site	enzyme-substrate complex
C ◯	substrate	active site	product
D ◯	active site	substrate	enzyme-substrate complex

10 The graph below shows the results of an investigation into
the effect of different limiting factors on photosynthesis.

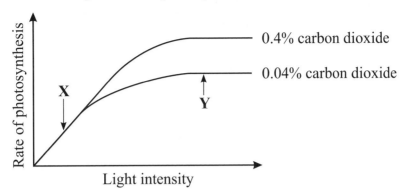

What are the limiting factors at points **X** and **Y**?

		Limiting Factor at **X**	Limiting Factor at **Y**
A	○	light intensity	temperature
B	○	carbon dioxide concentration	light intensity
C	○	light intensity	carbon dioxide concentration
D	○	temperature	carbon dioxide concentration

11 Which row shows the correct use of the ion in plants?

		Ion	Use
A	○	Nitrate	Making chlorophyll
B	○	Magnesium	Making amino acids and proteins
C	○	Nitrate	Making cell membranes
D	○	Magnesium	Making chlorophyll

12 Some symptoms of a dietary deficiency are shown below.

1. Tiredness

2. Shortness of breath

3. Pale skin

Which deficiency is most likely to cause these symptoms?

A kwashiorkor (protein deficiency)   ○

B vitamin D deficiency   ○

C iron deficiency   ○

D vitamin C deficiency   ○

13 Which row shows two correct functions for the chemical involved in digestion?

	Chemical	Function 1	Function 2
A ◯	hydrochloric acid	Giving the optimum pH for pepsin activity	Denaturing enzymes in harmful microorganisms
B ◯	bile	Neutralising the acidic mixture of food entering the duodenum	Giving the optimum pH for pepsin activity
C ◯	hydrochloric acid	Emulsifying fats to increase the surface area for digestion	Denaturing enzymes in harmful microorganisms
D ◯	bile	Giving the optimum pH for pepsin activity	Emulsifying fats to increase the surface area for digestion

14 The diagram shows the structure of a villus in the small intestine.

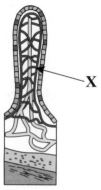

What is the role of structure **X**?

A To provide a good blood supply. ◯

B To absorb digested fats. ◯

C To provide energy from respiration. ◯

D To increase the surface area of the small intestine. ◯

15 How do nutrients move through a plant in translocation?

A In the xylem, from the source to the sink. ◯

B In the phloem, from the source to the sink. ◯

C In the xylem, from the sink to the source. ◯

D In the phloem, from the sink to the source. ◯

16 What is the function of a shunt vessel?

A To carry blood away from the heart. ◯

B To carry blood back to the heart. ◯

C To connect an artery to a vein. ◯

D To exchange substances with cells. ◯

17 The diagram below shows some blood cells under a microscope.

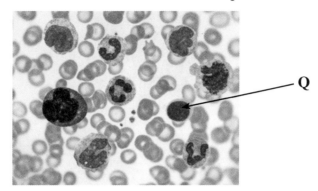

Q

What is the function of the cell marked **Q**?

A producing antibodies ○

B clotting ○

C phagocytosis ○

D transporting oxygen ○

18 Which statement would **not** be used when describing vaccination?

A Antigens trigger an immune response by lymphocytes. ○

B A dead or inactive pathogen with antigens is given. ○

C Memory cells are produced to give short-term, passive immunity. ○

D Lymphocytes produce antibodies against the antigens. ○

19 The diagram shows cells in the airways.

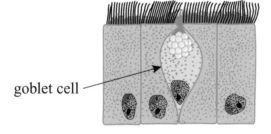

goblet cell

What is the purpose of the goblet cell?

A wafting mucus back up to the top of the throat ○

B producing antibodies ○

C transporting carbon dioxide ○

D producing mucus ○

20 Which statement about the removal of an oxygen debt is correct?

A Oxygen is needed for the aerobic respiration of lactic acid. ○

B Anaerobic respiration is used to break down lactic acid. ○

C Lactic acid is transported from the liver to the muscles. ○

D All lactic acid is broken down in the muscles. ○

21 The diagram shows the structure of the urinary system.

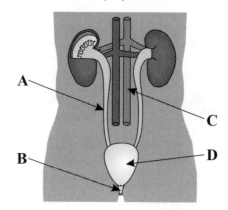

Which labelled structure is the urethra?

A ◯

B ◯

C ◯

D ◯

22 Which row correctly describes accommodation in the eye to look at distant objects?

	The ciliary muscles...	The lens becomes...	The amount of refraction...
A ◯	contract	more curved	decreases
B ◯	relax	more curved	increases
C ◯	contract	less curved	increases
D ◯	relax	less curved	decreases

23 Parts of the endocrine system are shown below.

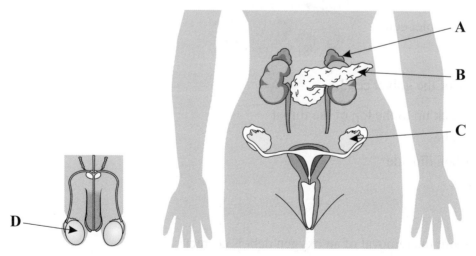

Which gland in the human body monitors and controls blood glucose concentration?

A ◯

B ◯

C ◯

D ◯

24 Which row correctly describes mechanisms to decrease body temperature?

	Erector muscles in hairs...	Amount of sweat...	Arterioles near the skin surface...
A ◯	contract	decreases	dilate
B ◯	relax	increases	constrict
C ◯	contract	increases	constrict
D ◯	relax	increases	dilate

25 The diagram shows an investigation into phototropism in cress seedlings.
The arrow shows the direction from which the light is coming.

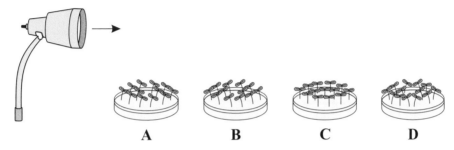

Which Petri dish shows the direction of seedling growth after two days?

A ◯

B ◯

C ◯

D ◯

26 The diagram shows a synapse.

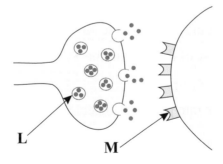

How would heroin act on this synapse?

A By dissolving neurotransmitters. ◯

B By stopping **L** releasing neurotransmitters. ◯

C By making **L** release more neurotransmitters. ◯

D By stopping neurotransmitters binding to **M**. ◯

27 Which row is correct?

		Produces genetic variation	Requires two parents	Produces offspring more quickly
A	○	sexual reproduction	asexual reproduction	sexual reproduction
B	○	asexual reproduction	sexual reproduction	sexual reproduction
C	○	sexual reproduction	sexual reproduction	asexual reproduction
D	○	asexual reproduction	asexual reproduction	asexual reproduction

28 The stages of development of a baby are shown.

1. fetus
2. zygote
3. embryo

What is the correct sequence of the stages?

A $2 \rightarrow 1 \rightarrow 3$ ○
B $1 \rightarrow 3 \rightarrow 2$ ○
C $2 \rightarrow 3 \rightarrow 1$ ○
D $3 \rightarrow 2 \rightarrow 1$ ○

29 Which statement would **not** be used when describing *in vitro* fertilisation?

A Eggs are collected from the woman's ovaries. ○
B Fertilised eggs are grown into embryos in an incubator. ○
C The hormones FSH and LH are given to stimulate several eggs to mature. ○
D Fertilisation takes place in the uterus. ○

30 The steps in protein synthesis are shown.

1. The gene coding for the protein remains in the **X**.
2. mRNA molecules carry a copy of the gene to the **Y**.
3. The mRNA passes through a **Z**.
4. The **Z** assembles amino acids into protein molecules.

What are the correct names for structures **X**, **Y** and **Z**?

		X	Y	Z
A	○	nucleus	cytoplasm	ribosome
B	○	cytoplasm	nucleus	ribosome
C	○	nucleus	cytoplasm	mitochondrion
D	○	cytoplasm	nucleus	mitochondrion

31 A diploid armadillo zygote contains 64 chromosomes.

How many chromosomes are in an armadillo gamete?

A 23

B 32

C 64

D 128

32 Red-green colour blindness is caused by a recessive allele (n) on the X chromosome. A man with red-green colour blindness has a child with a woman who is a carrier for the condition. The genetic diagram is shown.

		man	
		X^n	Y
woman	X^N	$X^N X^n$	$X^N Y$
	X^n	$X^n X^n$	$X^n Y$

What is the probability that the couple will have a child with red-green colour blindness?

A 0%

B 25%

C 50%

D 75%

33 The graph shows the percentage of UK blood donors with different blood groups.

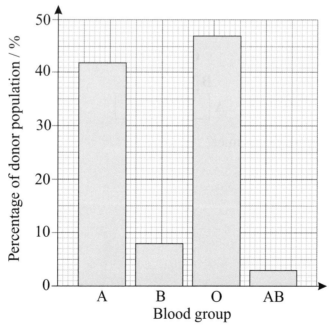

What percentage of donors have the I^B allele?

A 3%

B 8%

C 11%

D 55%

218

34 What term is given to the inherited functional features of an organism that increase its fitness?

A variation

B sex-linked characteristics

C mutations

D adaptive features

35 The diagram below shows a cross-section of a plant leaf.

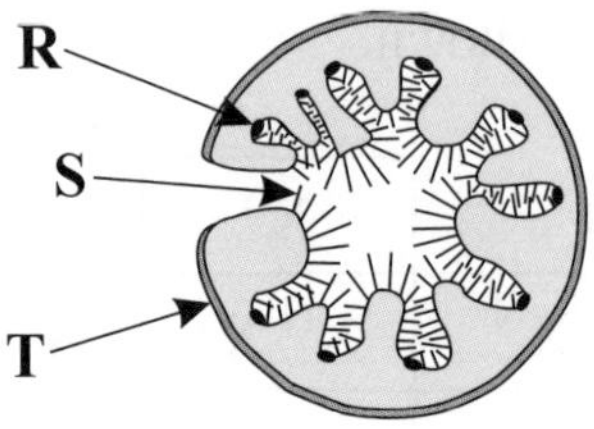

Which statement is **false**?

A The leaf is from a plant that is adapted to live in a dry climate.

B Structure **R** is sunk in a pit to increase transpiration.

C Structure **T** helps to reduce water loss by evaporation.

D Structure **S** helps to trap a layer of humid air close to the surface.

36 The diagram shows a pyramid of biomass.

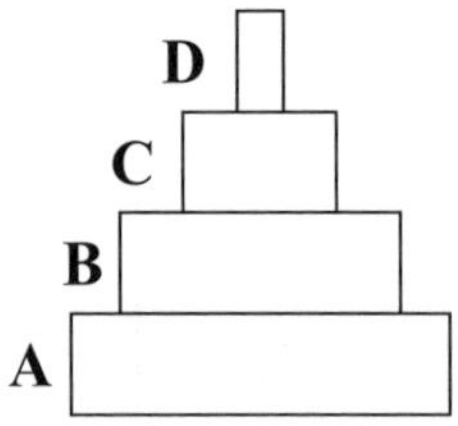

Which bar represents a primary consumer?

A

B

C

D

37 What is 'denitrification'?

A Turning NO_3^- in the soil into N_2 in the air.

B Turning NH_4^+ into NO_2^- and then NO_3^-.

C Turning N_2 in the air into nitrogen compounds.

D Turning proteins and urea into NH_4^+.

38 What is a 'community'?

A All of the populations of different species in an ecosystem. ○

B A group of organisms of one species, living in the same area at the same time. ○

C A unit containing organisms and their environment interacting together. ○

D A group of organisms that can reproduce to produce fertile offspring. ○

39 The diagram shows the genetic engineering of a bacterial plasmid.

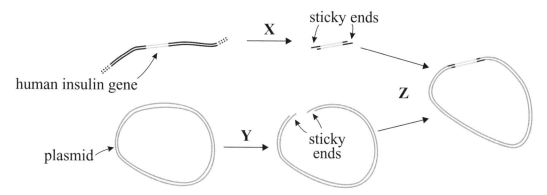

Which row of the table shows the correct enzymes for processes **X**, **Y** and **Z**?

	X	Y	Z
A ○	restriction enzymes	DNA ligase	restriction enzymes
B ○	DNA ligase	restriction enzymes	restriction enzymes
C ○	restriction enzymes	restriction enzymes	DNA ligase
D ○	DNA ligase	DNA ligase	restriction enzymes

40 The steps in eutrophication are shown.

1. The amount of dissolved oxygen in the water decreases.

2. The amount of decomposition increases, so aerobic respiration of decomposers increases.

3. Growth of producers such as algae increases, blocking out the light.

4. Organisms in the water that need dissolved oxygen die.

5. Fertilisers enter the water, providing extra nitrates and other ions.

What is the correct sequence of the steps?

A $5 \rightarrow 3 \rightarrow 1 \rightarrow 2 \rightarrow 4$ ○

B $5 \rightarrow 3 \rightarrow 2 \rightarrow 1 \rightarrow 4$ ○

C $5 \rightarrow 2 \rightarrow 3 \rightarrow 1 \rightarrow 4$ ○

D $5 \rightarrow 1 \rightarrow 2 \rightarrow 3 \rightarrow 4$ ○

END OF QUESTIONS

CGP — Practice Exam Paper Cambridge International GCSE Biology

Cambridge International GCSE Biology

Paper 3 Theory (Core)

In addition to this paper you should have:
- A pen and pencil.
- A ruler.
- A calculator.

Centre name					
Centre number					
Candidate number					

Time allowed:
- 1 hour 15 minutes

Candidate name
Candidate signature

Instructions to candidates
- Write your name and other details in the spaces provided above.
- Use blue or black ink to write your answers.
- Answer all questions in the spaces provided.
- Do all rough work on the paper.
- Cross out any work you do not want to be marked.
- In calculations, show clearly how you worked out your answers.

Information for candidates
- The marks available are given in brackets at the end of each question part.
- There are 80 marks available for this paper.

1   **Figure 1** shows a plant cell.

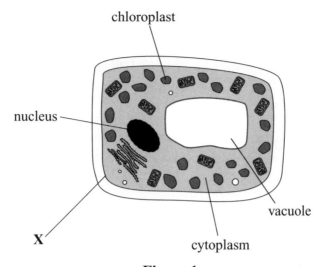

Figure 1

(a) (i)   State the name of part **X**.

....
[1]

(ii) State the function of part **X**.

....
[1]

(b) What part of the cell contains genetic material that controls the activities of the cell?

....
[1]

(c) Explain how this cell gets its food.

....

....

....
[2]

(d) (i)   Give **two** differences between this cell and an animal cell.

1. ....

2. ....
[2]

(ii) Give **one** similarity between this cell and an animal cell.

....
[1]

222

(e) A scientist viewed an individual plant cell under a microscope with × 150 magnification.
He calculated the real length of the plant cell to be 0.054 mm.
Calculate the length of the image of the plant cell. Use the formula:

$$\text{magnification} = \frac{\text{image size}}{\text{real size}}$$

....

....

.... mm

[2]

[Total 10 marks]

2 Enzymes are important in all living organisms.

(a) Define *enzyme*.

....

....
[1]

Biotechnology is where living organisms and biological processes are manipulated to produce a useful product. One use of biotechnology is in fruit juice production.

(b) (i) Name an enzyme commonly used in fruit juice production.

....
[1]

(ii) Explain why the enzyme you named in **(b) (i)** is used.

....

....

....
[2]

The anaerobic respiration of yeast is also exploited in biotechnology.

(c) (i) Complete the word equation for the anaerobic respiration of yeast.

.... → .... + carbon dioxide
[1]

(ii) State **two** uses of the anaerobic respiration of yeast in biotechnology.

1. ....

2. ....
[2]

[Total 7 marks]

Turn over ▶

3 The lung is a specialised gas exchange organ.

(a) What is meant by the term *organ*?

....

....
[1]

The lung contains millions of air sacs called alveoli.
Figure 2 shows an alveolus and a blood capillary.

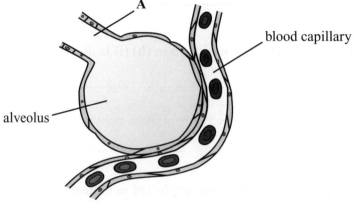

Figure 2

(b) Name the structure labelled **A**.

....
[1]

(c) State **three** features of alveoli, visible in **Figure 2**, that make them efficient
gas exchange surfaces.

1. ....

2. ....

3. ....
[3]

The composition of inspired and expired air is different.

(d) (i)   Complete **Table 1** by placing **one** tick in each row to show how the proportion of each gas changes between inspired air and expired air.

Table 1

	Change in Proportion from Inspired to Expired Air	
Name of Gas	Increases	Decreases
carbon dioxide		
oxygen		
water vapour		

[3]

(ii)   Explain how oxygen moves from an alveolus into a blood capillary.

....

....

....

....

[3]

[Total 11 marks]

4   The menstrual cycle is an important part of human reproduction.
Figure 3 shows how the uterus lining changes during one 28-day menstrual cycle.

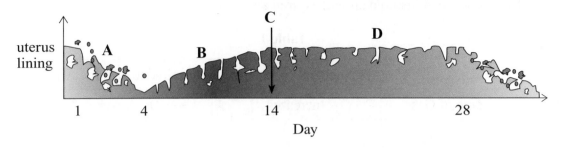

Figure 3

(a) Complete **Table 2** using letters from **Figure 3**. The first one has been done for you.

Table 2

Letter	Stage of the menstrual cycle
C	Ovulation occurs.
	The uterus lining is maintained ready for the implantation of a fertilised egg.
	The uterus lining thickens and grows.
	Menstruation occurs.

[3]

(b) (i)   Ovulation is the release of an egg from which organs in the female reproductive system?

....

[1]

   (ii)   State **two** adaptations of egg cells to their function in reproduction.

   1. ....

   2...

[2]

(c) Fertilisation takes place in the oviducts of the female reproductive system.

   Choose words from the list to complete the sentences about fertilisation.
   Each word may be used once, more than once or not at all.

   cell division   embryo   gamete   menstruation   ovary   zygote

   At fertilisation, one male and one female .... fuse to form

   a .... This then undergoes ....

   and develops into an ....

[4]
[Total 10 marks]

5   **Figure 4** shows a marine food web found near a hydrothermal vent.

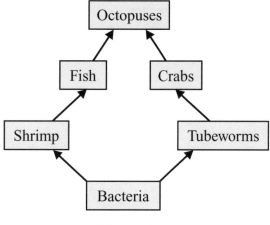

Figure 4

The producers in **Figure 4** are bacteria. They make their own organic nutrients using the energy they get from chemicals released by the hydrothermal vent.

(a) Give **one** similarity and **one** difference between these bacterial producers
    and typical plant producers.

Similarity: ....

    ....

Difference: ....

    ....

    [2]

(b) Name **one** primary consumer from the food web.

    ....

    [1]

The organisms in the food web in **Figure 4** are all interdependent.

(c) Suggest and explain how the removal of the population of **tubeworms** could affect the
    population sizes of:

(i)   the crabs,

        ....

        ....

        ....

        [2]

(ii) the shrimp.

        ....

        ....

        ....

        [2]

[Total 7 marks]

Turn over ▶

6   **Figure 5** shows a photograph of some human blood cells.

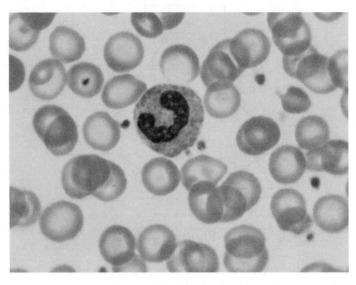

Figure 5

(a) Label a red blood cell and a white blood cell on **Figure 5**.

[1]

(b) (i)   Name **one** component of blood that is responsible for blood clotting.

....

[1]

(ii)   Suggest **one** symptom that a person might suffer from if they do not have enough of the blood component you named in **(b) (i)**.

....

[1]

The function of red blood cells is to carry oxygen from the lungs to all the cells in the body.

(c) Some athletes train in locations high above sea level for several weeks before a race.
This increases the number of red blood cells the athletes have.

Suggest how having more red blood cells might increase the amount
of energy available for muscle contraction during a race.

....

....

....

[2]

[Total 5 marks]

7 Cystic fibrosis is a genetic disorder caused by a recessive allele.
A couple have a baby boy. The doctor tells them that the baby has inherited cystic fibrosis.
Neither parent shows signs of the disorder.

(a) (i) Complete the diagram below to show how the baby inherited cystic fibrosis.
Use **F** to represent the dominant allele and **f** to represent the recessive allele.

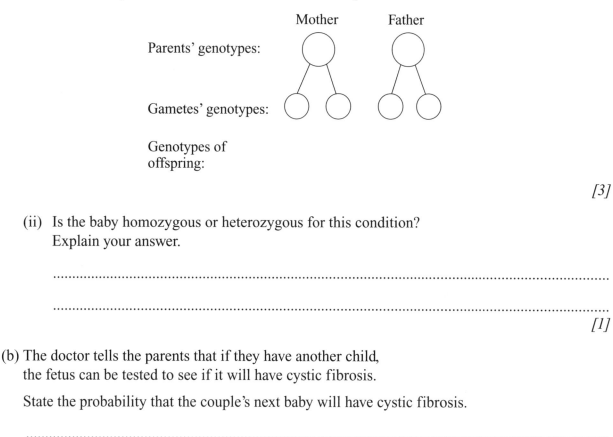

[3]

(ii) Is the baby homozygous or heterozygous for this condition?
Explain your answer.

....

....
[1]

(b) The doctor tells the parents that if they have another child,
the fetus can be tested to see if it will have cystic fibrosis.

State the probability that the couple's next baby will have cystic fibrosis.

....
[1]

The family pedigree in **Figure 6** below shows a family with a history of cystic fibrosis.

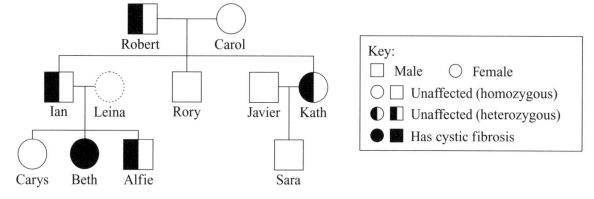

Figure 6

(c) Using the information given above, explain what Leina's genotype must be.

....

....

....
[2]

[Total 7 marks]

Turn over ▶

Practice Paper 3

8   The peppered moth is an insect that nests on the trunks of trees in Britain.
The moths are prey for birds such as thrushes.
The peppered moth exists in two varieties:

•   A light-coloured variety that is better camouflaged on tree trunks in unpolluted areas.
•   A dark-coloured variety that is better camouflaged on sooty tree trunks in badly polluted areas.

Figures 7 and **8** show these two varieties of moths on different tree trunks.

   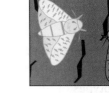

Figure 7   **Figure 8**

The dark variety of the moth was first recorded in the North of England in 1848.
It became increasingly common in polluted areas until the 1960s, when the number of soot-covered trees declined because of the introduction of new laws.

(a) The binomial name of the peppered moth is *Biston betularia*.
What is the moth's genus?

....

[1]

(b) (i)   Which variety of the moth has a better chance of survival in a soot-polluted area?

....

[1]

(ii) Using the idea of natural selection, explain why the variety of moth given in **(b) (i)**
became more common in soot-polluted areas.

....

....

....

....

[3]

Figure 9 shows the percentages of dark- and light-coloured peppered moths in two different towns.

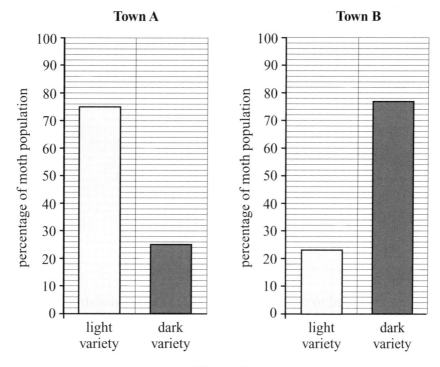

Figure 9

(c) Which town is the most polluted, **A** or **B**?
Explain your answer.

....

....

[1]

[Total 6 marks]

9 Humans can use genetic engineering to produce organisms with desired characteristics.

(a) What is meant by the term *genetic engineering*?

....

....

....

[2]

(b) Bacteria are often genetically engineered.
State **two** features of bacteria that make them suitable for this.

1. ....

2. ....

[2]

Selective breeding is also used to produce organisms with desired characteristics.

(c) Describe the process of selective breeding.

....

....

....

....

[3]

(d) Describe **one** way in which selective breeding of crop plants might be used to increase the human food supply.

....

....

....

[2]

[Total 9 marks]

10 **Figure 10** shows the carbon cycle.

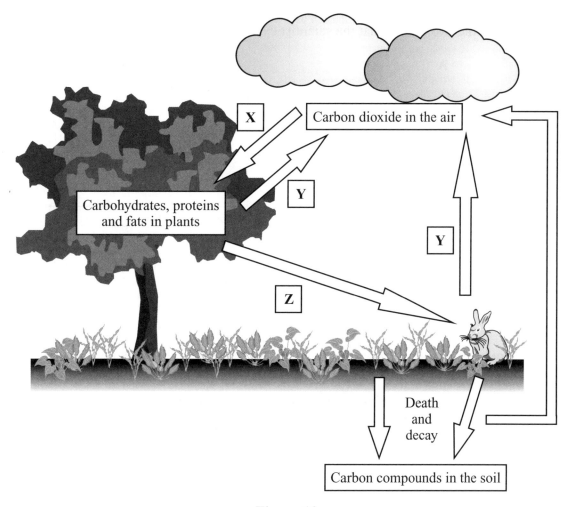

Figure 10

(a) Describe the movement of carbon occurring during processes marked **X**, **Y** and **Z** in **Figure 10**.

X ....

....

Y ....

....

Z ....

....

[3]

A scientist was examining some data to see if there is a link between the global human population and the carbon dioxide concentration in the atmosphere.

Figure 11 shows the two graphs that the scientist examined.

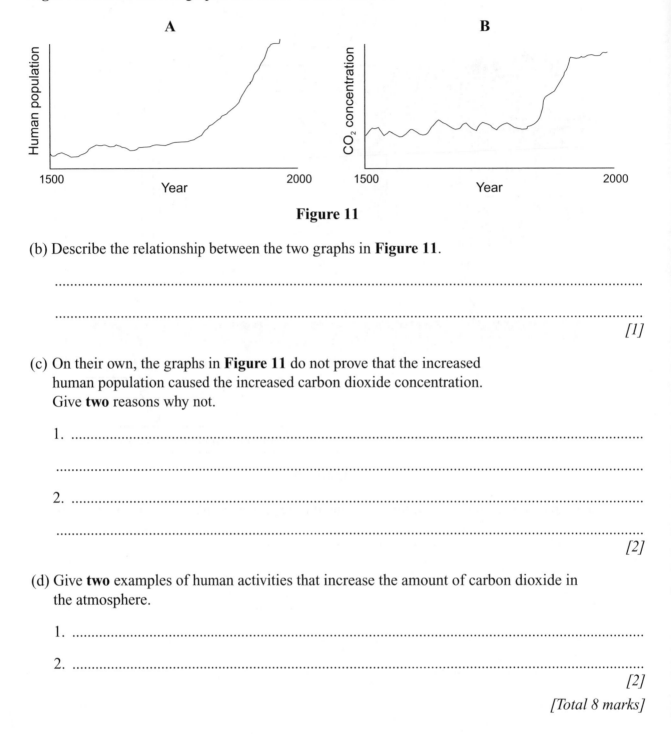

Figure 11

(b) Describe the relationship between the two graphs in **Figure 11**.

....

....

[1]

(c) On their own, the graphs in **Figure 11** do not prove that the increased human population caused the increased carbon dioxide concentration. Give **two** reasons why not.

1. ....

....

2. ....

....

[2]

(d) Give **two** examples of human activities that increase the amount of carbon dioxide in the atmosphere.

1. ....

2. ....

[2]

[Total 8 marks]

END OF QUESTIONS

Cambridge International GCSE Biology

Paper 4 Theory (Extended)

In addition to this paper you should have:
- A pen and pencil.
- A ruler.
- A calculator.

Centre name					
Centre number					
Candidate number					

Time allowed:
- 1 hour 15 minutes

Candidate name	
Candidate signature	

Instructions to candidates
- Write your name and other details in the spaces provided above.
- Use blue or black ink to write your answers.
- Answer all questions in the spaces provided.
- Do all rough work on the paper.
- Cross out any work you do not want to be marked.
- In calculations, show clearly how you worked out your answers.

Information for candidates
- The marks available are given in brackets at the end of each question part.
- There are 80 marks available for this paper.

1   Blood flows around the body in arteries, veins and capillaries.

(a) **Table 1** shows some of the features of these three different types of blood vessel.
    Complete the table by writing in the name of each type of blood vessel.

Table 1

	Type of blood vessel		
Walls	Thick, muscular	Very thin	Thin
Presence of valves	No	No	Yes
Pressure of blood in vessels	High	Low	Low

[2]

Figure 1 shows a human heart.

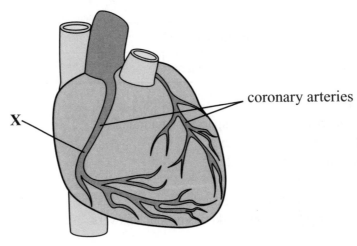

Figure 1

(b) Explain what would happen if the coronary artery was blocked at the point labelled **X**.

....

....

....

[2]

A patient has fatty deposits in the walls of one of his coronary arteries.
The patient's doctor recommends that the patient is treated using a stent.

(c) (i)   Explain how having a stent fitted could help the patient.

....

....

....

[2]

(ii) Give **one** other way of treating the patient surgically.

....

[1]

(iii) Suggest **one** change the patient could make to his diet
to reduce the risk of further fatty deposits developing.

....

[1]

[Total 8 marks]

2   **Figure 2** shows the structure of a DNA double helix.
The two strands are held together by cross-links between their bases.

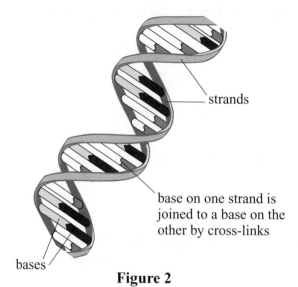

Figure 2

(a) Explain why there will always be equal amounts of bases A and T in a molecule of DNA.

....

....
[1]

(b) Name the part of a cell where strands of human DNA are found.

....
[1]

(c) Genes are lengths of DNA that code for a protein.
Exposure to some chemicals increases the rate of gene mutations.

(i)   What is meant by the term *gene mutation*?

....
[1]

(ii) Other than exposure to certain chemicals, what else can
increase the rate of mutation in DNA?

....
[1]

(iii) Enzymes are proteins. Explain why a mutation in a gene that codes for an enzyme could
negatively affect the function of the enzyme.

....

....

....

....
[3]
[Total 7 marks]

3   **Figure 3** is an extract from a report by a lifeboat crew member.

> "We were very concerned when we received news of a man lost overboard tonight because the sea is extremely cold at this time of year. Fortunately, we found him quickly and were able to rescue him before he suffered any serious ill effects. His skin was very cold when we picked him up, but his internal body temperature was normal."

Figure 3

(a) What name is given to the maintenance of a constant internal environment?

....

[1]

(b) Describe how the brain obtains information about the internal temperature of the body.

....

....

[1]

(c) (i) Explain how the man's blood vessels may have helped prevent his internal temperature from falling whilst he was in the sea.

....

....

....

[2]

(ii) Explain how the man's muscles may have helped prevent his internal temperature from falling whilst he was in the sea.

....

....

....

....

[3]

[Total 7 marks]

4   **Figure 4** shows the amount of energy contained within an area of plants.
    It shows how much energy from the plants is transferred to each trophic level in a food chain.

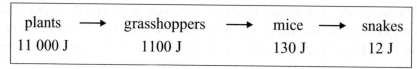

Figure 4

(a) (i)   State how much energy is available to the tertiary consumers in this food chain.

....

   [1]

   (ii) Describe how the plants in this food chain obtain their energy.

....

....

....

   [2]

   (iii) Calculate the percentage of energy in the grasshoppers that is transferred to the mice.
         Show your working.

.... %

   [2]

Figure 5 shows four pyramids of biomass.

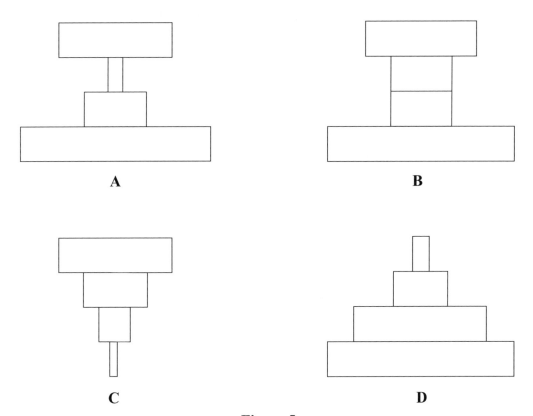

Figure 5

(b) Explain which pyramid of biomass (**A**, **B**, **C** or **D**) represents the food chain shown in **Figure 4**.

....

....

....

[2]

[Total 7 marks]

5 A student grew three plants in a windowsill tray.
She then put the plants in a cardboard box with a cut-out hole.

Figure 6 shows the same plants before and after three days in the cardboard box.

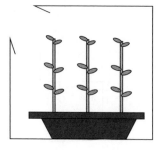
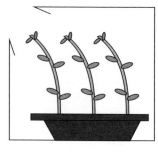

Start of experiment   After three days

Figure 6

(a) (i) Explain what caused the plants' response.

....

....

....

....

....

[3]

(ii) Name the response shown by the plants in this experiment.

....

[1]

(b) The plants responded in this way in order to maximise the
amount of light they received for photosynthesis.

(i) Complete the balanced chemical equation for photosynthesis.

$$\text{.................... } + \text{ .... } \xrightarrow{\text{light}} \text{ .... } + \text{ ....}$$

$$\text{....................}$$

[2]

(ii) Give **three** uses of the carbohydrates made in photosynthesis.

1. ....

2. ....

3. ....

[3]

(c) The student removed one of the plants from the tray.
She observed that the roots of the plant were growing downwards.

(i) Name the stimulus that causes the roots of a plant to grow downwards.

....
[1]

(ii) Suggest why it is beneficial for the roots of a plant to grow downwards.

....

....
[1]

[Total 11 marks]

6   A scientist measured the rate of transpiration in two plants over 48 hours.
The results are shown in **Figure 7**.

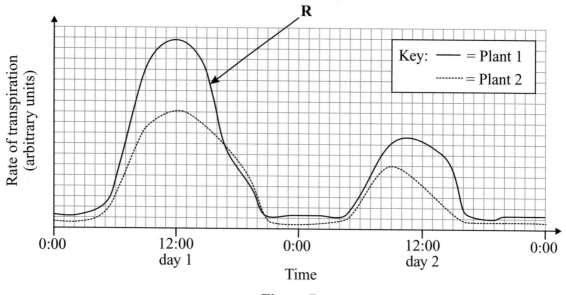

Figure 7

(a) At what time on **day 2** was the rate of transpiration highest for **plant 2**?

....

[1]

(b) The rate of transpiration for both plants was slower on **day 2** than on **day 1**.
Suggest **one** explanation for this.

....

....

....

[2]

(c) At time **R** on the graph, **plant 1** was wilting. Suggest **one** explanation for this.

....

....

....

[2]

(d) Explain how a transpiration pull moves water through a plant.

....

....

....

....

....

....

[4]

[Total 9 marks]

7   An example of a reflex action is the response of moving your hand away from a painful stimulus. **Figure 8** shows the parts of the nervous system involved in this reflex action.

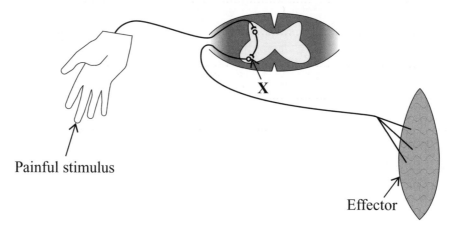

Painful stimulus

X

Effector

Figure 8

(a) Draw an arrow on **Figure 8** to show the direction in which the nerve impulse travels along the **motor neurone**.

[1]

(b) Explain how the structure labelled **X** ensures that nerve impulses only travel in one direction along a reflex arc.

....

....

....

....

....

....

[4]

(c) Describe the pathway from stimulus to response in this reflex arc.

....

....

....

....

....

....

....

....

[6]

[Total 11 marks]

8   The kidneys play a crucial role in filtering the blood.
Figure 9 shows a kidney tubule and the blood vessels associated with it.

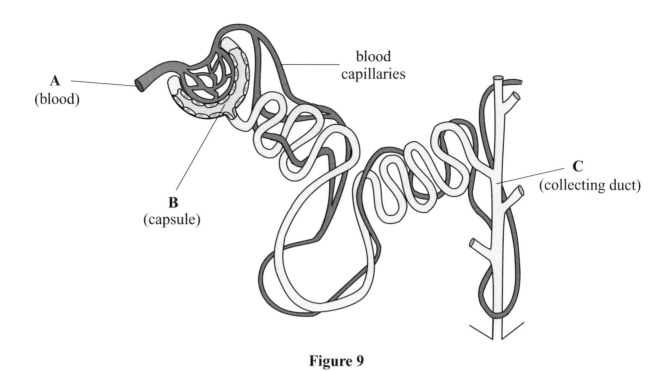

Figure 9

(a) Label the glomerulus on **Figure 9**.

[1]

(b) (i)   The concentration of urea is greatest at point **C**. Explain why.

....

....

[1]

   (ii)   Explain how the concentration of glucose at point **C** would compare to the concentration
of glucose at point **B**.

....

....

....

[2]

(c) On a cold day, an inactive person who drinks a large volume of water may produce a
larger volume of urine than on a warm day. Explain why.

....

....

....

[2]

People suffering from kidney failure may be treated using a kidney dialysis machine. **Figure 10** shows a type of dialysis machine.

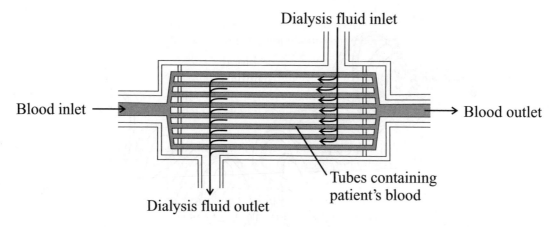

Figure 10

(d) (i)   Explain how a dialysis machine works.

....

....

....

....

[3]

(ii)   Describe **one** advantage of dialysis machines over kidney transplants as a treatment for kidney failure.

....

....

[1]

[Total 10 marks]

9 Sickle-cell anaemia is an inherited condition of the blood where the red blood cells become rigid and sickle-shaped. **Figure 11** shows a sickle-shaped red blood cell and some normal red blood cells.

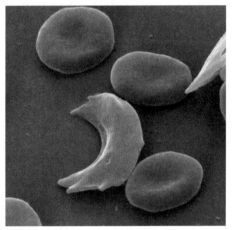

© EYE OF SCIENCE / SCIENCE PHOTO LIBRARY

Figure 11

(a) Outline how having sickle-cell anaemia causes sickle-shaped red blood cells.

....

....

....
[2]

(b) A person with sickle-cell anaemia may experience breathlessness.
Suggest an explanation for why they may experience this symptom.

....

....

....

....

....
[3]

250

(c) Two parents without sickle-cell anaemia have a child with sickle-cell anaemia.

(i) State the genotype of the child.

....
[1]

(ii) State the possible genotype(s) of the parents.

....
[1]

(d) Explain why sickle-cell anaemia is common in parts of Africa.

....

....

....

....

....
[3]

[Total 10 marks]

END OF QUESTIONS

Practice Paper 5

As part of your assessment, you will take either a practical test (Paper 5) or a written alternative to the practical test (Paper 6). You should check with your teacher which one of those options you'll be taking. Both papers will test your knowledge of experimental skills and investigations. This practice paper is the equivalent of Paper 6 in the exams.

CGP Practice Exam Paper Cambridge International GCSE Biology

Cambridge International GCSE Biology

Paper 5 Alternative to Practical

In addition to this paper you should have:
- A pen and pencil.
- A ruler.
- A calculator.

Centre name				
Centre number				
Candidate number				

Time allowed:
- 1 hour

Candidate name	
Candidate signature	

Instructions to candidates
- Write your name and other details in the spaces provided above.
- Use blue or black ink to write your answers.
- Answer all questions in the spaces provided.
- Do all rough work on the paper.
- Cross out any work you do not want to be marked.
- In calculations, show clearly how you worked out your answers.

Information for candidates
- The marks available are given in brackets at the end of each question part.
- There are 40 marks available for this paper.

1   Water diffuses through partially permeable membranes by osmosis.
     A student carried out an experiment to investigate osmosis using potatoes.
     First, the student cut cylinders out of the potatoes. He then measured and recorded the mass
     of each cylinder before placing them into different concentrations of sugar solution, as shown
     in **Figure 1**.

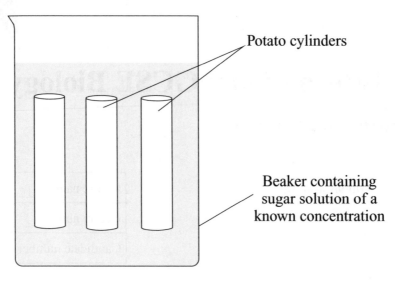

Potato cylinders

Beaker containing
sugar solution of a
known concentration

Figure 1

After 20 minutes in the sugar solution, the student dried the cylinders with tissue paper before
weighing them again.

(a) (i)   State **two** variables that the student would have had to keep the same to make the
          experiment a fair test.

          1. ....

          2. ....
                                                                                                                       [2]

    (ii)   Identify **one** source of error in the student's method and suggest an improvement.

           Error ....

           ....

           Improvement ....

           ....
                                                                                                                       [2]

(b) The student's results are shown in **Table 1**.

Table 1

Concentration of sugar solution / M	Change in mass / g			Mean change in mass / g
	Potato cylinder 1	Potato cylinder 2	Potato cylinder 3	
0.0	+0.67	+0.65	+0.69	+0.67
0.2	+0.30	+0.31	+0.33	+0.31
0.4	+0.04	−0.02	+0.04	+0.02
0.6	−0.27	−0.31	−0.25	−0.28
0.8	−0.48	−0.50	−0.47	−0.48
1.0	−0.71	−0.65	−0.72	−0.69
1.2	−0.78	−0.81	−0.82	

(i)   Complete **Table 1** by calculating the mean change in mass in the 1.2 M sugar solution. Show your working.

[1]

(ii) Explain why the student used three potato cylinders in each concentration of sugar solution, and took a mean of the results.

....

[1]

(c) Draw a graph of the mean change in mass against the concentration of sugar solution on the grid below. Draw a curve of best fit.

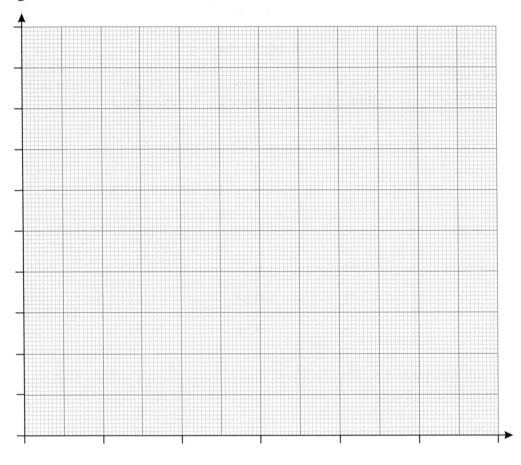

[5]

(d) Another student wanted to repeat the experiment with different concentrations of sugar solution. She was given test tubes containing the following glucose (sugar) concentrations: 0 M, 0.02 M, 0.1 M, 1 M. The test tubes were not labelled, so she was asked to perform tests on samples from the test tubes to determine which test tube contained which glucose solution.

(i) Describe a test she could carry out to try to distinguish between the glucose solutions.

....

....

....

[3]

(ii) **Table 2** shows the substance observed in the samples from the test tubes following the test that the student carried out. Complete the table to show which glucose solution (0 M, 0.02 M, 0.1 M, 1 M) each test tube contained.

Table 2

	Tube 1	Tube 2	Tube 3	Tube 4
substance observed	yellow precipitate	blue solution	red precipitate	green precipitate
glucose concentration / M	....	....	....	....

[1]

(e) Potato plants produce sugars when they photosynthesise. Some of these sugars are converted into starch and stored in structures called starch grains in the plants' cells. Starch grains can be stained. When viewed through a microscope they appear as circular structures and are darker in colour than the cytoplasm. **Figure 2** shows stained potato cells containing starch grains viewed through a microscope.

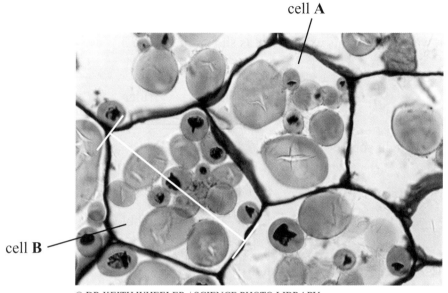

© DR KEITH WHEELER / SCIENCE PHOTO LIBRARY

Figure 2

(i)   Cell **A** in **Figure 2** measures 41 mm. Measure the length of the bar drawn on cell **B** and calculate the average length of the two cells.

average length = ... mm

[2]

(ii) Produce a large, labelled drawing of cell **A**.

[4]

[Total 21 marks]

Turn over ▶

2   A student decided to investigate the effect of light intensity on the rate of photosynthesis in pondweed. The student set up a test tube containing a solution of sodium hydrogencarbonate next to a light source. Sodium hydrogencarbonate dissolves in water and releases carbon dioxide, which plants need to photosynthesise. Next, she took a cutting of the pondweed and placed it into the test tube. She then measured the amount of gas collected in two hours.

She carried out this experiment five times, each time with the light source 10 cm further away from the test tube.

The apparatus that was used for this experiment is shown in **Figure 3**.

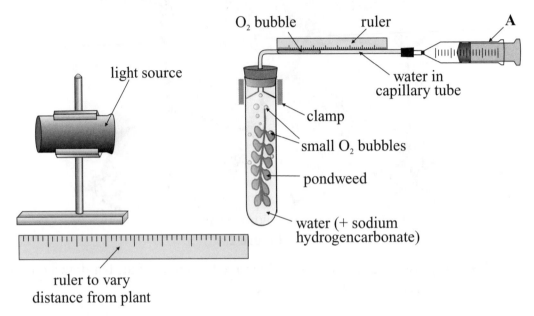

Figure 3

(a) (i)   Name the piece of equipment labelled **A**.

....

[1]

(ii)   Explain why it is important that the student adds the same amount of sodium hydrogencarbonate solution each time.

....

....

[1]

(b) The student started with the test tube 0 cm from the light source.
She repeated the experiment three times at each distance.
Prepare a table to record the results from her experiment.

[3]

(c) Once the experiment was completed the student processed her results and calculated the average rate of gas production at each distance. Her results are shown in **Table 3**.

Table 3

Distance away from light source / cm	Average rate of gas production / cm³/h
0	0.75
10	0.70
20	0.90
30	0.35
40	

(i) The average volume of gas collected when the distance was 40 cm was 0.20 cm³.
Complete **Table 3** by calculating the average rate of gas production at a distance of 40 cm.
[1]

(ii) The student thinks that one of the distances produced an anomalous result.
Suggest which distance this might be. Give a reason for your answer.

....

....
[2]

(iii) Ignoring the anomalous result identified in part **(c) (ii)**, use the results in **Table 3** to describe and explain the effect of the distance from the light source on the rate of gas production in pondweed.

....

....

....
[2]

(iv) Suggest **one** way in which you could increase your confidence in the answer you gave to part **(c) (iii)**.

....
[1]

d) Explain why it is important that the same light source is used each time the experiment is repeated.

....

....

....

[2]

e) After the experiment was conducted, a leaf from the pondweed was tested for starch. The leaf was boiled to stop any chemical reactions happening. The leaf was then heated in ethanol to remove chlorophyll. A few drops of iodine solution were then added.

(i) Suggest a safety precaution that should be taken when working with substances such as ethanol and iodine solution.

....

....

[1]

(ii) The leaf tested positive for starch.
How could the student tell that the leaf contained starch?

....

....

[1]

f) Describe how the student's original experiment could be altered to investigate the effect of temperature on the rate of photosynthesis, rather than light intensity.

....

....

....

....

....

[4]

[Total 19 marks]

END OF QUESTIONS

Answers

Section 1 — Characteristics and Classification of Living Organisms

Pages 9-10
Warm-Up Questions
1) Nutrition is the taking in of materials for energy, growth and development.
2) A species is a group of similar organisms that can reproduce to give fertile offspring.
3) Arthropods are invertebrates that have exoskeletons and segmented bodies.

Exam Questions
1 a) Stripes and spots *[1 mark]*
 b) Butterfly F *[1 mark]*
2 a) E.g. they feed, which means they require nutrition. / They are sensitive to chemicals in the water, allowing them to detect food. This shows they can respond to changes in their environment. / They are able to travel towards food, showing that they can move. *[3 marks]*
 b) respiration *[1 mark]*
 c) Excretion is the removal of the waste products of metabolism, toxic materials and substances that are in excess of what the organism needs *[1 mark]*.
 d) E.g. it may be smaller. / It may not be fully developed. *[1 mark]*
 e) *Asterias* *[1 mark]*
3 a) plants, animals, fungi, prokaryotes and protoctists *[1 mark]*
 b) Any two from: e.g. they are particles / they are not cells / they have a protein coat / they have DNA or RNA as their genetic material *[2 marks]*
4 a) The DNA sequences for the same gene in different organisms can be compared *[1 mark]*. The more similar the sequences are to each other, the more closely related the organisms are *[1 mark]*.
 b) Organism C *[1 mark]* because its DNA sequence has the highest percentage similarity to humans *[1 mark]*.

Section 2 — Organisation of the Organism

Page 17
Warm-Up Questions
1) Similarities — any two from: e.g. both an animal and a plant cell have a cell membrane. / Both an animal and a plant cell have a nucleus. / Both an animal and a plant cell have cytoplasm.
 Differences — any two from: e.g. an animal cell doesn't have a vacuole, but a plant cell does. / An animal cell doesn't have a cell wall, but a plant cell does. / An animal cell doesn't contain chloroplasts, but a plant cell does.
2) mitochondria
3) rough endoplasmic reticulum

Exam Questions
1 a) C *[1 mark]*
 b) They absorb light needed for photosynthesis to make food for the plant *[1 mark]*.
 c) It supports the cell and strengthens it *[1 mark]*.
2) The cell has a hair-like shape, which gives it a large surface area *[1 mark]* to absorb water and minerals from the soil *[1 mark]*.
3 a) real size = image size ÷ magnification *[1 mark]*
 = 7.5 ÷ 100
 = 0.075 mm *[1 mark]*
 b) 0.075 × 1000 = 75 µm *[1 mark]*

Section 3 — Movement In and Out of Cells

Page 26
Warm-Up Questions
1) Osmosis is the net movement of water molecules from a region of higher water potential to a region of lower water potential, across a partially permeable membrane.
2) E.g. diffusion is movement from an area of higher concentration to an area of lower concentration, whereas active transport is from an area of lower concentration to higher concentration. / Diffusion is caused by the kinetic energy of randomly moving molecules, but active transport requires additional energy from respiration in order to happen.

Exam Questions
1 a) The potato cylinder in tube D, because this tube contains the most concentrated sugar solution *[1 mark]* so this cylinder will have lost the most water by osmosis *[1 mark]*.
 b) Tube A contained pure water, so some of the water moved by osmosis into the potato cylinder *[1 mark]* from an area of higher water concentration to an area of lower water concentration *[1 mark]*.
2 a) diffusion *[1 mark]*
 b) As the size of the agar jelly cube increases, the time taken for the cube to become yellow increases *[1 mark]*. This is because the bigger cubes have a smaller surface area to volume ratio, which decreases the rate of diffusion *[1 mark]*.

Section 4 — Biological Molecules and Enzymes

Pages 33-34
Warm-Up Questions
1)   glucose
2 a)   Fats are made up of glycerol and fatty acids.
  b)   Proteins are made up of amino acids.
3)   Benedict's solution
4)   That starch is present in the sample.
5)   An enzyme is a protein that functions as a biological catalyst.
6)   active site
7)   The shape of an enzyme affects the shape of its active site, which determines what substrate it can bind to and what chemical reaction it can catalyse.
8)   When the temperature is too hot, the bonds holding the enzyme together break. This changes the shape of the enzyme's active site, so the substrate can't fit any more.

Exam Questions
1   A *[1 mark]*
2   A *[1 mark]*
3 a)   E.g. a dropping pipette *[1 mark]*
  b)   60 °C, as this was the temperature at which the iodine solution stopped turning blue-black first *[1 mark]*, meaning the starch had been broken down the fastest *[1 mark]*.
  c)   E.g. the amylase was denatured by the high temperature, so the starch was not broken down *[1 mark]*.
  d)   Any two from: e.g. the concentration of starch solution / the concentration of amylase / the volume of starch and amylase solution added to the iodine / the volume of iodine solution in the wells / the pH of the starch and amylase solution *[2 marks]*.
4   DNA has two strands coiled together in the shape of a double helix *[1 mark]*. Each strand contains chemicals called bases *[1 mark]*. The two strands are held together by cross-links between them that are formed by pairs of bases *[1 mark]*. The bases always pair up in the same way — it's always A-T and C-G *[1 mark]*.
5   E.g. water allows soluble molecules to be transported around the body in the blood *[1 mark]*. Digestive enzymes need to be in solution to work properly — water helps the body to digest food by acting as a solvent for the enzymes *[1 mark]*. In excretion, water transports metabolic waste products out of the body through, e.g. sweating and urination *[1 mark]*.

Section 5 — Plant and Human Nutrition

Pages 43-44
Warm-Up Questions
1)   chlorophyll
2)   making amino acids and proteins
3)   e.g. oxygen production
4)   A limiting factor is something present in the environment in such short supply that it restricts life processes.
5)   purple
6)   To increase the plants' growth so that more/ bigger tomatoes are produced.

Exam Questions
1 a)   carbon dioxide + water $\xrightarrow[\text{chlorophyll}]{\text{light}}$ glucose + oxygen *[1 mark]*
  b)   A *[1 mark]*
2 a)   At low light intensities, increasing the CO_2 concentration has no effect *[1 mark]*, but at higher light intensities, increasing the concentration of CO_2 increases the maximum rate of photosynthesis *[1 mark]*.
  b)   The rate of photosynthesis does not continue to increase because temperature or the level of carbon dioxide becomes the limiting factor *[1 mark]*.

You don't know if the temperature was kept constant or not, so either the level of carbon dioxide or temperature could have been the limiting factor here — there's no way of knowing.

3   delivers water and nutrients to the leaf — E *[1 mark]*
    helps to reduce water loss by evaporation — A *[1 mark]*
    where most of the chloroplasts in the leaf are located, to maximise the amount of light they receive — B *[1 mark]*
    allows carbon dioxide to diffuse directly into the leaf — D *[1 mark]*

4 a)

[1 mark]

  b)   Plants need both chlorophyll and light to photosynthesise and produce starch — there is only chlorophyll in the green area of the plant *[1 mark]*, and light can only reach parts of the leaf not covered by black paper *[1 mark]*.

Page 52
Warm-Up Questions
1) Any two from: activity level / age / gender / pregnancy / whether or not the person is breast-feeding
2) stomach, pancreas, small intestine
3) gripping and tearing food
4 a) amylase
   b) proteases
   c) lipases
5 a) simple sugars
   b) amino acids
   c) glycerol and fatty acids
6) E.g. a villus is a tiny finger-like projection that has microvilli on its surface. The villus has a single permeable layer of surface cells and contains a network of blood capillaries and a lacteal.
7) Egestion is the passing out of food that has not been digested or absorbed, as faeces through the anus.

Exam Questions
1 a)

 Place where bile is produced / liver

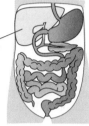

[1 mark]
   b) It neutralises the hydrochloric acid from the stomach *[1 mark]*.
   c) It emulsifies fats *[1 mark]* to give a much bigger surface area of fat for the enzyme lipase to work on *[1 mark]*.
2 a) marasmus *[1 mark]*
   b) E.g. they could have constipation which is caused by a lack of fibre/roughage *[1 mark]* and can lead to swelling of the large intestine/rectum *[1 mark]*. / They could have scurvy which is caused by a lack of vitamin C *[1 mark]* and leads to bleeding gums, poor wound healing and pain *[1 mark]*. / They could have vitamin D deficiency which is caused by not eating enough foods containing vitamin D or getting enough sunlight *[1 mark]* and can lead to e.g. bone deformation, bone pain and weak bones *[1 mark]*.
3 a) If the food is not removed then bacteria could build up and respire using sugar from the food *[1 mark]*. This will produce acid that dissolves enamel and dentine, causing dental decay *[1 mark]*.
   b) If the bone and cement are exposed, then acid produced by bacteria in the mouth would damage these parts of the tooth *[1 mark]*. The cement and the bone are responsible for holding the tooth in place and so if these are damaged then the tooth could be lost *[1 mark]*.

Section 6 — Transport in Plants and Animals

Page 58
Warm-Up Questions
1) Water moves from the root hair cells, through the root cortex cells, then through the xylem vessels and up to the mesophyll cells.
2) Transpiration is the loss of water vapour from plant leaves by evaporation of water at the surface of the mesophyll cells followed by diffusion of water vapour through the stomata.
3) A source is the place where a solute is made and a sink is a place where solutes are stored or used up in respiration and growth.
4) If there's no water in the soil, a plant starts to wilt because the cells lose water and become flaccid, meaning there is no turgor pressure to support the plant tissues.

Exam Questions
1 a) translocation *[1 mark]*
   b) phloem *[1 mark]*
   c) A *[1 mark]*
2 a) $(10 + 11 + 9) \div 3 = $ **10%** *[2 marks for correct answer, otherwise 1 mark for correct working]*
   b) The plants in Group B are at a higher temperature than those in Group A *[1 mark]*. At higher temperatures, the water particles have more kinetic energy to evaporate and diffuse out of the stomata *[1 mark]*, so the plant loses more mass *[1 mark]*.
   c) E.g. the more humid the air around a leaf, the slower transpiration happens *[1 mark]*. Humid air contains a lot of water, so there's not much of a concentration gradient between the inside and the outside of the leaf *[1 mark]*.

Pages 66-67
Warm-Up Questions
1) A system of blood vessels with a pump and valves to make sure that blood always flows in one direction.
2) E.g. using an ECG, by measuring pulse rate and by listening to the sounds of valves opening and closing.
3) They carry blood back to the heart.
4) They help the blood to clot at a wound.
5) Any three from: e.g. red blood cells / white blood cells / platelets / glucose / amino acids / carbon dioxide / ions / hormones.

Exam Questions

1 a) red blood cell *[1 mark]*

   b) Any one from: e.g. it has a biconcave disc shape *[1 mark]* to give a large surface area for absorbing oxygen *[1 mark]*. / It contains haemoglobin *[1 mark]*, which can bind to and release oxygen *[1 mark]*. / It doesn't have a nucleus *[1 mark]*, to give more room to carry oxygen *[1 mark]*.

   c) Any one from: e.g. white blood cell/phagocyte *[1 mark]*. It carries out phagocytosis *[1 mark]*. / White blood cell/lymphocyte *[1 mark]*. / It produces antibodies *[1 mark]*.

   d) E.g. they have permeable walls *[1 mark]*, so substances can diffuse in and out *[1 mark]*. Their walls are usually only one cell thick *[1 mark]*, which increases the rate of diffusion by decreasing the distance over which it occurs *[1 mark]*.

2 a) A disease where the coronary arteries that supply blood to the heart muscle get blocked by layers of fatty material building up *[1 mark]*.

   b) Any two from: e.g. eating a diet high in saturated fat and salt / high levels of stress / smoking / the genes you inherit / getting older / being male rather than female *[2 marks]*.

   c) Aspirin can thin the blood and so can prevent blood clots from forming in the arteries, which lowers the risk of a heart attack *[1 mark]*.

3 a) A is the right atrium. B is the left atrium. C is the septum. *[1 mark]*

   b) Deoxygenated blood enters the right atrium *[1 mark]* through the vena cava *[1 mark]*. The blood moves through to the right ventricle *[1 mark]* which pumps it through the pulmonary artery to the lungs *[1 mark]*.

   c) It needs more muscle because it has to pump blood around the whole body at high pressure *[1 mark]*, whereas the right ventricle only has to pump it to the lungs *[1 mark]*.

   d) They prevent the backflow of blood *[1 mark]*.

   e) Any one from: e.g. blood can be pumped around the body at a higher pressure. / Blood can be pumped around faster, so more oxygen can be delivered to the cells. *[1 mark]*

4 a) Clotting stops you losing too much blood *[1 mark]* and it stops pathogens from getting in *[1 mark]*.

   b) Fibrinogen is converted to fibrin *[1 mark]*. The fibrin fibres then tangle together to form a mesh in which platelets and red blood cells get trapped, forming a blood clot *[1 mark]*.

5 a) The lymph nodes filter anything harmful, e.g. pathogens or toxins out of the lymph *[1 mark]*. The lymph nodes also contain lots of lymphocytes to help destroy pathogens *[1 mark]*.

   b) The circulation of body fluids / the return of excess tissue fluid to the blood *[1 mark]*.

Section 7 — Diseases and Immunity

Page 73
Warm-Up Questions

1) antigens
2) A transmissible disease is a disease where the pathogen can be passed from one host to another.
3) The skin acts as a mechanical barrier to pathogens. If it gets damaged, blood clots quickly to seal cuts and keep microorganisms out.
4) Passive immunity is the short-term defence against a pathogen by antibodies made by a different organism.

Exam Questions

1 a) Hairs in the nose trap particles from the air that could contain pathogens *[1 mark]*.

   b) E.g. the stomach produces acid, which kills the majority of pathogens that are swallowed (e.g. in food) *[1 mark]*.

2 To prevent the contamination of food by pathogens that may be on the chefs' hands *[1 mark]*.

3 a) The process is called phagocytosis *[1 mark]*. It's where certain white blood cells/phagocytes engulf and digest pathogens *[1 mark]*.

   b) Antibodies are produced by lymphocytes *[1 mark]*. They lock on to specific antigens on the surface of a pathogen *[1 mark]* and either cause the direct destruction of the pathogen, or mark the pathogen for destruction by other white blood cells/phagocytes *[1 mark]*.

4 When vaccinated, child A was given dead or inactive rubella pathogens *[1 mark]*. These would have had antigens on their surface and so would have caused the child's lymphocytes to start producing antibodies *[1 mark]*. This would have also led to the production of memory cells *[1 mark]*. When child A was exposed to the rubella virus, the memory cells quickly made the specific antibodies against the virus, so child A didn't become ill *[1 mark]*. Child B did not have these memory cells, so when they were infected by the virus they didn't produce antibodies quickly enough and they became ill *[1 mark]*.

Section 8 — Gas Exchange and Respiration

Page 77
Warm-Up Questions
1) False

Inspired air has a greater proportion of oxygen than expired air.
Expired air has a greater proportion of carbon dioxide and water
vapour than inspired air.

2) limewater
3) Physical activity leads to an increase in breathing rate.
4) Ciliated cells waft mucus up to the back of
    the throat where it can be swallowed.

Exam Questions
1 a) E.g.

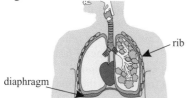

rib

diaphragm

[1 mark for a label pointing to the diaphragm,
1 mark for a label pointing to a rib].

b) bronchus *[1 mark]*
c) the alveoli *[1 mark]*
d) Any two from: e.g. they have a very large surface
    area *[1 mark]*. / They have a thin surface *[1 mark]*.
    / They have a good blood supply *[1 mark]*. / They
    have good ventilation with air *[1 mark]*.
2   **C** *[1 mark]*

Page 81
Warm-Up Questions
1) Any two from: e.g. for muscle contraction / for protein
    synthesis / for cell division / for active transport
    / for growth / for the passage of nerve impulses
    / to maintain a constant body temperature.
2) carbon dioxide and water

Aerobic respiration is the same in all organisms — it's anaerobic
respiration that can be different in different organisms.

3) $C_6H_{12}O_6 + 6O_2 \longrightarrow 6CO_2 + 6H_2O$
4) E.g. by keeping heart rate high/
    breathing depth high after exercise.
5) $C_6H_{12}O_6 \longrightarrow 2C_2H_5OH + 2CO_2$

Exam Questions
1 a) To transfer energy (from the breakdown of nutrient
    molecules) that cells need to do just about everything
    [1 mark].
b) Any two from: e.g. aerobic respiration uses oxygen,
    anaerobic respiration does not. / Aerobic respiration
    doesn't produce lactic acid, anaerobic respiration does.
    / Aerobic respiration releases more energy per glucose
    molecule than anaerobic respiration. *[2 marks]*
c) glucose + oxygen *[1 mark]* → carbon dioxide + water
    [1 mark]
2 a) glucose → lactic acid *[1 mark]*
  b) i) aerobic respiration *[1 mark]*
    ii) aerobic and anaerobic respiration *[1 mark]*

3   E.g. set up two test tubes containing soda lime granules
    and cotton wool, and put woodlice in one and glass beads
    in the other *[1 mark]*. Set up a respirometer and leave the
    apparatus in a water bath at a set temperature *[1 mark]*.
    Calculate the volume of oxygen taken in by the woodlice
    over a set time by using the scale on the respirometer to
    measure the distance moved by the liquid *[1 mark]*.
4   At lower temperatures, the rate of respiration was
    slow *[1 mark]*, but increased to a maximum at the
    optimum temperature *[1 mark]*. As temperature
    increased beyond the optimum, the rate of respiration
    decreased until it reached zero *[1 mark]*.

The speed of the fluid in the respirometer can be used to calculate
the rate of respiration — the faster the fluid moved, the faster the
rate of respiration.

Section 9 — Excretion in Humans

Page 86
Warm-Up Questions
1) the liver
2) the lungs
3) Deamination is the removal of the nitrogen-containing
    part of amino acids to form urea.
4) A bundle of capillaries at the start of a kidney tubule.
5) Carbon dioxide is toxic and will do us harm
    if it is allowed to build up in the body.

Exam Questions
1   It was a hot day and the runner was exercising, so
    she lost a lot of water through sweating *[1 mark]*.
    She didn't take in enough water to replace the water
    she'd lost, so she became dehydrated *[1 mark]*. This
    caused her kidneys to reabsorb more water into the
    blood *[1 mark]* so she produced a small volume
    of more concentrated (darker) urine *[1 mark]*.
2   **C** *[1 mark]*
3 a) The urea diffuses out through the dialysis membrane /
    into the dialysis fluid *[1 mark]*, because the concentration
    of urea in the blood is higher than in the dialysis fluid /
    because the dialysis fluid contains no urea *[1 mark]*.
b) The dialysis fluid contains the same concentration
    of glucose as healthy blood *[1 mark]*, so
    there is no concentration gradient and no
    net movement of glucose *[1 mark]*.
c) E.g. she will not have to have dialysis sessions three times
    every week for hours each time *[1 mark]*. /
    A kidney transplant is cheaper than dialysis in the
    long term *[1 mark]*.
d) E.g. there are long waiting lists for kidneys. / There's
    a risk that the donor kidney will be rejected by the
    patient's immune system. / The patient must take drugs
    to prevent rejection for the rest of her life. *[1 mark]*

Section 10 — Coordination and Response

Page 91
Warm-Up Questions
1) brain and spinal cord
2) nerve impulses / electrical signals
3) e.g. the pupil reflex (in response to bright light)

Exam Questions
1 a) X: sensory neurone *[1 mark]*
   Y: relay neurone *[1 mark]*
   Z: motor neurone *[1 mark]*
 b) synaptic cleft *[1 mark]*
 c) The effector is the muscle *[1 mark]* and
   it responds by contracting (which causes
   the man to drop the plate) *[1 mark]*.
2 a) A: cornea *[1 mark]*
   B: pupil *[1 mark]*
 b) It controls the diameter of the pupil / the
   amount of light entering the eye *[1 mark]*.
 c) i) rods *[1 mark]*, cones *[1 mark]*
   ii) the fovea *[1 mark]*
 d) Information is sent using impulses *[1 mark]*,
   via the optic nerve *[1 mark]*.

Page 96
Warm-Up Questions
1) A chemical substance, produced by a gland and
   carried by the blood, which alters the activity
   of one or more specific target organs.
2) a) ovaries
   b) testes
   c) adrenal glands
3) The maintenance of a constant internal environment.

Exam Questions
1 a) Erector muscles contract when it's cold, which
   makes the hairs stand up *[1 mark]*. This traps
   an insulating layer of air near the surface of the
   skin and so prevents heat loss *[1 mark]*.
 b) Sweat glands respond by producing very little sweat
   [1 mark], because sweat transfers heat from the body
   to the environment when it evaporates *[1 mark]*.
2 E.g. nervous responses are very fast and hormonal
   responses are slower *[1 mark]*. Nervous
   responses usually act for a short time while
   hormonal responses last for longer *[1 mark]*.
3 a) Organ A = pancreas *[1 mark]*, Organ B = liver *[1 mark]*
 b) The pancreas/organ A produces little or no insulin
   [1 mark]. This means that the liver/organ B is
   unable to remove glucose from the blood for
   storage *[1 mark]*. So blood glucose is able to
   rise to a dangerously high level *[1 mark]*.
 c) It makes the liver/organ B turn glycogen into glucose
   increasing blood glucose levels *[1 mark]*.

Page 99
Warm-Up Questions
1) A response in which parts of a plant grow towards or
   away from the direction from which light is coming.
2) auxin
3) In the shoot tips.
4) More auxin accumulates on the side of the shoot that's
   in the shade. This causes the cells on the shaded side to
   elongate faster, so the shoot bends towards the light.

Exam Questions
1 a) Selective weedkillers disrupt the normal growth
   patterns of weeds, which kills them *[1 mark]*.
 b) 2,4-D *[1 mark]*
2 a) The shoot has grown upwards, away from gravity. /
   The shoot is showing negative gravitropism. *[1 mark]*
 b) Auxin accumulated on the lower side of the
   shoot *[1 mark]*. This caused the cells on the
   lower side of the shoot to elongate faster,
   so the shoot bent upwards *[1 mark]*.
 c) The shoots will grow towards the light *[1 mark]*.
   This is because more auxin accumulates on the side that's
   in the shade *[1 mark]*, which stimulates these cells to
   elongate faster causing the shoot to bend towards the light
   [1 mark].

Section 11 — Drugs

Page 104
Warm-Up Questions
1) e.g. MRSA
2) A drug is any substance taken into the body that modifies or affects chemical reactions in the body.
3) It can increase the risk of infections such as HIV being passed between the users.
4) It's converted to morphine molecules in the brain, which have a similar shape to some neurotransmitter molecules. This means it can bind to receptors and block the neurotransmitters from binding.

Exam Questions
1 a) E.g. nicotine increases heart rate, which causes an increase in blood pressure *[1 mark]*. High blood pressure can damage the arteries and increase the risk of coronary heart disease *[1 mark]*.
  b) E.g. tar contains carcinogens *[1 mark]*, which are chemicals that can lead to cancers *[1 mark]*. / Tar damages the cilia in the bronchi and trachea and encourages more mucus than normal to be produced *[1 mark]*. This means that mucus can't be cleared very well, causing persistent coughing, which is a symptom of chronic obstructive pulmonary disease *[1 mark]*.
2 a) This means that alcohol reduces the activity of the nervous system and slows down reaction times *[1 mark]*.
  b) E.g. it leads to impaired judgement. / It can lead to a lack of self-control. / People can become addicted. / Alcohol addiction can lead to withdrawal symptoms. / It may cause people to resort to crimes. *[1 mark]*
  c) The liver has an important role in cleaning the blood by breaking down alcohol and other toxins *[1 mark]*. If the liver can't do this job properly because it is damaged, then dangerous substances start to build up and damage the rest of the body *[1 mark]*.
3 a) Any two from: e.g. infertility / hair loss / an increased risk of cancer *[2 marks]*
  b) Anabolic steroids improve sporting performance because testosterone can increase the amount of muscle *[1 mark]* and reduce the amount of fat in the body *[1 mark]*.
4 a) Antibiotics don't kill viruses, so prescribing antibiotics wouldn't have made the patient well again *[1 mark]*.
  b) Some of the bacteria may have been resistant to the antibiotic prescribed *[1 mark]*. This means that the antibiotic would have only killed the non-resistant bacteria infecting the patient *[1 mark]*. The resistant bacteria would have then gone on to reproduce in the patient and maintain the infection *[1 mark]*.

Section 12 — Reproduction

Page 110
Warm-Up Questions
1) Sexual reproduction is the process involving the fusion of the nuclei of two gametes to form a zygote and the production of offspring that are genetically different from each other.
2) Fertilisation is the fusion of gamete nuclei.
3) Self-pollination is the transfer of pollen grains from the anther of a flower to the stigma of the same flower or different flower on the same plant.

Exam Questions
1 a) X: Anther *[1 mark]*. It contains the pollen grains *[1 mark]*.
  Y: Ovary *[1 mark]*. It contains the female gametes/eggs *[1 mark]*.
  b) Flower B because e.g. long filaments hang the anthers outside the flower *[1 mark]*, so that a lot of pollen gets blown away *[1 mark]* / the large, feathery stigmas *[1 mark]* are efficient at catching pollen drifting past in the air *[1 mark]*.
  c) Any two from: e.g. brightly coloured petals to attract insects / scented flowers/nectaries to attract insects / large, sticky pollen grains that stick easily to insects / a sticky stigma to collect pollen from insects *[2 marks]*.
2 Because oxygen is needed for germination *[1 mark]* and oxygen was removed from the air in flask A by the sodium pyrogallate solution *[1 mark]*.

Page 115
Warm-Up Questions
1) E.g. nicotine / rubella virus.
2) For the first 12 weeks of the pregnancy, the fetus increases in complexity as different organs and body parts develop. For the rest of the pregnancy, once the fetus is fully developed, the fetus predominantly increases in size.
3) Any two from: e.g. she should not smoke. / She should not drink alcohol. / She may need to increase her intake of proteins/certain vitamins/certain minerals.

Exam Questions

1 a) X: Sperm duct *[1 mark]*
   Y: Urethra *[1 mark]*
   b) To produce the liquid that is added to sperm to make semen *[1 mark]*.
   c) E.g.

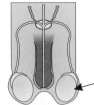

[1 mark for an arrow pointing to either of the testes]

2 a) It allows substances to be exchanged between the mother and the fetus *[1 mark]*.
   b) It protects the fetus against knocks/bumps. / It supports the fetus as it grows. / It allows the fetus to move. *[1 mark]*

3 a) To fertilise an egg. / To carry the male DNA to the female DNA (in the egg). *[1 mark]*
   b) E.g. it has a flagellum to enable it to swim to the egg *[1 mark]*. It has lots of mitochondria to provide energy for the flagellum to move *[1 mark]*. The acrosome contains enzymes to help the sperm digest a way through the jelly coat of the egg *[1 mark]*.

Pages 122-123

Warm-Up Questions

1) At the start of the menstrual cycle, menstruation starts and the lining of the uterus breaks down.
2) In the ovaries.
3) A diaphragm is a type of barrier birth control.
4) abstinence

Exam Questions

1 a) testosterone *[1 mark]*
   b) Any two from: e.g. extra facial/body hair / development of muscles / enlargement of penis/testes / production of sperm / deepening of voice *[2 marks]*
   c) E.g. growth of extra pubic/underarm hair / widening of the hips / development of breasts / start of periods/release of ova *[1 mark]*

2 a) A sexually transmitted infection is an infection that is transmitted via body fluids through sexual contact *[1 mark]*.
   b) HIV is spread via bodily fluids *[1 mark]*. By sharing needles there's a risk of injecting infected bodily fluids/blood from the previous user of the needle *[1 mark]*.
   HIV isn't just spread through sexual contact, although that's a common means of transmission.
   c) E.g. abstinence (not having sexual intercourse) / using a condom during sexual intercourse / limiting the number of sexual partners / getting tested for infection after unprotected sex or after contact with several sexual partners / taking medication to reduce the risk of passing the infection on to others *[1 mark]*
   d) AIDS occurs when a person's immune system deteriorates and eventually fails *[1 mark]*. This means a person does not have enough lymphocytes and cannot produce enough antibodies to fight infections *[1 mark]*.

3 a) FSH is needed to stimulate eggs to mature *[1 mark]*.
   b) Luteinising hormone / LH *[1 mark]* because it stimulates the release of an egg *[1 mark]*.

4 a) Keeping the oestrogen level permanently high inhibits production of FSH *[1 mark]*, so no eggs mature / so egg development and production stop *[1 mark]*.
   b) E.g. by stimulating the production of thick cervical mucus *[1 mark]*, which prevents any sperm getting through and reaching an egg *[1 mark]*.
   c) E.g. the contraceptive implant, as this is effective for three years once inserted *[1 mark]*, / the contraceptive injection, as this is effective for two to three months *[1 mark]*, / an intrauterine system, as this is effective for three to five years once inserted *[1 mark]*, / an intrauterine device, as this is effective for five to ten years once inserted *[1 mark]*, and so does not have to be thought about on a daily basis *[1 mark]*.
   d) By preventing sperm from reaching the egg *[1 mark]*.
   e) E.g. vasectomy / female sterilisation *[1 mark]*

5 a) Progesterone inhibits the release of FSH *[1 mark]*.
   b) day 14 *[1 mark]*
   c) The uterus lining will break down *[1 mark]*.
   d) E.g. a high level of progesterone is needed to maintain the lining of the uterus *[1 mark]*.
   e) In the ovaries and the placenta *[1 mark]*.

6 a) E.g. a mother is given FSH and LH to stimulate several eggs to mature *[1 mark]*. Several eggs are then collected from the mother and fertilised by sperm from the father in a laboratory *[1 mark]*. The fertilised eggs are grown into embryos in a laboratory incubator *[1 mark]*. Once the embryos are tiny balls of cells, one or two embryos are transferred into the mother's uterus *[1 mark]*.
   b) Any two from: e.g. the treatment may not work so repeated attempts may be needed, which could be upsetting/stressful/expensive for the couple. / It can result in multiple births which can be a risk to the health of the mother and the babies. / The mother may have a strong reaction to the hormones (e.g. pain, vomiting). *[2 marks]*

Section 13 — Inheritance

Page 128
Warm-Up Questions
1) XY
2) mitosis

Exam Questions
1 a) A chromosome is a thread-like structure of DNA, carrying genetic information in the form of genes *[1 mark]*.
   b) i) A diploid nucleus is a nucleus that contains two sets of chromosomes *[1 mark]*.
      ii) 23 *[1 mark]*
2 a) ribosome(s) *[1 mark]*
   b) The sequence of bases in the DNA/mRNA *[1 mark]*.
   c) Cell function is controlled by the production of proteins *[1 mark]*, which is controlled by the genes in DNA *[1 mark]*.
3 a) three *[1 mark]*
When a cell undergoes meiosis, each new cell ends up with half the number of chromosomes of the original cell.
   b) Meiosis produces cells that are genetically different to each other *[1 mark]*. It does this by forming new combinations of paternal and maternal chromosomes *[1 mark]*.

Page 134
Warm-Up Questions
1) Inheritance is the transmission of genetic information from generation to generation.
2) Genotype is the genetic make-up of an organism (the alleles present). Phenotype is the observable features of an organism.
3) on a sex chromosome

Exam Questions
1 Dd *[1 mark]*. Polydactyly is a dominant disorder, so if she was DD all of her children would be affected *[1 mark]*.
2 a) E.g.

Genotypes of parents: Rr Rr

Genotypes of gametes: R r R r

Genotypes of offspring: RR Rr Rr rr

Phenotypes of offspring: red eyes   red eyes   red eyes   white eyes

[1 mark for correct genotypes of the parents,
1 mark for correct genotypes of offspring,
1 mark for correct phenotypes of offspring]

You could have drawn a Punnett square instead here, for example:

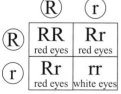

	R	r
R	RR red eyes	Rr red eyes
r	Rr red eyes	rr white eyes

   b) 1 in 4 / 25% *[1 mark]*

3 a) $I^A I^O$ *[1 mark]*
   b) i)

	I^B	I^B
I^A	$I^A I^B$	$I^A I^B$
I^O	$I^B I^O$	$I^B I^O$

[1 mark for correct alleles in parents,
1 mark for correct genotypes in offspring]
      ii) 0.5 / 50% / 1 in 2 *[1 mark]*
      iii) They will have blood group AB *[1 mark]*, because the I^A and I^B alleles are co-dominant / neither allele is dominant over the other / both alleles determine phenotype *[1 mark]*.

Section 14 — Variation and Selection

Page 141
Warm-Up Questions
1) Phenotypic variation is the differences in phenotype (the characteristics organisms display) and genetic variation is the differences in genotype (all of an organism's genes).
2) due to mutations
3) The probability of an organism surviving and reproducing in the environment in which it is found.
4) Individuals who are heterozygous for sickle-cell anaemia are resistant to malaria.

Exam Questions
1 E.g. webbed feet for swimming / streamlined body to reduce drag in water / lots of blubber/fat to stay warm *[2 marks]*.
2 A tall stem plant and a **dwarf** stem plant could be bred together. The offspring with the **highest** grain yield and **highest** bad weather resistance could then be bred together. Repeating this over several generations means the frequency of the desirable features **increases**. *[1 mark for each word in the correct place, up to a total of 4 marks.]*
3 Any two from: e.g. their leaves contain air spaces *[1 mark]* so they can float on the surface of the water and be exposed to the most light *[1 mark]*. / Stomata are usually only present on the upper surface of floating leaves *[1 mark]* to maximise gas exchange *[1 mark]*. / Their stems are flexible *[1 mark]* to prevent damage by currents *[1 mark]*.
4 Ancestors of this stingray showed variation in their appearance *[1 mark]*. These ancestors produced more offspring than could survive *[1 mark]*. Those offspring that looked like flat rocks were better camouflaged and so less likely to be seen by prey or predators *[1 mark]*. This means they were more likely to survive and reproduce *[1 mark]*. As a result, the alleles that caused the stingrays to look like flat rocks were more likely to be passed on to the next generation *[1 mark]*. Over time, the flat rock appearance became more common in the population, until all of the stingrays in the population had this appearance *[1 mark]*.

Section 15 — Organisms and Their Environment

Page 148

Warm-Up Questions

1) a producer
2) A herbivore is an animal that gets its energy by eating plants. A carnivore is an animal that gets its energy by eating other animals.
3) A trophic level is the position of an organism in a food chain, food web, pyramid of numbers or pyramid of biomass.
4) So much energy is lost at each trophic level that there's usually not enough left to support more organisms after five stages.

Exam Questions

1 a) E.g. the weevils eat platte thistles so could decrease this population, reducing the food available for honeybees *[1 mark]*. If the honeybee population decreases, the amount of wild honey produced will decrease *[1 mark]*.
  b) decomposers *[1 mark]*
2 a) The concentration of DDT in organisms increases as you go up the trophic levels *[1 mark]*.
  b) $13.8 \div 0.04 =$ **345 times**
    [2 marks for correct answer, otherwise 1 mark for using 13.8 and 0.04 in calculation]
  c) E.g. because DDT is stored in the tissues of animals and a pyramid of biomass represents the mass of the living tissues *[1 mark]*.

Page 153

Warm-Up Questions

1) Lightning makes nitrogen react with oxygen in the air to form nitrates (which plants can take up from the soil and use).
2) Decomposers break down animal and plant proteins and turn them into ammonia — this forms ammonium ions in the soil.
3) Water vapour rises. When it gets higher up it cools and condenses, forming clouds.
4) E.g. deforestation means there are fewer trees to take in carbon dioxide during photosynthesis, so more stays in the atmosphere. / Carbon dioxide is released into the atmosphere when trees are burnt to clear land.

Exam Questions

1 a) i) photosynthesis *[1 mark]*
    ii) carbon dioxide *[1 mark]*
  b) respiration *[1 mark]*
  c) Microorganisms/detritus feeders break down/decompose material from dead organisms *[1 mark]* and return carbon to the air as carbon dioxide through respiration *[1 mark]*.
  d) i) Fossil fuels are formed from dead animals and/ or plants which contain carbon *[1 mark]*.
    ii) Carbon is released into the atmosphere as carbon dioxide when fossil fuels are burnt *[1 mark]*.
2 C *[1 mark]*

Page 157

Warm-Up Questions

1) A population is a group of organisms of one species, living in the same area, at the same time.
2) An ecosystem is a unit containing the community of organisms and its environment, interacting together.
3) The human population size has increased rapidly in the last 250 years, especially in the 20th century.
4) There are just a few individuals, so the rate of reproduction is slow and the population is increasing slowly.

Exam Questions

1 C *[1 mark]*
2 E.g. rapid human population growth has implications for human health as it may make overcrowding worse so diseases are more likely to spread/ it may increase pollution leading to disease/ it may increase health problems caused by a lack of nutrition *[1 mark]*. Rapid population growth can also result in more conflict *[1 mark]*.
3 a) the exponential (log) phase *[1 mark]*
  b) E.g. at 12 hours, the population couldn't grow any bigger due to limiting factors (e.g. food, water) *[1 mark]*. At 7 hours, the population size was increasing quickly as the environment had enough resources to support more individuals *[1 mark]*.

Section 16 — Genetic Engineering and Biotechnology

Pages 163-164
Warm-Up Questions
1) E.g. bacteria.
2) Plasmids are used to transfer the desired genes from one organism to another.
3) DNA ligase
4) Any two from: e.g. amylases / proteases / lipases.
5) Any two from: e.g. temperature / pH / oxygen levels / nutrient levels.

Exam Questions
1 a) Genetic engineering is the changing of an organism's genetic material by removing, changing or inserting individual genes *[1 mark]*.
  b) E.g. bacteria have been genetically engineered to produce human insulin that can be used to treat diabetes *[1 mark]*.
  c) Restriction enzymes *[1 mark]* are used to recognise and cut the desired gene from the organism's DNA *[1 mark]*.
  d) A plasmid is cut open using the same restriction enzyme used to cut out the desired gene *[1 mark]*. The desired gene is then inserted into the plasmid using DNA ligase *[1 mark]*. The plasmid is then inserted into the target bacterium *[1 mark]*. The modified bacterium replicates to produce lots of bacteria with the desired characteristics *[1 mark]*.
2 a) i) Any one from: e.g. herbicide resistance / insect resistance / a greater nutritional value. *[1 mark]*
    ii) E.g. there would be more maize/food for the growing population to eat, as the yield with herbicide-resistant/insect-resistant plants is usually greater *[1 mark]*. / The maize/food would be better for the growing population as it would provide more nutrients from the same amount of food than the non-genetically engineered crops *[1 mark]*.
  b) Any two from: e.g. some people worry that transplanted genes may be passed on to other organisms. / Some people worry that changing an organism's genes could have unforeseen problems that could get passed on to offspring. / Some people worry that genetically engineered crops could have a negative impact on food chains/human health. / Genetically engineered crops might be expensive. *[2 marks — 1 mark for each correct answer.]*
3 a) Any two from: e.g. bacteria reproduce very quickly in the right conditions. / Bacteria can produce complex molecules. / There aren't ethical concerns about using bacteria. / The genetic code in bacteria is the same as in other organisms. / Bacteria have plasmids which can be easily modified and transferred. *[2 marks — 1 mark for each correct answer]*
  b) E.g. enzymes work best at their optimum temperature / if the temperature gets too high, the enzymes will denature *[1 mark]*. So the temperature needs to be controlled to maximise the rate of lactose breakdown *[1 mark]*.
4 a) *Penicillium* *[1 mark]*
  b) To supply oxygen *[1 mark]* for the fungus/*Penicillium* to respire aerobically *[1 mark]*.
  c) E.g. to circulate the culture medium inside the fermenter, so the fungus can always access the nutrients needed for growth *[1 mark]*. This should increase the yield of penicillin *[1 mark]*.
  d) E.g. nutrients *[1 mark]*.

Section 17 — Human Influences on Ecosystems

Page 169
Warm-Up Questions
1) Any three from: e.g. agricultural machinery / chemical fertilisers / insecticides / herbicides / selective breeding
2) E.g. the high input costs of farming can make it too expensive for people in some countries to start or maintain food production, meaning not enough food is produced.
3) Famine is when there isn't enough food to feed a population.
4) Any three from: e.g. an unequal distribution of food / drought / flooding / increasing population / poverty

Exam Questions
1 a) Any two from: e.g. if there's a pest or disease that affects the species, it could kill all of the crop being grown. / Monocultures can require lots of pesticides which can pollute water. / Monocultures can reduce biodiversity, as they contain fewer plant species than a natural ecosystem, so they don't provide habitats for as many organisms. *[2 marks]*
  b) E.g. waste from livestock can build up, causing the spread of disease and pollution of water sources. The chemicals used to treat disease can pollute the environment. *[2 marks]*
2 a) E.g. to increase the area of land available for food crop growth/livestock production/housing *[1 mark]*. For the extraction of natural resources *[1 mark]*.
  b) Any two from: e.g. loss of soil / flooding / increase of carbon dioxide in the atmosphere *[2 marks]*
  c) E.g. loss of soil — nutrients are lost when soil is washed away, which makes it harder for new trees to grow. / Flooding — without trees to slow down how quickly rain reaches the ground, flooding is more likely/trees are not there to take up water from the soil. / Increase of carbon dioxide in the atmosphere — the carbon dioxide released when trees are burnt contributes to atmospheric pollution. *[1 mark for each correct explanation, up to a total of 2 marks]*
3 E.g. the more land needed for food, the less land there is available for people to live on. / If food is scarce, it may become too expensive for some people to afford. *[1 mark]*

Page 175
Warm-Up Questions
1) E.g. insecticides / herbicides / nuclear fall out
2) E.g. methane / carbon dioxide / sulfur dioxide / nitrogen oxide

Exam Questions
1 C *[1 mark]*
2 a) E.g. if organisms eat plastic by mistake they can be poisoned/suffer from intestinal blockages. Organisms can be trapped/entangled/strangled by plastic items. *[2 marks]*
  b) Any two from: e.g. they can take up valuable space in landfills that could be used to feed/house the increasing global population. / They can release toxic gases when they are burnt. / They can release carbon dioxide when they are burnt, which contributes to global warming. / They can release poisons that can enter and contaminate food chains, killing many organisms. *[2 marks]*

270

3 a) Any two from: e.g. using coal that contains less sulfur / 'washing' the coal before it is burnt to remove some of the sulfur / installing 'scrubbers' in chimneys to remove sulfur dioxide / producing energy without using fossil fuels *[2 marks]*.

b) Increasing levels of greenhouse gases in the atmosphere *[1 mark]* have enhanced the greenhouse effect *[1 mark]* causing global warming/the Earth to warm up — this is climate change *[1 mark]*.

4 a) E.g. chemical waste from industry can be washed into water. / Discarded waste can build up in waterways. / Untreated sewage and fertilisers can contaminate the environment. *[1 mark]*

b) E.g. it can cause male aquatic organisms to become feminised *[1 mark]*. It may cause men to have a reduced sperm count *[1 mark]*.

c) The number of decomposer microorganisms increases downstream of the sewage discharge pipe *[1 mark]*. The sewage provides extra nutrients causing rapid algal growth *[1 mark]*. The algae block out light from plants causing them to die *[1 mark]*. The dead plants provide food for decomposer microorganisms, causing the number of decomposer microorganisms to increase *[1 mark]*.

Page 180
Warm-Up Questions
1) A sustainable resource is one which is produced as rapidly as it is removed from the environment so that it does not run out.
2) Any three from: e.g. paper / glass / plastic / metal
3) Any three from: e.g. screening / sedimentation / aerobic digestion / anaerobic digestion

Exam Questions
1 E.g. more offspring will survive to reproduce if the Siberian tigers are bred in captivity as there is less infant mortality *[1 mark]*. Some of these individuals can then be released into the wild *[1 mark]*.

2 Any three from: e.g. organisms can't adapt to climate change quickly enough. / Habitat destruction reduces the area that an organism can live in. / Animals are killed by hunters. / Species can be affected by pollution in their environment. / Organisms can't defend themselves against or compete with an introduced species. *[3 marks]*

3 B *[1 mark]*

4 a) E.g. it protects a source of food for humans. / It may stop other species (that feed on the fish) from becoming extinct. / It may allow ecosystem functions, like nutrient cycling, to be maintained. *[1 mark]*

b) E.g. restocking restores the fish that have been removed *[1 mark]*. Education can be used to tell people about the importance of conserving them/help them make informed choices when shopping for fish *[1 mark]*. Legal quotas put limits on the number and size of fish that can be caught in certain areas, as well as the time of year they can be caught in *[1 mark]*.

Paper 1 Multiple Choice (Core)
Pages 194-206
1 C *[1 mark]*
2 B *[1 mark]*
3 C *[1 mark]*
Image size = magnification × real size, so 0.08 mm × 100 = 8 mm.
4 B *[1 mark]*
In the diagram, the concentration of oxygen molecules is higher in the cell than in the tissue fluid. So the oxygen molecules will move from the cell to the tissue fluid down the concentration gradient.
5 A *[1 mark]*
6 C *[1 mark]*
7 C *[1 mark]*
8 D *[1 mark]*
9 B *[1 mark]*
10 D *[1 mark]*
11 B *[1 mark]*
12 A *[1 mark]*
13 A *[1 mark]*
14 C *[1 mark]*
15 B *[1 mark]*
16 C *[1 mark]*
17 C *[1 mark]*
18 D *[1 mark]*
19 D *[1 mark]*
20 A *[1 mark]*
21 D *[1 mark]*
22 D *[1 mark]*
23 C *[1 mark]*
24 B *[1 mark]*
25 A *[1 mark]*
26 B *[1 mark]*
27 D *[1 mark]*
You needed to recognise that the flower is from a wind-pollinated plant.
28 C *[1 mark]*
29 A *[1 mark]*
30 C *[1 mark]*
31 A *[1 mark]*
32 A *[1 mark]*
33 C *[1 mark]*
34 D *[1 mark]*
35 B *[1 mark]*
36 A *[1 mark]*
37 D *[1 mark]*
38 B *[1 mark]*
39 C *[1 mark]*
40 B *[1 mark]*

Answers

Paper 2 Multiple Choice (Extended)

Pages 207-219

1   A *[1 mark]*
2   B *[1 mark]*
3   B *[1 mark]*
4   C *[1 mark]*
Start by converting everything to the same units:
12 µm ÷ 1000 = 0.012 mm.
Magnification = image size ÷ real size, so
24 mm ÷ 0.012 mm = 2000.
5   C *[1 mark]*
The rate of diffusion will be faster in dish A because the temperature is higher. It will be faster in dish B because the acid is more concentrated. It will be faster in D because the surface area to volume ratio of the agar cubes is larger. The rate of diffusion will be slower in C because the acid is less concentrated.
6   A *[1 mark]*
7   C *[1 mark]*
8   B *[1 mark]*
9   D *[1 mark]*
10   C *[1 mark]*
11   D *[1 mark]*
12   C *[1 mark]*
13   A *[1 mark]*
14   A *[1 mark]*
15   B *[1 mark]*
16   C *[1 mark]*
17   A *[1 mark]*
18   C *[1 mark]*
19   D *[1 mark]*
20   A *[1 mark]*
21   B *[1 mark]*
22   D *[1 mark]*
23   B *[1 mark]*
24   D *[1 mark]*
25   B *[1 mark]*
26   D *[1 mark]*
27   C *[1 mark]*
28   C *[1 mark]*
29   D *[1 mark]*
30   A *[1 mark]*
31   B *[1 mark]*
32   C *[1 mark]*
33   C *[1 mark]*
8 + 3 = 11% (or 100 − 42 − 47 = 11%). Whichever method you used, you needed to realise that all the people with blood group B and all the people with blood group AB have the I^B allele.
34   D *[1 mark]*
35   B *[1 mark]*
36   B *[1 mark]*
37   A *[1 mark]*
38   A *[1 mark]*
39   C *[1 mark]*
40   B *[1 mark]*

Paper 3 Theory (Core)

Pages 220-234

1 a) i)   cell membrane *[1 mark]*
    ii) Holds the cell together/controls what enters and leaves the cell *[1 mark]*.
  b)   the nucleus *[1 mark]*
  c)   The cell uses its chloroplasts *[1 mark]* to produce food from photosynthesis *[1 mark]*.
  d) i) Any two from: e.g. a plant cell has a cell wall, but an animal cell does not. / A plant cell has chloroplasts, but an animal cell does not. / A plant cell has a vacuole, but an animal cell does not. *[2 marks]*
    ii) E.g. it has a nucleus/cytoplasm/cell membrane *[1 mark]*.
  e)   image size = magnification × real size
       = 150 × 0.054
       = 8.1 mm
     [2 marks for correct answer, otherwise 1 mark for correct working]

2 a)   An enzyme is a protein that functions as a biological catalyst *[1 mark]*.
  b) i) E.g. pectinase *[1 mark]*
    ii) E.g. pectinase breaks down pectin in fruit cell walls *[1 mark]* so that the fruit produces juice more easily *[1 mark]*.
  c) i) **glucose → alcohol** + carbon dioxide *[1 mark]*
    ii) E.g. bread making *[1 mark]* and the production of ethanol for biofuels *[1 mark]*.

3 a)   A group of different tissues that work together to perform a certain function *[1 mark]*.
  b)   bronchiole *[1 mark]*
  c)   E.g. alveoli have a large surface area. Alveoli have a thin surface. Alveoli have a good blood supply. *[3 marks]*
  d) i)

Name of Gas	Change in Proportion from Inspired to Expired Air	
	Increases	Decreases
carbon dioxide	✓	
oxygen		✓
water vapour	✓	

    [1 mark for each correct tick]
    ii) There is a higher concentration of oxygen in the alveolus than in the blood capillary *[1 mark]*, so oxygen diffuses *[1 mark]* down its concentration gradient (into the blood capillary) *[1 mark]*.

4 a)

Letter	Stage of the menstrual cycle
C	Ovulation occurs.
D	The uterus lining is maintained ready for the implantation of a fertilised egg.
B	The uterus lining thickens and grows.
A	Menstruation occurs.

    [1 mark for each correct letter]
  b) i) ovaries *[1 mark]*
    ii) E.g. they have energy stores in their cytoplasm *[1 mark]*. They have a jelly coating that changes at fertilisation *[1 mark]*.
  c)   At fertilisation, one male and one female **gamete** *[1 mark]* fuse to form a **zygote** *[1 mark]*. This then undergoes **cell division** *[1 mark]* and develops into an **embryo** *[1 mark]*.

5 a) Similarity: e.g. both make their own organic nutrients *[1 mark]*. Difference: e.g. the bacteria use the energy from chemicals released by the hydrothermal vent, whereas plants use energy from the Sun *[1 mark]*.

b) shrimp / tubeworms *[1 mark]*

c) i) The population of crabs might decrease in size *[1 mark]*, as there would be no tubeworms for them to eat *[1 mark]*.

ii) The population size of the shrimp could rise *[1 mark]*, as there would be more bacteria for them to eat *[1 mark]*.

6 a) E.g.

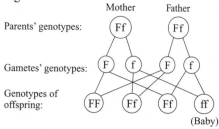

— white blood cell

— red blood cell

[1 mark for both a white blood cell and a red blood cell correctly labelled]

b) i) E.g. platelets *[1 mark]*

ii) E.g. excessive bleeding/bruising when injured *[1 mark]*

c) Having more red blood cells means that more oxygen can be carried to the muscles for aerobic respiration *[1 mark]*. This means more energy can be released for muscle contraction *[1 mark]*.

7 a) i) E.g.

Mother   Father

Parents' genotypes: Ff   Ff

Gametes' genotypes: F   f   F   f

Genotypes of offspring: FF   Ff   Ff   ff

(Baby)

[1 mark for showing that the parents both have the Ff genotype, 1 mark for showing the gametes' genotypes as F or f, 1 mark for correctly showing all three possible genotypes of the couple's offspring.]

The parents must both have one copy of the recessive allele for cystic fibrosis — so they're both Ff.

ii) Homozygous, because he has two alleles the same/ both of his alleles are recessive *[1 mark]*.

b) 1 in 4 / 25% *[1 mark]*

c) Ff *[1 mark]*. Ian has the genotype Ff, so Leina must also have the genotype Ff in order for her children to inherit the genotypes: FF (Carys), ff (Beth) and Ff (Alfie) *[1 mark]*.

8 a) *Biston [1 mark]*

b) i) the dark variety *[1 mark]*

ii) The dark variety is less likely to be eaten by predators in soot-polluted areas (because they are better camouflaged) *[1 mark]*, so they are more likely to survive to reproduce *[1 mark]*, meaning that the genes for the characteristics that made them successful / genes for dark colouring are more likely to be passed on to the next generation and become more common in the population *[1 mark]*.

c) Town B, because it contains a higher proportion of dark moths *[1 mark]*.

9 a) Genetic engineering is the changing of the genetic material of an organism *[1 mark]* by removing, changing or inserting individual genes *[1 mark]*.

b) E.g. bacteria have a rapid reproduction rate *[1 mark]*. Bacteria are able to make complex molecules *[1 mark]*.

c) Organisms with desirable features are selected *[1 mark]*. These organisms are crossed with each other to produce the next generation *[1 mark]*. The offspring with the most desirable features in this generation are then selected and crossed together (so the desirable feature becomes more common in the population) *[1 mark]*.

d) E.g. selective breeding could be used to develop crop plants that grow faster/are disease-resistant *[1 mark]*. This will increase production, creating more food for humans *[1 mark]*.

10a) X — carbon dioxide is being removed from the atmosphere by plants (photosynthesis) *[1 mark]*. Y — carbon dioxide is being released into the atmosphere by plants and animals (respiration) *[1 mark]*. Z — carbon compounds in the plants are being transferred to animals as they eat the plants (feeding) *[1 mark]*.

b) E.g. the two sets of data show roughly the same pattern/ a significant increase at the same time *[1 mark]*.

c) Any two from: e.g. the two sets of data may follow similar patterns by chance. / Some other factor may have caused both increases. / The concentration of carbon dioxide varied even when human population was low/fairly constant. *[2 marks]*

d) E.g. deforestation, burning fossil fuels. *[2 marks]*

Paper 4 Theory (Extended)

Pages 235-250

1 a)

	Type of blood vessel		
	Artery	Capillary	Vein
Walls	Thick, muscular	Very thin	Thin
Presence of valves	No	No	Yes
Pressure of blood in vessels	High	Low	Low

[2 marks for all three correct, otherwise 1 mark for two correct.]

b) E.g. the blood supply to the area below the blockage would be cut off/reduced *[1 mark]*. Not enough oxygen would reach this part of the heart muscle, resulting in cells being unable to respire/damage/death of the muscle tissue/a heart attack *[1 mark]*.

c) i) A stent will keep the coronary artery open *[1 mark]*, making sure that enough blood/oxygen can reach the heart muscle *[1 mark]*.

ii) E.g. angioplasty / coronary bypass surgery *[1 mark]*

iii) E.g. reduce the amount of saturated fat in his diet *[1 mark]*.

2 a) Because the A and T bases in a DNA molecule always pair up with each other *[1 mark]*.

b) nucleus *[1 mark]*

c) i) A change in the base sequence of DNA *[1 mark]*.

ii) E.g. exposure to ionising radiation *[1 mark]*.

iii) E.g. a mutation/change in the base sequence of DNA could lead to a change in the amino acid sequence of the enzyme *[1 mark]*. This could alter the shape of the enzyme's active site *[1 mark]*, which could mean it is unable to bind to its substrate and catalyse a reaction (preventing the enzyme from functioning) *[1 mark]*.

3 a) homeostasis *[1 mark]*

b) Receptors monitor the temperature of the blood and the brain coordinates a response based on signals from these receptors *[1 mark]*.

c) i) Arterioles supplying skin capillaries may have constricted / vasoconstriction may have taken place in the arterioles supplying the skin capillaries *[1 mark]*. This would have reduced the amount of heat radiated from his skin to the environment *[1 mark]*.

ii) They may have started to shiver/contract in spasms *[1 mark]*. This would have increased respiration in the muscle cells *[1 mark]*, which would have released more heat to warm the body *[1 mark]*.

4 a) i) 130 J *[1 mark]*
Tertiary consumers are the third consumers in a food chain — so in this case the tertiary consumers are the snakes.

ii) The plants absorb energy from the Sun *[1 mark]* during photosynthesis *[1 mark]*.

iii) $(130 \div 1100) \times 100\% = \mathbf{12.0\%}$
[2 marks for correct answer, otherwise 1 mark for using 130 ÷ 1100 in working]

b) D *[1 mark]*, because the biomass of the organisms decreases at each trophic level and the bars on this pyramid get smaller at each trophic level *[1 mark]*.

5 a) i) Light coming through the hole in the box caused more auxin to accumulate on the shaded sides of the shoots *[1 mark]*. This made the cells on the shaded sides of the plants grow/elongate faster *[1 mark]*, so the shoots bent towards the light *[1 mark]*.

ii) phototropism *[1 mark]*

b) i) $6CO_2 + 6H_2O \xrightarrow[\text{chlorophyll}]{\text{light}} C_6H_{12}O_6 + 6O_2$
[1 mark for correctly completing the balanced equation, 1 mark for chlorophyll]

ii) Any three from: e.g. for respiration / for making cellulose / for making amino acids / for storage as fats/oils / for storage as starch *[3 marks]*.

c) i) gravity *[1 mark]*

ii) E.g. so the roots grow into the soil, where they can absorb water/mineral ions *[1 mark]*.

6 a) 9:00 a.m. *[1 mark]*

b) E.g. day 2 was colder, so the water evaporated/diffused more slowly. / Day 2 was more humid, so there was a smaller concentration gradient between the inside and outside of the leaf so diffusion couldn't happen as quickly *[1 mark for reason, 1 mark for explanation]*.

c) The plant has lost too much water/has lost water faster than it could be replaced through the roots *[1 mark]* so its cells have become flaccid/there's not enough turgor pressure to support the plant *[1 mark]*.

d) Transpiration/diffusion of water from the stomata creates a slight shortage of water in the leaf *[1 mark]*. This draws more water into the leaf, which causes a column of water molecules to be drawn up through the plant's xylem vessels *[1 mark]*, as the water molecules are cohesive (stick together) *[1 mark]*. This in turn means that more water is drawn up from the roots, and so there's a constant transpiration pull of water through the plant *[1 mark]*.

7 a) E.g.

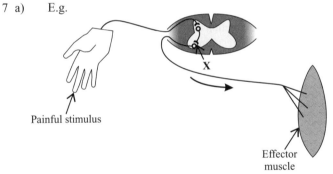

Painful stimulus

X

Effector muscle

[1 mark for an arrow anywhere on the neurone after the X, pointing towards the effector]

b) When the nerve impulse reaches X/the synaptic cleft, it triggers the release of neurotransmitters *[1 mark]*. These neurotransmitters diffuse across X/the synaptic cleft to bind with receptor molecules on the membrane of the next neurone *[1 mark]*, causing the nerve impulse to continue in the next neurone *[1 mark]*. The receptors are only on one side of X/the synaptic cleft, so the impulse can only travel in one direction *[1 mark]*.

c) The stimulus is detected by receptors in the hand *[1 mark]* and converted into a nerve impulse, which travels along a sensory neurone *[1 mark]* to a synapse in the CNS/central nervous system/spinal cord *[1 mark]*. The impulse then travels along a relay neurone to another synapse *[1 mark]* before travelling along the motor neurone *[1 mark]* to the effector muscle, which responds by contracting to move the hand away from the source of pain *[1 mark]*.

8 a)

glomerulus

[1 mark]

b) i) Urea is not reabsorbed into the blood, so its concentration increases through the tubule as water is reabsorbed *[1 mark]*.

ii) The concentration of glucose at point B would be high and there would be no glucose at point C *[1 mark]*, as all glucose is reabsorbed back into the blood in the first part of the tubule *[1 mark]*.

c) If the person has taken in more water than they have lost through sweating *[1 mark]*, the kidneys will reabsorb less water than usual and produce a greater volume of urine *[1 mark]*.

d) i) The person's blood flows between partially permeable membranes *[1 mark]*. The dialysis fluid contains the same concentration of glucose and dissolved salts as healthy blood, which ensures that glucose and useful salts are not lost *[1 mark]*. Waste products/ urea and excess salts and water are able to diffuse out of the blood into the dialysis fluid *[1 mark]*.

ii) E.g. dialysis is available immediately/there is no need to wait a long time for a donor organ to become available *[1 mark]*.

9 a) A change in the base sequence of the gene for haemoglobin *[1 mark]* results in abnormal haemoglobin and sickle-shaped red blood cells *[1 mark]*.

b) E.g. the function of red blood cells is to transport oxygen to respiring cells *[1 mark]*. The sickle-shaped cells are more rigid than normal red blood cells and they are the wrong shape, which could result in them being unable to fit through the capillaries *[1 mark]*. This could reduce/block the blood supply to respiring cells, meaning that not enough oxygen is transported to the cells, resulting in breathlessness *[1 mark]*.

If you don't have enough oxygen for respiration, your breathing rate increases to get more oxygen into your blood. In a person with sickle-cell anaemia, the lack of oxygen may cause their breathing rate to increase so much that they feel breathless.

c) i) Hb^SHb^S *[1 mark]*

ii) Both parents must have the genotype Hb^AHb^S *[1 mark]*.

d) People who are carriers for the sickle-cell allele/Hb^S are resistant to malaria *[1 mark]*. So in areas such as parts of Africa where malaria is common, being a carrier/heterozygous is an advantage *[1 mark]*. This has led to an increase in the number of carriers over time, which has therefore led to an increase in the number of people with sickle-cell anaemia *[1 mark]*.

Paper 5 Alternative to Practical

Pages 251-258

1 a) i) Any two from: e.g. the type of potato used for each cylinder / the size of potato cylinder / the volume of sugar solution / the temperature *[2 marks]*.

ii) E.g. the amount of sugar solution removed when the potato cylinders are dried with tissue paper may vary for each cylinder *[1 mark]*. Make sure the method of drying the potato cylinders is the same each time *[1 mark]*.

b) i) $(-0.78 + -0.81 + -0.82) \div 3 = -2.41 \div 3 = -0.8033...$ $= -0.80$ g (to 2 s.f.) *[1 mark]*

ii) To give more reliable results *[1 mark]*.

c)

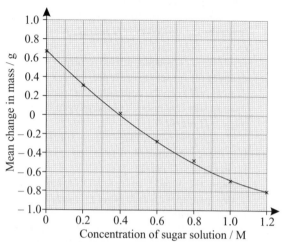

[1 mark for choosing suitable scales, 1 mark for a curve of best fit, 1 mark for having axes labelled correctly with independent variable on the x-axis and dependent variable on the y-axis (with correct units), 2 marks for all points plotted correctly (or 1 mark for at least 5 points plotted correctly). Plotting marks may still be given if an incorrect answer to 1 (b) (i) has been plotted correctly or if variables are on the wrong axes.]

d) i) E.g. she should add Benedict's solution to a sample of solution from each of the test tubes using a pipette *[1 mark]*. She should then place the samples in a water bath set at 75 °C *[1 mark]*. She should look out for a colour change and note the final colour of each solution *[1 mark]*.

ii)

	Tube 1	Tube 2	Tube 3	Tube 4
substance observed	yellow precipitate	blue solution	red precipitate	green precipitate
glucose concentration / M	**0.1**	**0**	**1**	**0.02**

[1 mark]

The higher the concentration of glucose in the solution, the further the colour change goes along the following scale: blue — green — yellow — orange — brick red. If no precipitate forms then there are no reducing sugars in the solution.

e) i) E.g. (41 + 45) ÷ 2 = **43 mm**
      *[2 marks for an answer between 42.5 mm and 43.5 mm,
      otherwise 1 mark for correct measurement of cell B
      between 44 mm and 46 mm]*

   ii) The drawing should occupy at least half of the available
       space *[1 mark]*. The drawing should not include
       any colouring/shading and should be drawn with
       clear, unbroken lines *[1 mark]*. Structures inside the
       cell should be drawn in proportion *[1 mark]*. The
       cytoplasm and starch grains should be labelled using
       straight, uncrossed lines drawn with a ruler *[1 mark]*.

2 a) i) gas syringe *[1 mark]*

   ii) E.g. so the same volume of carbon dioxide is released
       each time *[1 mark]*.

   b) E.g.

Distance away from light source / cm	Gas collected / cm³		
	Repeat 1	Repeat 2	Repeat 3
0			
10			
20			
30			
40			

*[1 mark for a neatly drawn table with cells for 15 results,
1 mark for column/row with the distances away from
light source completed, 1 mark for appropriate row/
column headers with units.]*

   c) i) 0.20 ÷ 2 = **0.10 cm³/h** *[1 mark]*

      ii) 20 cm *[1 mark]*. The volume of gas collected is higher
          than that for 10 cm *[1 mark]*.

      iii) As the distance from the light source increases, the rate
           of gas production decreases *[1 mark]*. This is because the
           intensity of the light reaching the plant decreases as the
           light source is placed further away *[1 mark]*.

      iv) E.g. by repeating the experiment at a greater distance
          from the light source *[1 mark]*.

   d) E.g. different light sources may produce different
       intensities of light *[1 mark]*, so using the same
       light source helps to ensure that the distance
       between the light source and the test tube is the
       only thing affecting the light intensity *[1 mark]*.

   e) i) E.g. wear gloves / a lab coat / safety goggles / keep away
         from naked flames *[1 mark]*.

      ii) The leaf will have turned blue-black *[1 mark]*.

   f) E.g. the student could carry out the experiment as
       described, but instead of varying the distance, the student
       should keep the light source at the same distance from
       the test tube throughout the experiment *[1 mark]*. She
       should instead vary the temperature, by carrying out
       the experiment at a range of different temperatures,
       e.g. 10 °C, 20 °C, 30 °C, 40 °C *[1 mark]*. To vary the
       temperature she should put the test tube in a water bath
       set to a constant temperature *[1 mark]* and monitor the
       temperature using a thermometer *[1 mark]*.

Glossary

absorption	The movement of small food molecules and ions through the wall of the intestine into the blood.
active immunity	The defence against a pathogen by the production of antibodies in the body.
active site	The part of an enzyme where the substrate binds.
active transport	The movement of particles across a cell membrane from a region of lower concentration to a region of higher concentration using energy from respiration.
adaptive feature	(Core) An inherited feature that helps an organism to survive and reproduce in its environment. (Extended) An inherited functional feature of an organism that increases its fitness.
aerobic respiration	The series of chemical reactions in cells that uses oxygen to break down nutrient molecules to release energy.
allele	A version of a gene.
anaerobic respiration	The series of chemical reactions in cells that breaks down nutrient molecules to release energy without using oxygen.
antibiotic	A drug used to kill bacteria.
antibiotic resistance	When bacteria aren't killed by an antibiotic.
antibody	A protein produced by white blood cells to help destroy pathogens.
antigen	A molecule on the surface of a cell, e.g. a pathogen, that causes a response from white blood cells.
asexual reproduction	The process resulting in the production of genetically identical offspring from one parent.
assimilation	The movement of digested food molecules (and water) into the cells of the body where they are used, becoming part of the cells.
balanced diet	A diet that gives you all the essential nutrients you need in the right proportions.
binomial system	An internationally agreed system to scientifically name organisms using their genus and species.
biotechnology	When living things and biological processes are manipulated to produce a useful product.
carnivore	An animal that gets its energy by eating other animals.
catalyst	A substance which increases the rate of a reaction, without being changed or used up in the reaction.
chemical digestion	The breakdown of large, insoluble molecules into small, soluble molecules.
chromosome	A thread-like structure of DNA, which carries genetic information in the form of genes.
community	All the populations of different species living in an ecosystem.

Glossary

consumer	An organism that gets its energy by feeding on other organisms.
cross-pollination	The transfer of pollen grains from the anther of a flower to the stigma of a flower on a different plant of the same species.
deamination	The removal of the nitrogen-containing part of amino acids to form urea.
decomposer	An organism that gets its energy from breaking down dead material and waste.
diffusion	The net movement of particles from a region of their higher concentration to a region of their lower concentration as a result of their random movement.
diploid nucleus	A nucleus that contains two sets of chromosomes.
DNA	A molecule that carries the genetic information necessary to make proteins in a cell.
dominant allele	An allele that is expressed if it is present.
drug	Any substance taken into the body that modifies (changes) or affects chemical reactions in the body.
ecosystem	A unit containing the community of organisms and its environment, interacting together.
effector	A group of cells that responds to a stimulus, e.g. a muscle or gland.
egestion	The passing out of food that has not been digested or absorbed, as faeces, through the anus.
enzyme	A protein that functions as a biological catalyst.
evolution	The change in adaptive features of a population over time as the result of natural selection.
excretion	The removal from organisms of the waste products of metabolism, toxic materials, and substances in excess of requirements.
fertilisation	The fusion of the nuclei of two gametes.
fitness	The probability of an organism surviving and reproducing in the environment in which it is found.
flaccid cell	A plant cell that is limp and wilted due to loss of water.
food chain	A chain showing the transfer of energy from one organism to the next, starting with a producer.
food web	A network of interconnected food chains.
gamete	A sex cell, e.g. a sperm or an egg cell.
gene	A length of DNA that codes for a protein.
gene mutation	A change in the base sequence of DNA.

Glossary

genetic engineering	The changing of an organism's genetic material by removing, changing or inserting individual genes.
genotype	The genetic make-up of an organism (the alleles present).
gravitropism	A response in which parts of a plant grow towards or away from gravity.
growth	(Core) A permanent increase in the size of an organism. (Extended) A permanent increase in the size and dry mass of an organism, by an increase in cell number, cell size or both.
haploid nucleus	A nucleus containing a single set of unpaired chromosomes.
herbivore	An animal that gets its energy by eating plants.
heterozygous	Having two different alleles of a particular gene.
homeostasis	The maintenance of a constant internal environment.
homozygous	Having two identical alleles of a particular gene.
hormone	A chemical substance, produced by glands and carried by the blood, which alters the activity of one or more specific target organs.
ingestion	The taking of substances (e.g. food and drink) into the body through the mouth.
inheritance	The transmission of genetic information (DNA) from generation to generation.
limiting factor	Something present in the environment in such short supply that it restricts life processes.
mechanical digestion	The breakdown of food into smaller pieces without chemical change to the food molecules.
meiosis	(Core) Nuclear division that gives rise to four genetically different cells. (Extended) Reduction division in which the chromosome number is halved from diploid to haploid resulting in genetically different cells.
metabolism	The chemical reactions that happen in cells, including respiration.
mitosis	Nuclear division that gives rise to two genetically identical cells.
movement	An action by organisms or parts of organisms causing a change of place or position.
mutation	Genetic change.
natural selection	The process that results in organisms that are better adapted to their environment being more likely to survive and reproduce.
nerve impulse	An electrical signal that passes along nerve cells called neurones.
neurone	A nerve cell.
nutrition	The taking in of materials for energy, growth and development.

Glossary

organ	A group of different tissues that work together to perform specific functions.
organ system	A group of organs working together to perform body functions.
osmosis	(Core) The diffusion of water molecules through a partially permeable membrane. (Extended) The net movement of water molecules from a region of higher water potential to a region of lower water potential, across a partially permeable membrane.
passive immunity	The short-term defence against a pathogen by antibodies made by a different organism.
pathogen	A disease-causing organism.
phenotype	The observable features of an organism.
photosynthesis	The process that plants use to manufacture carbohydrates (glucose) from raw materials (carbon dioxide and water) using energy from light.
phototropism	A response in which parts of a plant grow towards or away from the direction from which light is coming.
plasmolysis	When the cytoplasm starts to shrink and the membrane pulls away from a plant cell wall because the cell is short of water.
pollination	The transfer of pollen grains from the anther of a flower to the stigma.
population	A group of organisms of one species living in the same area at the same time.
process of adaptation	The process, resulting from natural selection, by which populations become more suited to their environment over many generations.
producer	An organism that makes its own organic nutrients (food), usually using energy from the Sun during photosynthesis.
receptor	A group of cells that can detect a change in the environment (a stimulus).
recessive allele	An allele that is only expressed when there is no dominant allele of the gene present.
reflex action	A rapid, automatic response to a certain stimulus that doesn't involve the conscious part of the brain.
reproduction	The processes that make more of the same kind of organism.
respiration	The chemical reactions that happen in cells to break down nutrient molecules and release energy for metabolism.
selective breeding	When humans artificially select the plants or animals that are going to breed so that the frequency of the alleles for desired characteristics increases in a population.
self-pollination	The transfer of pollen grains from the anther of a flower to the stigma of the same flower or different flower on the same plant.

Glossary

sense organ	A group of receptor cells that respond to specific stimuli (e.g. light, sound, touch, temperature and chemicals).
sensitivity	(Core) The ability to detect and respond to changes in the environment. (Extended) The ability to detect and respond to stimuli in the internal or external environment.
sex-linked characteristic	A characteristic in which the gene responsible is located on a sex chromosome, making it more common in one sex than in the other.
sexual reproduction	The process involving the fusion of the nuclei of two gametes to form a zygote and the production of offspring that are genetically different from each other.
sexually transmitted infection (STI)	An infection that is transmitted via body fluids through sexual contact.
species	A group of similar organisms that can reproduce to give fertile offspring.
stem cell	An unspecialised cell that divides by mitosis to produce daughter cells that can become specialised for specific functions.
stimulus	A change in the environment.
sustainable development	Development providing for the needs of an increasing human population without harming the environment.
sustainable resource	A resource which is produced as rapidly as it is removed from the environment so that it does not run out.
synapse	A junction between two neurones.
tissue	A group of similar cells that work together to carry out a shared function.
translocation	The movement of sucrose and amino acids in phloem from sources (regions of production) to sinks (regions of storage or use).
transmissible disease	A disease where the pathogen can be passed from one host to another.
transpiration	The loss of water vapour from plant leaves by evaporation of water at the surface of the mesophyll cells followed by the diffusion of water vapour through the stomata.
trophic level	The position of an organism in a food chain, food web, pyramid of numbers or pyramid of biomass.
turgid cell	A plant cell that is plump and swollen.
turgor pressure	The pressure of water against an inelastic plant cell wall.
variation	The differences between individuals of the same species.
water potential	The likelihood of water molecules to diffuse out of or into a solution.
zygote	A fertilised egg cell.

Index

Index

Index

Index